The Birds
of Lundy

Publication of this book has been aided by financial assistance from:

Devon Bird Watching & Preservation Society
Lundy Field Society
Tom Bedford
Hugh Boyd
The Landmark Trust
Claude & Margaret Pike Woodland Trust
Ian Farrell
John Turner
Devon Asphalte Company Limited
Michelmore Hughes

The Birds of Lundy

Tim Davis & Tim Jones

Illustrated by Mike Langman

Devon Bird Watching & Preservation Society
and Lundy Field Society

Published for Devon Bird Watching & Preservation Society and Lundy Field Society
by Harpers Mill Publishing, Berrynarbor, Devon EX34 9TB

Produced and designed by Harpers Mill Publishing

ISBN-10: 0-954-0088-7-1
ISBN-13: 978-0-954-0088-7-1

This publication should be cited as:
Davis, T.J. & Jones, T.A. 2007. *The Birds of Lundy*. Devon Bird Watching &
Preservation Society and Lundy Field Society, Berrynarbor, Devon.

A CIP catalogue record for this book is available from the British Library.

Printed by Short Run Press Limited, Bittern Road, Sowton Industrial Estate, Exeter,
Devon EX2 7LW

Text set in Verdana and Palatino

Printed on Greencoat Velvet 80% recycled paper combined with fibre harvested
from sustainably managed forests

Cover illustration: Wheatear in South West Field by Mike Langman
Back cover photograph: Puffin off Lundy's North East Point by Stuart Leavy

Photographs:
Tim Ball (page 26)
Richard Campey (pages 15, 16, 17, 18, 30)
Tim Davis (pages 27, 33, 42)
Paul James (page 14 top)
Tim Jones (pages 14 bottom, 19, 20, 21, 29, 40)

Contents

This book is dedicated to
Tony Vickery,
birdwatcher and mentor, without
whose inspiration none of this would
have been possible,
and in memory of
Barbara Snow,
pioneering ornithologist and
Lundy warden 1954–1958.

*Tony Vickery (centre) repairing the Quarter Wall Heligoland
trap in 1966 in an illustration by John Dyke for the
17th LFS Annual Report.*

Foreword

My brief spell as LFS warden (1948–1949) was a wonderful start to a professional life devoted to ornithology and conservation. As queries put to me by Tim Davis and Tim Jones in the course of preparing this book have shown, my recollections of that time are vague and unreliable. Young people, as well as old ones, forget, or never knew. That is one reason why another account of Lundy's birds, 27 years after Nick Dymond's, will be useful. Any study of birds is a study of continual change, by a changing group of observers with changing equipment, drawing on a growing body of knowledge that will never be as complete as we would like. A work like this not only brings the story up to date, it also enables us to use what has become known recently to interpret more fully the records from the past.

"What's hit's history, what's missed's mystery" was the ornithologists' slogan in the nineteenth century, when bird identification was far harder than it is now. In 1948 there was no model for recording in the daily log what we had seen in the detail that is now required for critical identifications. I don't recall any photographs of 'rarities' that could have been used to back up our claims. Any that there had been would have been developed well after the event, when the photographer had returned to the mainland. Now, digital images can be sent on the internet within minutes.

Though sightings of 'rare' species excite the 'twitchers', they are much less useful than regular tallying of variations in the numbers of breeding and wintering birds and the numbers and timing of passage migrants. In 1948 we had begun to realise that changes in farming affected what birds lived and bred where. The impact of fisheries on seabirds remained un-thought about, though the immediate effects of oil pollution were obvious. In the last 40 years I have spent a lot of time looking for the effects of climate on Arctic-nesting birds: in 1948 climate change hadn't entered the vocabulary of birdwatchers.

In recent years birdwatching on Lundy has somewhat gone out of fashion – people fly to Mauritius or the Falkland Islands instead, avoiding delays in Ilfracombe or Bideford (though not at Stansted or Heathrow). The attractions of Lundy as an island continue to be obvious. My greatest hope for this book is that it will help a resurgence of interest in detailed local recording, which provides the foundations of better understanding of what is going on around us.

Hugh Boyd
Ottawa, Canada
August 2007

Hugh pictured on Lundy in July 1948 after a day's seabird ringing.

Acknowledgements

The task of writing this book has been both long and challenging and we would undoubtedly have failed had it not been for the unstinting enthusiasm, support and sheer hard work of many other individuals whose names and contributions we are privileged to acknowledge here.

Firstly, we are indebted to Tony Taylor, who, since 1985, has prepared the annual Lundy Field Society (LFS) logbook and shouldered the considerable burden of analysing and summarising its contents for the *LFS Annual Report*. Tony also coordinates bird ringing on the island, produces an annual ringing report, and liaises with the Devon Birds Records Committee to ensure that LFS records are integrated annually into the *Devon Bird Report* and that rarity descriptions are forwarded to the appropriate authorities. These are not easy undertakings, requiring both attention to detail and, at times, great patience and diplomacy. A generation of Lundy birdwatchers has Tony to thank for his quiet efficiency and we are delighted that Tony reviewed drafts of all of the species accounts in the Systematic List and Appendix, making many valuable comments.

We were also hugely fortunate to have James Diamond as a technical reviewer for all of the species texts. James undertook this task with great dedication and good humour, and the final texts have benefited from numerous improvements as a consequence of his careful reading, knowledge and in-depth experience of Lundy and its birds.

Special thanks go to Mike Langman for his excellent cover painting and for the exquisite series of line drawings that appear throughout the Systematic List.

It was a particular delight to work with Hugh Boyd, LFS warden in 1948 and 1949, who went on to a highly distinguished international career in ornithology and conservation. We are honoured that Hugh readily agreed to contribute the Foreword and that he also reviewed and commented on all of the species texts – approaching a potentially tedious task with inspirational enthusiasm.

Nick Dymond, LFS warden in 1972 and 1973 and author of *The Birds of Lundy* (1980), encouraged us from the outset and kindly shared notes he had made in the 1990s updating his 1980 manuscript.

Roger Doble, Mike Lock, Peter Reay and Paul Stubbs of the Devon Bird Watching & Preservation Society (DBWPS) and Roger Chapple, Keith Hiscock, Paul James, Colin McShane, Frances Stuart, Myrtle Ternstrom and Chris Webster of the Lundy Field Society are thanked for their support. In particular the authors thank both societies for their financial contributions, without which publication of this book may not have been possible.

Richard Campey, a former LFS island representative and long-time Lundy bird aficionado, maintains the Lundy bird sightings website (www.lundybirds.org.uk) which provides an invaluable means of keeping in touch with recent ornithological happenings. Richard can often be seen creeping about the island with unfeasibly heavy-looking photographic equipment, some of the fruits of which adorn the background chapters. Tim Ball, Paul James and Stuart Leavy are also thanked for their photographic contributions.

We thank the Lundy wardens during this book's gestation period – Liza Cole, Ben Sampson and Nicola Saunders – for their interest and for assistance rendered.

Helen Booker of the RSPB's South-West England regional office provided breeding-season updates for the Manx Shearwater account. Mark Darlaston and James Leonard assisted greatly with Peregrine. Simon Griffith, Nancy Ockendon and Shinichi Nakagawa contributed to the House Sparrow text, while John Hutchinson provided us with details of his colour-ringing studies of Lundy's Skylarks. David Price supplied data on breeding seabirds and information on the Seabird Recovery Project, as well as commenting on the seabird accounts. Others who helped in various ways were former LFS wardens Peter Davis and the late Barbara Snow (née Whitaker), David Snow, Tony Parsons, Leigh Lock, Grant Sherman, Ian Taylor, Dudley Iles, Kirsty Meadows of JNCC, and British Trust for Ornithology (BTO) Librarian Carole Showell.

Sophie Wilcox at the Alexander Library, University of Oxford, provided considerable help with pre-LFS references. David Morgan lent us back numbers of *British Birds* containing Rarities Committee (BBRC) reports. Peter Fraser, the BBRC statistician, patiently fielded our enquiries concerning national rarities recorded on Lundy, while Jacquie Clark at the BTO provided the file of Lundy ringing recovery and control data that enabled us to build on the information published in *LFS Annual Reports*.

Ian Farrell and John Turner, in addition to providing us with continual encouragement, also made financial contributions in memory of John's late wife, Janet Kear, a much-missed friend, expert adviser and enthusiastic supporter of this project. Additional thanks are due to Ian for the enormous amount of help he gave in a variety of areas, including looking up old DBWPS record cards, assigning the book's ISBNs, advising on the book's marketing, and – especially – creating and managing the birdsoflundy.org.uk website.

Chris Jones produced the map of Lundy and also scanned the photographs (improving many in the process) and illustrations. Mark Couch and staff at Short Run Press were ever helpful during the production stage and especially in the days before we finally hit the print button. And we thank Martin Grant of Grant Turner Imprint, Okehampton, for contributing the pre-publication leaflet at reduced cost.

We are grateful to all the sponsors listed on page 2, and the British Trust for Ornithology are thanked for their generous in-kind support through distribution of a flyer for the book to BTO members.

Mark Young very kindly hosted the launch of the book at his South Molton bookshop and provided the purchasing facility on the website.

Lastly, we thank our friends and fellow Lundy birdwatchers, especially Tom Bedford and Sue Ziebland, Richard Campey, Sheelagh Darling, James Diamond and Jacqueline Hill and their baby, Emma Primrose (who made her debut on Lundy on 25 August 2007), Paul and Kim Etherton, Dave Flumm, Mary Gade, Alan Kitson, Grahame Madge, Keith Mortimer, Brian Owens, Amanda Richardson, Geoff Taylor, Tony Vickery and Steve Wing, whose pleasurably idiosyncratic company we have shared on visits to the island and elsewhere over the years. We are grateful to Andrew Coughlan and Bruno Drolet, vagrants to Lundy from the New World, in whose snowbound Quebec home we finally began drawing this project to a close.

Our greatest debt of gratitude goes to Tony Vickery who led us to discover Lundy and whose birdwatching skills and love of the island have continued to inspire and enthuse. Tony first went to Lundy in 1953. During the fifties and sixties he helped run the activities of the Lundy Field Society from its then headquarters in the Old Light, including a stint as Maintenance Officer which must have brought some unique challenges. He continued to visit regularly and contribute records to the island logbook over another three decades. While the march of time means that Tony no longer gets across to the island from his home on the North Devon mainland, we have been fortunate to draw on his memory and notebooks for previously unpublished information and he has assiduously run to ground many details from past *Devon Bird Reports* and other published sources. We are proud to dedicate this book to him, and to the the memory of Barbara Snow, former LFS warden who died shortly before we went to press.

The views expressed in these pages are those of the authors and are not necessarily the views of the Devon Bird Watching & Preservation Society, the Lundy Field Society or any other organisation or individual. The responsibility for any errors or omissions is ours alone.

We welcome comments or readers' views on the book and these can be emailed via the website – www.birdsoflundy.org.uk.

Tim Davis & Tim Jones
September 2007

Lundy South

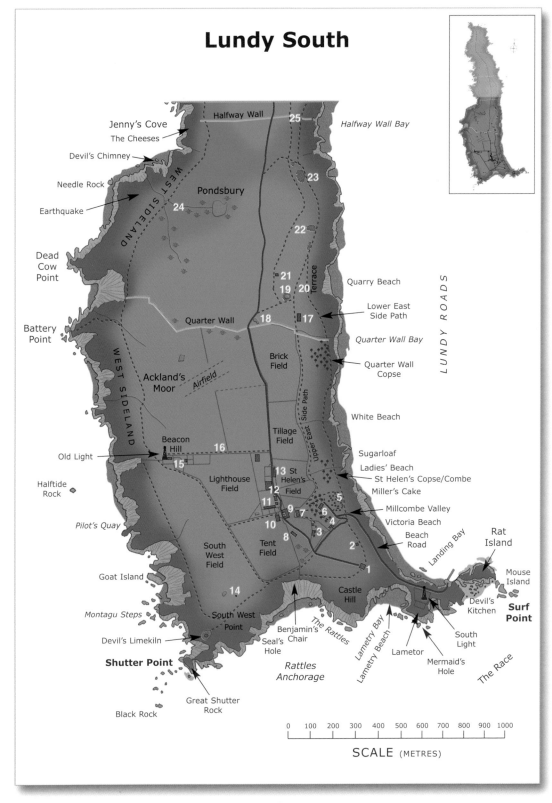

Jenny's Cove
The Cheeses
Devil's Chimney
Needle Rock
Earthquake
Dead Cow Point
Battery Point
Halftide Rock
Pilot's Quay
Goat Island
Montagu Steps
Devil's Limekiln
Shutter Point
Black Rock
Great Shutter Rock

Halfway Wall
Pondsbury
WEST SIDELAND
Quarter Wall
Ackland's Moor
Airfield
Beacon Hill
Old Light
Lighthouse Field
Brick Field
Tillage Field
St Helen's Field
South West Field
Tent Field
South West Point
Benjamin's Chair
Seal's Hole
Rattles Anchorage
Castle Hill

Halfway Wall Bay
Quarry Beach
Lower East Side Path
Quarter Wall Bay
Quarter Wall Copse
White Beach
Sugarloaf
Ladies' Beach
St Helen's Copse/Combe
Miller's Cake
Millcombe Valley
Victoria Beach
Beach Road
Landing Bay
Rat Island
Mouse Island
Devil's Kitchen
Surf Point
South Light
Lametor
Mermaid's Hole
Lametry Bay
Lametry Beach
The Rattles
The Race

LUNDY ROADS
Terrace
Upper East Side Path
WEST SIDELAND

25 23 24 22 21 19 20 18 17 16 15 13 12 11 10 9 7 6 5 4 3 2 8 1 14

0 100 200 300 400 500 600 700 800 900 1000

SCALE (METRES)

Lundy North

Hen and Chickens

North West Point

Virgin's Spring
Kittiwake Gully
Puffin Gully
Seal's Rock

North
Light

North East Point

Puffin Slope

Constable Rock

John O'Groats House

Long Roost

North End

Old Copper Mine

Bird Island

Gannets' Rock

Gannets' Combe

Gannets' Bay

Slipper Rock

Squire's View

St John's Stone

St Peter's Stone

Sanky Bay

Devil's Slide

Mousehole & Trap
Frenchman's Landing
Brazen Ward

St James's Stone

WEST

Widow's Tenement

East Side Path

Threequarter Wall

Threequarter Wall Bay

Knoll Pins

St Mark's Stone

Ally Sloper Rock

Aztec Bay

St Philip's Stone

Tibbett's

Tibbett's Point

Gull Rock

SIDELAND

Middle Park

EAST SIDELAND

Knight Templar Rock

The Pyramid

Halfway Wall

Halfway Wall Bay

Jenny's Cove

Number key

1 Marisco Castle
2 Hanmers
3 St John's Valley, Old School & Big & Little St John's
4 Brambles Villa
5 The Ugly
6 Millcombe House
7 Government House
8 Church of St Helena
9 Old House & Marisco Tavern
10 Black Shed
11 Campsite, Quarters (Pig's Paradise) & Reservoir Pond
12 Shop, Museum & High Street
13 Barton Cottages
14 Rocket Pole, Rocket Pole Pond & Rocket Pole Marsh
15 Stoneycroft & Cemetery
16 Water Tanks
17 Quarter Wall Cottages
18 Quarter Wall Pond & Quarter Wall Trap
19 Quarry Pond
20 Terrace Trap
21 Old Hospital
22 VC Quarry
23 North Quarry
24 Punchbowl Valley
25 Logan Stone

Beginnings

These opening words were written on a glorious May day on the southern slopes of Jenny's Cove, on Lundy's West Side, an easterly breeze filtering down the steep grassy slopes to ruffle the waters of the Atlantic a hundred metres below. On calm days or when the wind is in the easterly quarter, Jenny's is a wonderful place to tuck yourself away, be it in quiet contemplation or to watch birds playing on the wind.

Lundy's name is derived from the Old Norse words 'lundi' (meaning Puffin) and 'ey' (island). While once these cliffs held breeding Puffins in their thousands, numbers have dwindled to the edge of extinction. The few pairs that return each spring are to be found a little to the north of Jenny's Cove and though breeding was successful in 2007, the population hangs by the narrowest of threads. We can only hope that the conservation measures described later in this book will help Puffin numbers to increase and that Lundy's iconic bird will continue to enthral visitors for years to come.

Whatever the future holds for Puffins, the island will remain a magnet for birdwatchers, drawn by the sheer variety and number of birds that – given the right time of year and weather conditions – can be encountered within a relatively tiny area. The island plateau, covering some 445 hectares, provides a haven for landbirds, resident and migrant alike, while the heavily indented coastline, with its long grassy sidelands, towering cliffs, rocky shoreline and open sea – to the east the Bristol Channel, to the west the Atlantic Ocean – attract many species typical of such habitats, and some completely atypical. The unexpected is part of Lundy's magic, drawing human visitors back to this remote granite outcrop year after year.

The wealth of Lundy's bird life can be enjoyed whether visiting for a few hours on a day trip or, better still, by staying on the island, either camping or in one of the self-catering cottages run by the Landmark Trust. Spring (from March to early June) and autumn (August to November) are the periods of greatest interest for birdwatchers. Migrant birds are passing through at these times, with spring also providing the draw of breeding sea and landbirds. An added attraction for birdwatchers on the island, particularly in autumn, is 'seawatching'. Comparatively little of this peaceful (if sometimes uncomfortable) pastime has been done from Lundy's cliff-tops, but with modern optics there is always the chance of finding unusual shearwaters, seaducks, divers, terns, skuas, non-breeding gull species and perhaps even phalaropes. There is certainly plenty of potential for adding some exciting new records.

About this book

This book documents the birds of Lundy from the earliest fragments of historical information, through the first more detailed accounts of the late nineteenth and early twentieth centuries, to the formation of the Lundy Field Society (LFS) in 1946 and the instigation of regular ornithological recording that continues to this day. The opening chapters provide background and context, with a brief description of the island and the history of human habitation and land use that has produced the mosaic of natural, semi-natural and entirely manmade habitats to be found on the island today and which is partly responsible for the sheer diversity of Lundy's birds. We have also drawn together a brief history of ornithology and bird conservation on the island, an indication of what birds to expect – or hope for – at various times of year, and hints on some of the most promising places to look for birds when visiting Lundy. The latter include four suggested routes of varying distance to assist those new to the island and keen to make the most of limited time, particularly if on a day trip.

The Systematic List of birds recorded on the island constitutes the heart of the book. This is followed by an Appendix containing brief accounts of species which, for varied reasons, cannot be accorded full status in the Systematic List. Both the Systematic List and the Appendix are based largely on the compilation and analysis of information contained in the daily logbook maintained on the island by the LFS since 1969, the *LFS Annual Reports* covering the years 1947 to 2005, and the annual *Devon Bird Reports* published by the Devon Bird Watching & Preservation Society (DBWPS). We have also taken into account all records contained in the LFS logbooks for the whole of 2006 and up to 25 August 2007. In addition, the species accounts draw on two previous publications: *A List of the birds of Lundy* by Peter Davis, published by the LFS in 1954, and *The Birds of Lundy* by Nick Dymond, published by

DBWPS in 1980. Historical information on the island's birds prior to the commencement of LFS recording has been taken from a wide variety of other sources, referenced where appropriate and included in the Bibliography.

All place names mentioned in the text are shown on the map of Lundy on pages 10 & 11.

For the sake of completeness and to assist future studies, we have investigated as thoroughly as possible all published records where crucial information appeared to be lacking or where we suspected an error had been made. Inconsistencies found in the details published at national, county and island levels are included in a series of endnotes which detail our findings and conclusions in each case (see page 293).

Whether you have already been visiting Lundy for many years or are a newcomer to the island, and regardless of whether you think of yourself as a birdwatcher, we hope you will find within these pages much that is informative and entertaining and that will add to your enjoyment of Lundy and its birds.

Documenting bird records

The means of documenting and authenticating records has changed over the years. Until 1947, responsibility depended entirely on the thoroughness of individual observers – for example, the Heaven Diaries 1870–1905; entries for Lundy in *The Birds of Devon* by D'Urban & Mathew, published in 1892 and updated with a supplement in 1895; in *Lundy, its history and natural history* by Lewis Loyd, published in 1925; and the personal observations of Felix Gade between 1926 and 1974, many of which were published in *My Life on Lundy* in 1978. Between 1947 and 1967 and again in 1972–1973, the LFS employed seasonal wardens who were responsible for maintaining ornithological records that were published in the *LFS Annual Report*. At these times there was no formal system for integrating Lundy records into the *Devon Bird Report*. With the establishment of the *British Birds Rarities Committee* (BBRC) in 1958, a new standard was set for the recording of nationally rare bird species and for the first time it became necessary to submit a detailed written description (supported by photographic evidence if possible) for review and authentication by the BBRC. Consequently, records of rare birds on Lundy since 1958 must have been accepted by the BBRC to be included in the Devon or Lundy lists.

As identification techniques, optical equipment and observer skills have become ever more sophisticated, so the system of recording has been refined. Today, the BBRC continues to assess reports of national rarities, while the Devon Birds Records Committee considers records of nationally scarce migrants and the LFS deals with other Lundy vagrants. The latter include birds such as Magpie or Jay that are commonplace on the mainland but which are extremely rare on Lundy and which therefore require acceptance of a written description if they are to be included in the island annals. Most descriptions are entered in the LFS logbook which is kept in the Tavern and in which all wildlife observations may be recorded.

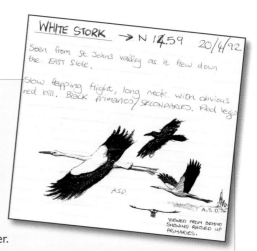

Bird logging

An entry by the LFS secretary in the 1968 *LFS Annual Report* states: "We have decided also to keep a Visitors Log Book on Lundy so that any sightings or observations made by visitors to the island may be recorded." The first such logbook was established in 1969 and the practice continues today, offering visitors the opportunity to record and share their wildlife sightings while on the island, whether on a day-trip or staying for longer.

The LFS logbook entry for Lundy's only record of a White Stork (see page 74).

Variation in observer coverage and recording methods

One of the challenges inherent in preparing the Systematic List has been to take due account of variations in coverage of the island by experienced birdwatchers. This applies to variation within and between months, seasons and years. As already mentioned, in many years past a bird warden was employed who was responsible, among other tasks, for maintaining detailed, standardised records. In other years coverage has fallen to visiting birdwatchers; in some weeks there may be many observers present, in others none at all. Hence, the main migration period of some species may be missed entirely in any given year or season. In recent years, coverage has been especially poor in winter and for some weeks in midsummer. The presence of bird ringers is similarly patchy, nowadays being concentrated mainly into a few short weeks in spring and again in mid to late autumn.

Not only does the number and experience of observers vary, but also the methods used: from detailed counts of birds actually seen, to estimated numbers of those seen, to extrapolation for the whole island based on counts from a limited area. Furthermore, many common species usually thought of as nocturnal migrants – such as Blackcap, Willow Warbler or Goldcrest – may also pass through the island by day; a fact clearly revealed by ringing studies combined with careful observation (e.g. the number of individual Willow Warblers seen at any one time in St John's Valley may never reach double figures on a given day, even though the ringing totals for the same day show that more than 50 had moved through). Regrettably, visiting birdwatchers don't always enter their observations in the LFS logbook, meaning that valuable information is lost. Even the many visitors who do use the log are often tempted to put a fairly meaningless 'tick' against a species name rather than a count or estimate of the number seen.

This variation makes drawing direct comparisons from year to year fraught with uncertainty and is one of the reasons we have not repeated the histograms compiled by Dymond (1980) from daily LFS counts. With few birdwatchers present for large parts of the year since the cessation of the position of LFS bird warden (at the end of 1973), such histograms would nowadays reveal more about the movements of birdwatchers than the birds themselves!

A close encounter with a well-camouflaged Long-eared Owl (above) in Millcombe, 5 May 2007.

A portrait of the island

Geography and geology

Straddling the confluence of the Atlantic Ocean and the Bristol Channel, the island of Lundy (geographical coordinates 51°11'N 4°40'W) lies some 18 kilometres north-north-west of the North Devon mainland at Hartland Point and approximately 48 kilometres south of the two nearest points on the South Wales coast at St Govan's Head (Pembrokeshire) and Worms Head (Gower). The island's modest dimensions – about five kilometres long and a little over one kilometre at the widest point – belie its variety of landscapes. This is due in no small part to the deeply indented coastline, which extends greatly the island's perimeter.

Given that the length of Lundy lies virtually north–south, the island's western coast is exposed to the full force of Atlantic storms, while the eastern shore, facing inland towards the Bristol Channel, is usually much more sheltered (though a fearful place in easterly gales!). This difference in exposure to the elements is reflected in the contrast between the dramatic ruggedness of the West Side, with its pounding seas, towering cliffs and thrift-carpeted sidelands, and the softer landscape of the East Side, with its more gently sloping sidelands and well-vegetated combes.

The majority of the island is composed of granite, except for the south-easternmost corner which consists of shale and basalt, with cliffs rising to over 100 metres and only a handful of landing places accessible from both plateau and sea – on the West Side at Montagu Steps, Pilot's Quay and Pyramid Rock, and on the East Side at Brazen Ward, Quarry Beach and, of course, the Landing Bay, where the island supply vessel, *MS Oldenburg*, berths alongside the jetty completed in 1999.

The gently undulating plateau, which covers an area of about 445 hectares, and much of the southern half of the island is more than 120 metres above sea level (a.s.l), rising to 141 metres a.s.l. at Beacon Hill, site of the Old Light. The northern half generally lies between 80 and 100 metres a.s.l., but reaches 128 metres at Tibbett's Hill.

Human habitation and use

Lundy has a long history of human habitation, evidence of which can be seen all over the island, from the medieval long-house at Widow's Tenement near Threequarter Wall, or the early Christian burial site at Beacon Hill, to the Castle and relatively much more recent artefacts such as the quarries, the Terrace and associated buildings, the Battery, and of course the three lighthouses. Lundy's human history has been the subject of painstaking research over many years and readers are referred for further information to books such as *The Island of Lundy* by A.F. Langham (1994b) and the papers published in the Lundy Field Society's *Annual Reports*. For the purposes of this book it is simply important to underline that Lundy's apparently wild landscape is in fact the product of centuries of human influence, ranging from the keeping of rabbits, the farming of sheep and cattle, the release at different times of various kinds of deer on the island, and the rearing of Lundy's famous ponies, to cultivation of cereal crops, hay-making, quarrying for granite and, more recently, tourism and recreation. The impacts of these activities are discussed further in the section on conservation.

The ownership of the island by the Heaven family, from 1834 to 1916, marked a significant point in the more recent natural history of Lundy, since it was the construction of Millcombe House in 1840 as the Heavens' residence that led to the extensive planting of trees and shrubs in Millcombe. These plantings were added to by Martin Coles Harman in the first half of the twentieth century. It was Mr Harman who was also responsible for introducing an astonishing variety of birds and mammals to the island; these included Mute Swan, Red Grouse, Grey Partridge, Moorhen, Red Deer, Roe Deer, Fallow Deer, Rock Wallaby, Red Squirrel and even Guinea Pigs. Most failed while others such as Brown Hare and Pheasant succeeded temporarily. Two of Mr Harman's introductions, Soay Sheep and Japanese Sika Deer, persist to this day (see 'Feral grazing animals' on page 18).

In 1969 ownership of Lundy passed to the National Trust, which leases the island to the Landmark Trust. In the time since, the Landmark Trust has undertaken an enormous programme of renovation and reconstruction, providing the infrastructure and services that visitors are now able to enjoy. Access from spring to autumn is by the island's supply vessel, *MS Oldenburg*, which once plied the waters of the Wadden Sea but which nowadays links Lundy with the North Devon ports of Bideford and Ilfracombe. Increasing numbers of people are coming to the island, with more than 20,000 visitors in 2006. In winter the boat service is replaced by a helicopter shuttle that runs between Hartland Point and Lundy.

The village, looking north-west towards Beacon Hill and the Old Light.

Natural and semi-natural habitats

The island provides varied habitats for birds, including:

○ **Shallow inshore waters** (e.g. the Landing Bay) favoured by feeding auks and Shags.

○ **Boulder beaches and rocky platforms** close to sea level (e.g. Quarry Beach, North West Point) used by small numbers of feeding and roosting waders, including breeding Oystercatchers, migrants such as Curlews, Whimbrels and Turnstones, and roosting/resting gulls and Shags.

○ **Sea cliffs** (e.g. Jenny's Cove, Long Roost) used by breeding Fulmars, Shags, Kittiwakes, Razorbills, Guillemots, Peregrines, Ravens and Rock Pipits. Lundy's remaining Puffins nest in burrows at the junction of the cliff tops and the grassy sidelands.

○ **Sidelands** (e.g. between Battery Point and Old Light) used by breeding Manx Shearwaters and nesting Meadow Pipits, Wrens and Wheatears, and as feeding and resting places for a wide range of passerine migrants.

Quarter Wall Pond, with the Old Hospital top left.

○ **Wet moorland** (e.g. around Pondsbury and Punchbowl Valley) which supports relatively few species but with numerous Meadow Pipits nesting amongst the grassy tussocks, and Snipe occasionally flushed from autumn to spring. It is perhaps also the most likely area in which to see migrant harriers or Short-eared Owls.

○ **'Waved' heathland** with wind-pruned 'waved'-form gorse and heather (e.g. on the northern slopes of Tibbett's Hill and at the southern end of South West Field) which supports nesting Stonechats and Linnets and migrant warblers.

○ **Freshwater habitats** (e.g. Pondsbury, Rocket Pole Pond, Quarry Pond, Quarter Wall Pond, streams, flushes and temporary pools). Pondsbury, the only sizeable area of open water on Lundy, is favoured by visiting wildfowl and waders, as well as flocks of migrant Swallows and martins which feed and drink on the wing, while the smaller pools may attract waders and are often magnets for smaller migrants, including Sedge Warblers, which feed in fringing vegetation.

○ **Vegetated combes.** Millcombe and St John's Valley, St Helen's Copse and Quarter Wall Copse are the only significant areas of trees and shrubs and hence attract the great majority of migrant warblers and flycatchers, alongside a wide range of other species including breeding Woodpigeons, Dunnocks, Robins, Blackbirds, Song Thrushes and Chaffinches, and passage or wintering Water Rails, Woodcocks and Sparrowhawks.

○ **Grazed, semi-improved grassland** (e.g. Middle Park, South West Field) favoured by Skylarks, Wheatears, pipits, buntings, plovers and Whimbrel.

○ **Improved grassland, farm and village buildings, drystone walls.** The intensively farmed grassland tends to attract relatively few birds, though wagtails, Carrion Crows, Ravens and Starlings feed among the domestic sheep. The buildings provide nesting and roosting sites for House Sparrows (which also benefit from numerous nestboxes), Starlings, Pied Wagtails and occasional pairs of Swallows, while the island's extensive network of drystone walls are favoured as perches by birds as varied as Merlin, Turtle Dove, Cuckoo, chats and finches.

Native flora and fauna

The island's only native resident mammals are Pygmy Shrew and Atlantic Grey Seal. Bats (Long-eared and Pipistrelle), Common Seals and cetaceans (dolphins, porpoises and even the odd passing whale) are seen from time to time and Basking Sharks and occasionally Sunfish occur in summer. There is a rich insect fauna, including migratory butterflies and moths, such as Red Admiral and Hummingbird Hawk-moth. Among Lundy's flora, the most notable species is Lundy Cabbage, which is unique to the island and supports its own species of flea beetle – the Bronze Lundy Cabbage Flea Beetle – also found nowhere else in the world. The rare Small Adder's-tongue Fern is abundant in Middle Park and South West Field in late spring, while the wet heathland around Pondsbury holds a variety of specialised, though not rare, wetland plants including Bog Asphodel, Round-leaved Sundew and Heath Spotted-orchid. Other notable plants include Balm-leaved Figwort (e.g. along the Lower East Side Path) and Royal Fern (e.g. in some of the quarries), and Golden Hair Lichen which thrives in the clean air of Lundy. A complete checklist of Lundy's flora was compiled by Elizabeth Hubbard (1971) and updated by Lorna Gibson (1992).

Lundy Cabbage

Feral grazing animals

Lundy has a long history of grazing by domestic and feral livestock, currently including domestic and Soay sheep, goats, Lundy Ponies, Sika Deer and rabbits. Other grazing animals introduced in the past have included cattle, as well as Red Deer and Brown Hare, both of which have died out. The April 2007 feral mammal survey recorded 186 Soays, 58 goats and 99 Sika Deer, but only 193 rabbits following a severe outbreak of myxomatosis in 2006. These animals have a tremendous impact on Lundy's vegetation, bringing both advantages and disadvantages for conservation (see following page).

Sika Deer, goats, Lundy Ponies and Soay Sheep are all part of the Lundy landscape.

Bird conservation on Lundy – past, present and future

The present-day mosaic of habitats on Lundy that supports such a wide range of birds is the product of hundreds, even thousands, of years of human activity. Ploughing, grazing, burning, construction of buildings, stone walls, roads and tracks, and the installation of drains, dams and boreholes have all changed the island's natural landscape and vegetation. Nowadays, conservation is about managing present and future human activities to ensure that the rich diversity of habitats is maintained and enhanced, and that potentially damaging impacts are reduced to an absolute minimum or avoided altogether.

In the past Lundy's seabirds provided valuable protein through their eggs and meat and they were hunted for the income generated by the sale of wings and feathers to the fashion industry (see 'The slaughter of Lundy's seabirds', pages 36 & 37). In the early days of ornithology during the nineteenth century it was standard practice for any unusual bird to be shot in order that its identity might be established and proven. Fortunately times have changed and nowadays the accent is very much on protection and conservation and there are few direct threats remaining.

Since 1976 the majority of Lundy's land area – with the exception of the village and farm – has been designated as a Site of Special Scientific Interest (SSSI) in recognition of its valuable natural and semi-natural habitats, including 'waved' heath (see page 17), unimproved grassland and seabird cliffs.

The East Side, showing a recently cleared area and the extent of the remaining rhododendron in May 2007.

The waters around the island were designated in 1986 as the UK's first statutory Marine Nature Reserve (MNR) and since April 2005 have been listed as a Special Area of Conservation (SAC) under the European Union Habitats Directive. Management of the terrestrial SSSI and MNR/SAC is led by a partnership of Natural England, the Landmark Trust and the National Trust, and coordinated through a management forum which includes representation from other bodies such as the Lundy Field Society, Devon Sea Fisheries Committee and the RSPB. The management plan for the terrestrial SSSI guides the stocking densities and grazing regime for different parts of the island, sets out climbing restrictions during the breeding season and has provided the framework for rhododendron control and rat eradication (see below). Parts of the island that are outside the SSSI but which have important conservation value, such as South West Field and Ackland's Moor, have been entered into agri-environment schemes where the government financially rewards conservation-friendly stocking and grazing regimes. The stocking density of domestic sheep for the farm as a whole has been reduced significantly in recent years, but there continues to be application of significant quantities of synthetic fertilisers, which inevitably leach into water courses and unimproved/semi-improved grassland. As of February 2007, Natural England assessed the condition of the SSSI as 40.5% 'favourable', 45.5% 'unfavourable recovering' and 14% 'unfavourable declining' (explanations of these categories are available from Natural England's website: www.naturalengland.org.uk).

The highest-profile bird conservation project of recent years has been the Seabird Recovery Programme initiated in 2001 as a joint venture of English Nature (now Natural England), the Landmark Trust, National Trust and the RSPB. The first phase of this was a rat eradication programme, following research establishing that the island's huge rat population was the single most important threat to nesting Manx Shearwaters – a species for which the UK has international responsibility. Over the winters of 2002/03 and 2003/04 the entire island was covered with a 50-metre grid of more than 2,000 poison bait stations. This extraordinary effort appears to have been successful, with no signs of rats since February 2004 and the island having been declared 'rat free' in 2006. However, monitoring continues and an emergency control plan is ready to swing into action should rats ever return to the island. There have already been promising signs that the Seabird Recovery Project has helped both Manx Shearwaters and Puffins (and possibly also Storm Petrels) to nest successfully, but it will be many years before the long-term prospects for these and other seabirds are clear.

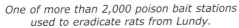

One of more than 2,000 poison bait stations used to eradicate rats from Lundy.

The other most visible conservation project of recent years has been the progressive clearance of the dense stands of rhododendron that at one time threatened to overwhelm the island, excluding native flora, notably Lundy Cabbage and its endemic invertebrate fauna. Rhododendron self-seeds abundantly on the island, with seeds carried far and wide on the wind. It also produces a highly acidic leaf litter, while the shrub's roots exude substances that are toxic to other plants. These effects, combined with the casting of dense shade, mean that nothing else can grow. While the remaining rhododendron stands undoubtedly provide roosting, feeding and nesting opportunities for some birds (e.g. nesting Robins, Chaffinches, Woodpigeons and staging migrants) these benefits are heavily outweighed by the threat that rhododendron poses to natural habitats and food-chains. The target is to eradicate rhododendron from the island by 2012.

Grazing pressure from domestic and feral livestock tends to vary significantly from year to year, according to the numbers of each animal (e.g. the rabbit population goes through huge peaks and troughs related to outbreaks of disease) and the lushness of growth in a given season, which itself depends on variations in rainfall and temperature. The significance for Lundy's birds is that without feral grazers the island's landscape would consist of a very different, probably much less varied, range of habitats. Each type of grazing animal has a different impact on the vegetation – according to the plant species preferred, the height above ground at which they are grazed off, whether the stems are nibbled or pulled, and the degree of trampling or poaching involved – and it is a constant challenge to maintain a beneficial balance without parts of the island becoming either overgrazed or (where a short, open sward is required) undergrazed.

Continued vigilance for rats, the careful management of domestic and feral grazing livestock, further clearance of rhododendron, planting of native tree species within existing treed areas to enhance nesting, feeding and roosting opportunities for resident and migrant landbirds, and ongoing restrictions on climbing during the breeding season will all benefit Lundy's birds. Areas deserving of greater conservation focus in future include the possible negative impacts of water abstraction (very much greater nowadays than in the past) and fertiliser application on the island's vegetation and wetlands, and the benefits that the organic cultivation of small areas of weed-seed and cereal crops would have for resident, migratory and wintering birds.

While the conservation measures taken on the island itself play a vital role in securing the future for Lundy's birds, there are other factors affecting them that can only be tackled through national or even international environmental protection policies and action. For example, the island's seabirds remain highly vulnerable to the effects of marine pollution – whether the nightmare scenario of a major accident causing direct pollution of Lundy's shoreline during the breeding season or the hidden toll that is taken when birds are dispersed at sea at other times of year. Climate change also poses threats ranging from the warming of the seas around Britain and consequent changes in the distribution and availability of sand-eels and other food for seabirds, to the expansion of deserts along migration routes and in the wintering areas used by the warblers, chats, flycatchers and hirundines that pass through Lundy every year.

The eastern end of Threequarter Wall with the heather-clad slopes of North End beyond.

A chronology of Lundy ornithology

Below are some of the most important milestones in Lundy's ornithological history, beginning in the second half of the nineteenth century. Details of all the publications mentioned can be found in the Bibliography.

1870–1905	Entries in the diaries of the Heaven family, owners of Lundy from 1834 to 1916, provide the first dated records for several species.
1871	First definitive list of the birds of Lundy published by John Roberts Chanter.
1876	Edward Parfitt publishes an updated list of the birds of Lundy, based largely on Chanter, in Part XIV of *The Fauna of Devon*.
1877	Chanter updates his 1871 list as part of his monograph on Lundy.
1892	*The Birds of Devon* by William D'Urban and the Rev. Murray Mathew (revised 1895) contains numerous references to birds on Lundy.
1903	Last year for which details of nesting Gannets are available; all five nests fail and the colony dies out altogether in the next few years.
1925	Lewis Loyd's book *Lundy, its history and natural history* contains an extensive section on the island's birds.
1938	An attempt to reintroduce Gannets from the Welsh colony on Grassholm fails.
1940	Richard Perry's account of a spring and summer spent observing breeding seabirds on Lundy – *Lundy Isle of Puffins* – is published.
1944	Fulmars breed for the first time.
1946	The Lundy Field Society (LFS) is founded and the island joins the network of British and Irish Bird Observatories. A list of Lundy's birds, compiled by N.V. Allen, is published in Mervyn Palmer's *The fauna and flora of the Ilfracombe District of North Devon*.
1947	First *LFS Annual Report* is published, containing the first annual list of bird sightings on the island. Bird ringing commences, focusing in particular on the island's breeding seabirds.
1950	A summary by Hugh Boyd of the ornithological records in the Heaven Diaries is published in the *LFS Annual Report*.
1952	American Robin on Lundy is the first for Britain.
1954	*A list of the birds of Lundy* by warden Peter Davis is published by the LFS, giving full status to 220 species. Common Yellowthroat on Lundy is the first for Britain.
1954–1957	Barbara Snow (née Whitaker) undertakes detailed studies of Lundy's breeding Shags.
1955	Sardinian Warbler on Lundy is the first for Britain.
1958	Baltimore Oriole on Lundy is the first for Britain.
1959	Last nesting by Cormorants; four young raised.
1962	Bimaculated Lark on Lundy is the first for Britain.
1966	Eastern (Rufous-sided) Towhee and Spanish Sparrow on Lundy are both firsts for Britain, with the Towhee also the first for the Western Palearctic. Two Least Sandpipers caught on Lundy are the first to be ringed in Britain.
1973	Last successful breeding by Curlew.

1978	In the year of his death, Felix Gade's *My Life on Lundy* is published, containing many ornithological observations, especially prior to and during World War II.
1980	Nick Dymond's *The Birds of Lundy* is published by Devon Bird Watching & Preservation Society, giving full status to 274 species. Seven study plots are set up for monitoring Lundy's breeding seabirds.

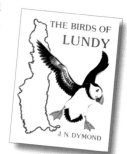

1985	160 species – still the highest annual total – are recorded.
1986	A 'Breeding Seabird Site Register' is established following surveys in 1980, 1982 and 1986.
1987	Eastern Phoebe on Lundy is the first for Britain and the Western Palearctic.
1990	Ancient Murrelet on Lundy is the first for Britain and the Western Palearctic.
1991	A long-term study of House Sparrows commences, initially by the University of Leicester and subsequently by the University of Sheffield.
1994	A seven-year study of Skylarks by Dr John Hutchinson begins.
2000	Last confirmed breeding of Lapwing.
2001	The Seabird Recovery Project commences with a rat eradication campaign.
2004	Manx Shearwaters breed successfully for the first time in living memory.
2006	The island is declared rat free, though monitoring continues. Green-winged Teal becomes the latest addition to the Lundy list.
2007	Puffins are few in number but include up to four active burrows, with breeding confirmed in July. This new book on the island's birds is published, giving full status to 317 species.

Lundy Wardens 1947–2007

1947	Rowland Barker	**1972–1973**	Nick Dymond
1948	Rosemary Studdy (April–June)	**1974**	position discontinued
1948–1949	Hugh Boyd	**1975–1977**	LFS Rep: Michael Rogers
1950	Stan Ball (March–April)	**1978–1980**	LFS Rep: Richard Campey
1950–1951	David Lea	**1980–1983**	LFS Rep: Keith Mortimer
1951–1954	Peter Davis	**1984–1991**	LFS Rep: Mary Gade
1954–1958	Barbara Whitaker	**1986–1988**	Neil Willcox
1958	Bill Workman	**1989–1994**	Andrew Gibson
1959–1964	Michael Jones	**1994–1996**	Emma Parkes
1965	Jonathan Sparrow, Tony Prater	**1996–2002**	Liza Cole
1966–1967	Clifford Waller	**2002–2005**	Ben Sampson
1968–1971	position discontinued	**2006–**	Nicola Saunders

The position of warden from its instigation in 1947 to 1967 was funded by the Lundy Field Society. It was discontinued for lack of funds between 1968 and 1971 but was reinstated with the financial assistance of the Landmark Trust in 1972 and 1973. Individual staff on the island acted as LFS representative between 1975 and 1991, with responsibility for maintaining the LFS logbook. Since 1996 the position of Marine Nature Reserve/Wildlife Warden has been supported by the Landmark Trust and Natural England.

Bird ringing on Lundy

"Much of the excitement of ringing on an island is derived from the rarities but these are, almost by definition, individuals which are atypical in their migration behaviour; it is the everyday ringing of common species in large numbers which is most valuable in providing information about bird movements and life histories."

Tony Taylor, 1981 *LFS Annual Report*

Bird ringing on Lundy began in 1947 following the founding a year earlier of the Lundy Field Society and the setting up of an 'observatory' in the Old Light. The new observatory quickly joined the network of bird observatories around the coast of Britain and Ireland, coordinated by the Bird Observatories Committee of the British Trust for Ornithology (BTO), the organisation responsible for running the British Ringing Scheme. In these early years, ringing – largely carried out by the LFS warden and concentrating on nestlings and cliff-nesting seabirds – was combined with a daily 'Cruise', a walk of a little under four miles each morning around the southern half of the island, covering in particular the south-eastern slopes which support most of the vegetative cover on the island. Its aim was to provide numerical records of resident and migrant birds for comparative use year on year.

Various methods of catching birds have been employed on Lundy over the years. These have ranged from large, immobile Heligoland traps and smaller, portable versions, to mist-nets, drag-nets (useful for catching grassland species like Skylark and Meadow Pipit), fleyg nets (mesh nets akin to a butterfly net), chardonneret traps (small mesh cages for catching passerines), wader traps, clap-nets, dazzling (using a torch at night to catch birds at roost), and ringing of pulli (nestlings). Keepers at the North and South Lighthouses also contributed to the yearly ringing totals, catching birds attracted to the lights at night.

Heligoland traps

The idea of constructing a Heligoland trap – a tunnel of fine wire mesh with a catching box at one end, named after the site of the first such trap on the island of Heligoland off north-west Germany – was first raised by LFS Secretary Leslie Harvey in a letter to Martin Coles Harman, the owner of Lundy, in March 1946. That autumn the first trap was built between Millcombe House and the Manor Farm Hotel. It was badly damaged shortly afterwards by winter gales and twice destroyed during the first half of 1947, after which it was relocated for a short time in St John's Valley.

The Garden Trap.

In 1949 a small Heligoland trap was erected in the garden adjacent to the Old Light. Though prone to damage by strong winds and destroyed more than once in its early days, the 'Garden Trap', as it was known, proved very successful. In its first year 183 birds of 24 species were caught, among them Pied Flycatcher, Wood Warbler, Grasshopper Warbler and Icterine Warbler. It was destroyed again by gales in 1959, restored for a final time a year later but has long since disappeared.

Another Heligoland trap was constructed in 1950 in the southernmost quarry, initially with little catching success, the mouth of the trap being too high, allowing birds to fly out over the heads of the ringers. At the same time, two portable traps (clap-nets) were introduced and used around the farm, catching 11 Chaffinches and a Blackbird in their first year of use. In 1951 the quarry trap was dismantled and a new one constructed on the Terrace. This proved far more successful, catching 218 birds in its first year, including the first ever Melodious Warbler ringed in Britain, the second Little Bunting and third Wood Sandpiper. The Terrace trap, which was moved to its present location in 1962, has since been rebuilt or extensively repaired in 1963, 1972, 1988 and 1998. The Quarter Wall Heligoland trap was constructed in 1953 and rebuilt with double entrances in 1973; the east-facing opening was later removed because the bulky nature of the construction discouraged birds from entering. In 1973, the last year in which the Terrace and Quarter Wall traps were operational on a full-time basis, they contributed more than 700 of the 878 full-grown birds caught.

Seabird ringing

Seabirds were the early focus of ornithological work for the LFS wardens and considerable effort went into ringing nestling Shags, gulls and auks. Three papers published in the 1956 *LFS Annual Report* summarise the results in terms of the dispersal of Lundy-bred birds away from the island. Later, in 1973 and 1974, Kittiwakes were the subject of a concerted ringing effort, with 714 nestlings ringed. The movements of these birds included only the second British Kittiwake recovery from Morocco. More recently, a week of seabird ringing at the end of June in both 1995 and 1996 resulted in 204 Lesser Black-backed Gulls being ringed, more than doubling the grand total for this species over the previous 47 years and reflecting the great increase in their numbers since the last serious efforts to ring seabirds in the early 1970s. Another week in June 1999 saw a further 131 Lesser Black-backed Gulls ringed. Summaries of ringing controls and recoveries for all seabirds are given in the species accounts in the Systematic List.

The advent of mist-nets

Mist-nets were first used on Lundy in 1958. The introduction to the *LFS Annual Report* for the year states: "The mist nets which [have been] introduced [by LFS warden Bill Workman] have proved very adaptable to conditions on Lundy and have yielded very profitable harvests, although they will not of course be expected to replace the existing Heligoland traps." Their impact was immediately noticeable, just two nets contributing 358 of the year's 1,234 captures. By this time the permanent traps were generally in poor condition and as the constant repairs needed to the Heligoland traps were straining the LFS's limited finances, mist-nets soon became the prime means of catching birds. Light, easily portable (aside from the carrying of 12-foot bamboo support poles) and simple to erect, mist-nets gradually led to the focus of the ringing effort moving away from breeding seabirds to migratory passerines. A comparison of Lundy's 'Top Ten' ringed birds between the end of 1966 (Table 1) and the end of 2006 (Table 2) demonstrates the shift in emphasis that has persisted to this day.

Since the demise of the LFS warden position at the end of 1973, bird ringing on Lundy has relied entirely on volunteers, albeit trained and qualified ringers in their own right, holding the requisite BTO ringing permit. The spring and autumn migration seasons are naturally the time of most interest, so ringing coverage has largely been restricted to these periods. With the Heligoland traps again in a state of disrepair and their future uncertain, most of the ringing effort is nowadays concentrated in St John's

Table 1. Lundy's 'Top Ten' ringed birds 1947–1966			Table 2. Lundy's 'Top Ten' ringed birds 1947–2006		
1.	Herring Gull	2,670	1.	Willow Warbler	12,814
2.	Guillemot	2,479	2.	Goldcrest	8,353
3.	Willow Warbler	2,245	3.	Chaffinch	6,885
4.	Whitethroat	1,790	4.	Swallow	6,155
5.	Kittiwake	1,648	5.	Blackcap	4,140
6.	Blackbird	1,115	6.	Blackbird	4,008
7.	Razorbill	1,106	7.	Chiffchaff	3,979
8.	Shag	963	8.	Meadow Pipit	3,215
9.	Starling	705	9.	Whitethroat	2,977
10.	Chiffchaff	622	10.	Herring Gull	2,930

Valley and Millcombe, and it is here that you are most likely to see mist-nets being operated, usually for a few weeks in spring and for slightly longer in autumn.

In his ringing report in the 1979 *LFS Annual Report*, Tony Taylor noted that the list of most frequently ringed species had changed considerably since the early 1970s, with only a handful of cliff-nesting seabirds ringed in the intervening years, largely owing to the absence of a full-time warden. This shift in emphasis had a delayed effect on the number of controls and recoveries. Four years later Tony wrote: "The number of recoveries and controls of ringed birds has been dropping steadily in recent years because seabirds, which used to make up the bulk of the records, have not been ringed in significant numbers since 1973 and the number of ringed individuals still alive has therefore been dwindling." Nevertheless, some seabird ringing still takes place, with much of the current effort devoted to Manx Shearwaters and to a lesser extent Storm Petrels.

Ringing a Willow Warbler.

That ringing can reflect annual trends or short-term seasonal phenomena was demonstrated in 1985 when the total of 48 Siskins ringed on the island was greater than the combined number ringed in the preceding 34 years; in the autumn of 1985 an exceptional influx of continental Siskins reached Britain. Generally, a dearth of rarities during a year is reflected in the ringing. For instance, a Little Bunting ringed in 1991, a year in which the autumn migration was disappointing due to a prolonged period of poor weather, was the only national rarity caught.

By the end of 2006, 85,741 birds of 172 species had been ringed on Lundy. The highest number of species caught in any one year is 70 in 1966, while the highest annual total of birds ringed is 3,675 in 1988. Willow Warbler is the most commonly caught species, numbering 12,814, while 35 species have just one ring to their name. These include Lundy vagrants such as Little Grebe, unusual visitors like Moorhen, scarce migrants such as Spotted Crake, and national rarities like Citrine Wagtail and Red-flanked Bluetail. See page 289 for a complete list of species ringed and ringing totals.

Among many fascinating, and sometimes astonishing, controls and recoveries of birds ringed on the island are a Woodcock almost 3,000 kilometres away in Russia and two Sedge Warblers trapped 4,000 kilometres from Lundy in Djoudj National Park, Senegal, West Africa. Travelling in the other direction, a Chiffchaff ringed in that same Senegalese National Park was controlled on Lundy two months later during its spring migration. Among the resident birds, a Raven ringed as a chick on the island in 1965 was still going strong 13 years later.

Ringing of birds on Lundy has certainly revealed much about their life-cycles and seasonal movements, as can be seen from the species accounts. At a national level, for instance, ringing has helped to show that declines in the number of Sedge Warblers breeding in Britain are linked to lower levels of rainfall in their African wintering quarters. Yet for all that we have learnt, there remains an infinite amount still to be discovered.

The science of bird ringing

Bird ringing is a scientific research method based on the individual marking of birds. Any record of a ringed bird, either through recapture and subsequent release (generally termed 'retrap' for a resident bird or 'control' for a migrant) or on the occasion of its final 'recovery' as a dead bird, will tell us a lot about its life, particularly its movements. Tracking back the journeys of ringed birds allows us to define their migratory routes and staging areas, so providing crucial information for the planning of networks of protected areas for birds. Other information derived from controls and recoveries includes estimates of survival (longevity) and lifetime reproductive success, factors that are essential in determining the causes of changes in population sizes.

Adapted from **www.euring.org** – the European Union for Bird Ringing

Birds through the seasons

Spring

Spring migration through Lundy begins, for some species, as early as February, and extends, for others, into June. It tends to be very much a go-stop-go affair, heavily dependent on weather. Clear starlit nights, typical of settled, anticyclonic conditions, often lead to thin pickings for birdwatchers, since night migrants tend to overfly the island, having no need to stop. On the other hand, the same fine weather may bring impressive movements of daytime migrants, such as Swallows and martins which sometimes occur in their thousands, skimming low over the top of the island or hugging the shoreline in the lee of the cliffs.

The earliest migrants, in late February or early March, include Pied and White Wagtails, Meadow Pipits and Stonechats, followed a little later in March by Wheatears, Sand Martins and Chiffchaffs and perhaps the odd Ring Ouzel, Black Redstart or Firecrest. By the end of March the first few Swallows and Willow Warblers are likely to be seen, but it is typically the beginning of April when larger arrivals of Chiffchaffs and Willow Warblers signal that migration is in full swing. During the rest of April and into May the variety of birds gradually increases, common migrants including Grasshopper Warbler, Sedge Warbler, Whitethroat and Spotted Flycatcher, plus a scattering of Wood Warblers, Reed Warblers, Pied Flycatchers and Redstarts; these species occurring mainly in the sheltered, vegetated combes of the East Side, especially Millcombe, and along the Terrace.

On the plateau, large numbers of Wheatears stop off on their way to northern breeding grounds, mixing temporarily with the Lundy nesting population, while small numbers of Golden Plovers and Whimbrels can often be encountered on areas of semi-natural grassland, such as Middle Park, Ackland's Moor and South West Field. In some years a 'trip' of brightly coloured but cryptically

Kidney Vetch and Thrift mark spring on Rat Island.

patterned Dotterels may set the pulse of a lucky birdwatcher racing. These beautiful and enigmatic mountaintop nesters favour the same areas used by Golden Plovers and the two can sometimes be seen together.

Though renowned as the harbinger of spring, Cuckoos are sadly rather unusual on Lundy nowadays, but during late April and May the odd one may be seen perched on a stone wall or flying low over the ground, usually pursued by an attack squadron of Meadow Pipits. Sand Martins, House Martins, Swallows and Swifts are all common spring migrants, with the first three species sometimes to be seen lining up side-by-side on fence lines, typically in the vicinity of St Helen's Field and the eastern part of Quarter Wall.

Changeable weather, with cloudy or misty / drizzly conditions towards dawn after a fine night, can sometimes ground large numbers of birds, as was the case on 2 May 2004 when we witnessed an extraordinary 'fall' of hundreds of warblers, chats, flycatchers and other migrants. As quickly as they came, most had moved on by the following day.

The vast majority of migrants passing through Lundy are unseen, as evidenced by the following extract from the **1972 *LFS Annual Report***:

"On the night of 5/6th [May], calm and thick fog, there was a considerable attraction of migrants at the South Lighthouse, species involved including Curlew, Whimbrel, Dunlin, Common Sandpiper, Redstart, Whinchat, Spotted Flycatcher, Willow Warbler and Sedge Warbler. The only evidence of these migrants on the ground on the 6th were 22 Dunlin and a few Common Sandpipers."

Throughout the spring migration period, but particularly from the second half of April to the beginning of June, there is always the chance of seeing something out of the ordinary. Among the nationally scarce migrants that have occurred at this time of year are Purple Heron, Hoopoe, Wryneck, Bluethroat and Golden Oriole (the latter being virtually annual in May). Even rarer species occur from time to time and these have included Britain's fourth Eastern Bonelli's Warbler (April 2004), second Rüppell's Warbler (June 1979) and first – and, to date, only – Eastern Phoebe (April 1987). Perhaps more mundane for some, but of great excitement for regular Lundy birdwatchers are the sightings of species that are commonplace on the mainland but very unusual on this isolated granite outcrop. For example, we vividly recall watching a lone Rook, accompanied by a single Jackdaw, flying high to the north-east, away from the island and into a strong headwind on a clear but crisp May morning. On another occasion, this time in mid-April 1987, we ventured out to find a superb male Yellowhammer in full song at the top of Millcombe, only for it to be gone the next day.

Breeding birds and summer visitors

The facts and figures detailing the species that are known – or suspected – to have bred on Lundy are presented on pages 34 & 35. However, such a dry listing doesn't do justice to the rich experience of being on the island during the height of the breeding season. Early nesters include Ravens, which favour the inaccessible cliffs of the West Side and South End, stealing seabirds' eggs to feed their already well-grown or even fledged young. Shags, auks (Razorbills, Guillemots and Puffins), Fulmars and Kittiwakes return to their breeding ledges, mainly along the West Side, in early spring, sometimes putting in brief appearances during fine spells in late winter. Sitting anywhere between Jenny's Cove and the Devil's Slide, particularly early in the morning when the birds are most active and the light is ideal for looking offshore towards the west, watching the comings and goings of the nesting seabirds is one of the highlights of birdwatching on Lundy. Further out to sea, Gannets and Manx Shearwaters can be seen passing by, while the shortest of forays out of doors on a moonless night during the spring and summer is likely to be rewarded by the eerie and unmistakable calls of Manx Shearwaters flying low over the sidelands.

> *"Six or seven pairs [of Lapwing] believed to have nested, though only four nests found. A flock thought to comprise the breeding population remained until the end of September."*
>
> **1949 *LFS Annual Report***
> (Lapwing is now extinct as a nesting species on Lundy)

Wheatears, Rock Pipits, Meadow Pipits and even Wrens nest commonly on the western sidelands, and their songs – which have to be powerful enough to compete with roaring seas and howling winds – are characteristic accompaniments to any spring or early summer bird walk. In the same vein, a penetrating *kleep-kleep* call will often draw attention to a pair of territorial Oystercatchers on the rocks far below.

While Kestrel, Sparrowhawk, Buzzard and, in the long-distant past, even Osprey and White-tailed Eagle, all feature in the list of confirmed or reported breeding species, the bird of prey that is most characteristic of Lundy nowadays is undoubtedly the Peregrine, whose spectacular aerial displays of territorial or courtship behaviour enthral birdwatchers and non-birdwatchers alike. Lundy's breeding Peregrines are, as elsewhere, strictly protected by law and climbing restrictions are in force to prevent disturbance of their nests. Sadly, Peregrines remain a target for egg-collectors, unscrupulous falconers and a minority of pigeon fanciers, and any suspicious activity should be reported immediately to the Lundy wildlife warden.

The walled gardens in Lower Millcombe, a haven for nesting songbirds.

The plateau supports very healthy breeding populations of both Skylark and Meadow Pipit, with the skies between Quarter Wall and Threequarter Wall literally alive with song-flighting males from early spring to early summer, especially in still, sunny conditions first thing in the morning. The careful and patient observer is certain to be rewarded with views of both species at their nests, but as with all breeding birds, take care to avoid causing any disturbance.

The gorsy heathland of the plateau and the scrubby eastern sidelands nowadays support a small breeding population of Stonechats, which raise several broods in good seasons, but which are vulnerable to the effects of cold weather – apparently a limiting factor in the past, but perhaps no longer in these times of global warming.

Nesting Woodpigeons, Dunnocks, Robins, Blackbirds, Song Thrushes, Chaffinches and Linnets are largely confined to the East Side, especially from Millcombe to the Terrace, while Pied Wagtails nest in drystone walls, holes in buildings or natural cavities, chiefly on the south-eastern part of the plateau. A thriving colony of House Sparrows breeds mainly in nestboxes erected for them around the farm and in Millcombe, while Starlings are to be found nesting under the eaves of several buildings, including the Church and Old Light. Other species breeding from time to time around the village include Swallow and Collared Dove.

These are Lundy's 'bread and butter' breeding birds, but each year there is something out of the ordinary; perhaps a nesting pair of Greenfinches, as in 1985, or Lesser Whitethroats, as in 2003. On other occasions an unusual species has summered on the island; none more exceptional than the Ancient Murrelet that maintained a lonely vigil among the breeding auks in Jenny's Cove over three breeding seasons in the 1990s.

By July, bird song has ceased, the seabirds are beginning to move offshore and young landbirds fledged on the island are mixing with those dispersing from the neighbouring mainland. In ornithological terms, autumn has begun!

Wet flushes like this one on the West Side are good places to look for migrating waders.

"Large numbers of Starlings and Chaffinches, with other species, begin to move through in the first or second weeks of October, but these movements are southerly until the end of the month or the first days of November. At this time the tide suddenly turns, and many thousands of birds pass to the north-west and north."

Former LFS warden **Peter Davis** (1954b) describing his observations of late autumn migrants presumed to be heading for Irish wintering grounds

Autumn

As at other coastal migration hotspots, including such famous locations as the Isles of Scilly, the north Norfolk coast and Fair Isle, autumn is the season during which most rare birds occur and hence the time when many birdwatchers choose to visit Lundy. However, autumn birdwatching on the island offers much more than the possibility of a chance encounter with a stray waif from North America or Siberia, exciting though such moments are.

Autumn is a long and subtly changing season on Lundy. At the time when the island is full of human visitors during the peak of the school holidays in late July and August, migrants are already moving south, with small numbers of waders and insect-eaters such as Swifts, warblers and flycatchers among the first to move. By mid to late August, suitable weather conditions can bring significant overnight arrivals of Sedge Warblers, Willow Warblers and Whitethroats to Millcombe and elsewhere along the East Side, with the main migration of Pied and Spotted Flycatchers, Redstarts and Wood Warblers also occurring at this time, along with increasing numbers of Swallows, martins and wagtails on the plateau. Unfortunately, coverage by birdwatchers – at least by those who enter their sightings in the LFS logbook – tends to be rather poor and much remains to be discovered and recorded about these early autumn movements.

September is a fickle month that may bring long periods of fine, settled and hot weather, while in other years, depression after depression sweeps in off the Atlantic bringing gales and lashing rain. As in spring, calm, clear conditions often presage low levels of visible migration, most birds choosing to push south while the going is good, not needing to take advantage of the food and shelter offered by Lundy in less favourable periods. However, anticyclonic weather in September can favour the arrival of scarce migrants from continental Europe, which may drift further west than normal when moving south with an easterly element in the wind. Among the species occurring relatively regularly have been Wryneck, Icterine and (especially) Melodious Warblers, Barred Warbler, Firecrest and Ortolan Bunting. And if it's hot and sunny and there are few birds around, what better way to pass the time than by lying on the Terrace watching for a passing Basking Shark or Sunfish?

Unsettled conditions – particularly day-to-day changes in wind direction and periods of rain or showers interspersed with clearer spells – tend to bring both higher numbers of birds and a greater diversity of species, with variety generally increasing as September merges imperceptibly with October. The first Lapland Buntings – something of a Lundy speciality – are typically seen (or more often heard) in the last week of September, while significant movements of Blackcaps, Chiffchaffs, Meadow Pipits and Goldcrests begin from about the middle of September and continue well into October, when they are joined by flocks of migrating finches and thrushes. The autumn Chaffinch migration is one of the highlights of the birdwatching year on Lundy; in favourable seasons tens of thousands may be seen streaming south in a single day, perhaps interspersed with much smaller numbers of Bramblings and Siskins.

South-westerly or westerly gales in September and October favour the arrival of birds from the other side of the Atlantic, with Lundy having an exceptional track record for North American waders and landbirds blown off course by fast-moving storms. September is the peak month for American waders, such as Buff-breasted Sandpiper, Pectoral Sandpiper or Semipalmated Sandpiper, while October is the most likely month for finding a Nearctic passerine such as Red-eyed Vireo (the most frequent transatlantic vagrant, with seven Lundy records), American Robin or Rose-breasted Grosbeak. National rarities and scarce migrants have arrived from all points of the compass in October, with some eastern species such as Richard's Pipit, Yellow-browed Warbler and Red-breasted Flycatcher being virtually annual, while others remain extreme vagrants; for example, Olive-backed Pipit, Red-flanked Bluetail, Radde's Warbler and Black-faced Bunting.

North or north-west winds in October or November may bring small arrivals of wildfowl, such as the family party of Whooper Swans that graced Pondsbury in November 2001, or the group of up to ten Pink-footed Geese that remained on the island for some weeks from October to December 2006. Other migrants with a northerly origin worth keeping an eye open for include Merlin and Snow Bunting, while late autumn is also perhaps the most likely time to see a Short-eared Owl or Hen Harrier quartering the moorland, or to flush a Woodcock from bracken or one of the copses.

The final departing Swallows, flycatchers and most warblers are usually seen in the last days of October or early November, while Black Redstarts, Chiffchaffs and Blackcaps continue to pass through for another few weeks. Autumn movements of pipits, thrushes, Goldcrests, finches and Starlings continue throughout November – and for some species even well into December, particularly if conditions remain mild. Indeed, the onset of winter, always deferred by Lundy's maritime location in the mild south west, seems to be getting later and later, with 'Indian Summer' – once applied to warm spells in September – now occurring in November in some years. A quick glance at the LFS logbook for 2006, for example, shows significant numbers of Swallows still passing through, alongside migrant butterflies and moths such as Painted Ladies and Hummingbird Hawk-moths.

Wintering

Unsurprisingly, winter is the season when coverage of the island by birdwatchers is at its sparsest. Even during the years when Lundy was part of the national Bird Observatories Network and the LFS employed a bird warden, coverage was largely confined to the period from spring to autumn. More recently, it has only been when a member of the island staff has had a personal interest in birdwatching that there has been anything like regular recording in winter – bird censusing not being part of the wildlife warden's already onerous duties. Among those who have gathered much of the information on wintering birds are: Felix Gade (1920s to 1970s), Nick Dymond (1972/73), Richard Campey (1978/79), Keith Mortimer (early 1980s) and Andrew Jewells (1990s).

Resident passerines such as Wren, Dunnock, Blackbird, House Sparrow and Chaffinch continue to be evident along the East Side and are occasionally joined by an overwintering Chiffchaff or Blackcap, or perhaps something even rarer (for Lundy) such as a Great Spotted Woodpecker, Blue Tit, Great Tit or Bullfinch. Lower Millcombe might host a wintering Water Rail. Most of the seabirds spend the winter at sea, but a visit to the West Side in mild, settled weather later in the season may be rewarded by the sight of the first returning Shags, auks or Fulmars visiting the nesting cliffs.

On the island plateau, small numbers of Meadow Pipits and Skylarks may be seen, but whether any of these are birds that breed on the island, or whether they are migrants from elsewhere, is entirely unknown. Other species that might be seen include Snipe, Woodcock, Redwing, Fieldfare, Starling, perhaps small numbers of Lapwing or Golden Plover and even the odd Jack Snipe. Though Lundy does not seem to attract many wintering waders typical of rocky shores, such as Oystercatcher, Turnstone, Curlew or Purple Sandpiper, it is always worth keeping an eye open, while the sheltered inshore waters may turn up a diver, grebe, seaduck or, as in both January 2006 and January 2007, Little Auk.

Freezing weather on the surrounding mainland can result in significant influxes of birds to Lundy in search of refuge and food. Peter Davis, then LFS warden, experienced a cold snap in late January and early February 1954 when snow lay for two days on the island, but covered the nearby mainland for a much longer period:

> "The first birds to arrive, on January 27th, were a number of Redwings, with a few Fieldfares and Song-thrushes and perhaps the single Jack Snipe seen. On 29th a few Woodcocks and Snipe had come in, to be followed on 30th by 10 Teal, a Golden Plover, a few Snipe, a Curlew and 2 Black-headed Gulls. About 50 other ducks, probably Teal, flew over, – the largest number seen at Lundy for many years. On January 31st there were 30 Teal

clustering in one of the open runnels: 18 Golden Plovers, a large number of Snipe, and new flocks of Skylarks, Fieldfares, Song-thrushes, Redwings and 2 Linnets appeared…By February 3rd they had begun to die: several Redwings, Song-thrushes, a Teal and a Lapwing were picked up, and the number of corpses increased on each ensuing day. Most of these were Redwings, but more Lapwings and a Curlew were found" (Davis 1954b).

The most severe British winter in living memory, that of 1962/63, when freezing conditions set in by late December and continued until early March, also affected Lundy. Felix Gade (1978) captured the severity of the time in his memoirs:

"Large flocks of birds arrived, and it is impossible to say how many died of cold, starvation and thirst, but there must have been thousands…Great black-backed gulls were slaughtering lapwings, curlews and woodcocks and eating their meagre bodies, and rats were killing the birds for food. Vince Squire found a rat's nest with a store of dead skylarks in it, and Mary [Squire, Gade's daughter] found forty-three dead starlings in a hole in the barn."

The 1962 *LFS Annual Report* elaborates:

"Large flocks of Snipe and Woodcock arrived at the beginning of January; a hundred of each being a very conservative estimate; and along with these Curlew, Lapwing, Starlings, Thrushes and Blackbirds – all of these birds suffered from the cold and starvation. Sixty Starlings were found dead in the church while many more were discovered wedged, three and four at a time, inside any sheltering crevice or hole around the farm. Curlews and a small group of Larks were frozen to death as they crouched huddled together under tree roots or behind tufts of grass or bush. Thrushes, Blackbirds, Curlews and Lapwings lay openly around – dead. Birds were exhausted and on one occasion a Lapwing was seen buffeted to the ground as it attempted to fly, and was knocked dead. Fights were frequent amongst those feeding around the patches of food put out by the Islanders and even a Song Thrush was watched while it pecked one of its own kind to death in order to guard its share."

Mass death is not, however, confined to very cold weather. At the beginning of November 1980, for instance, easterly gales over a six-day period resulted in large numbers of birds – mainly tired migrants such as Blackbirds and Chaffinches – dying from starvation, their corpses found in the lee of walls and other sheltered areas away from the unforgiving wind.

Such events are, thankfully, extremely rare and in most years the approach of spring is marked by the steadily increasing variety and duration of bird song in Millcombe during January and February and the acrobatic displays of Ravens as they twist and roll high over their cliff-top territories, their loud 'cronking' calls carrying far across the island plateau.

Pondsbury in late autumn – with a visiting family of Whooper Swans just discernible on the water.

Lundy's breeding birds

The average number of species recorded annually on Lundy between 1980 and 2005 was 144, with the all-time record being 160 species in 1985. The number of breeding species is much lower, being typically around 30 to 35 per year. Taking all years into consideration, 68 species are known to have bred, with 'possible' breeding by a further 16 species.

Twenty-two species are likely to have bred in every year since 1947 (commencement of LFS recording):

Fulmar

Shag

Oystercatcher

Lesser Black-backed Gull

Herring Gull

Great Black-backed Gull

Kittiwake

Guillemot

Razorbill

Puffin

Skylark

Meadow Pipit

Rock Pipit

Wren

Dunnock

Robin

Wheatear

Blackbird

Carrion Crow

Raven

Chaffinch

Linnet

Seventeen species have bred regularly since 1947 but not in every year:

Manx Shearwater – thought to be
    largely unsuccessful until
    eradication of rats in 2004

Mallard – introduced

Kestrel

Peregrine

Lapwing – last bred 2000

Woodpigeon – possibly in every year

Cuckoo – last bred 1999

Swallow

Pied Wagtail

Stonechat

Song Thrush

Chiffchaff

Willow Warbler

Spotted Flycatcher

Starling

House Sparrow

Goldfinch

Fifteen species bred (or probably bred) regularly in the past but have not done so for many years:

Gannet – until the early 1900s

Cormorant – last bred 1959

White-tailed Eagle – listed by
    nineteenth century authors as
    a former breeding species

Buzzard – last successful 1954;
    last attempted breeding 1965

Osprey – said to have bred regularly
    until 1838

Pheasant – introduced; last bred 1972

Grey Partridge – introduced;
    last bred 1928

Quail – 13 or 14 nests in 1870

Corncrake – last nest found 1928;
    may have bred 1935

Curlew – last bred 1973

Rock Dove – likely to have bred
    historically

Mistle Thrush – last bred 1943

Whitethroat – last bred 1978

Chough – until late nineteenth century

Yellowhammer – last thought to have
    bred 1951

Fourteen species have nested very occasionally:

Sparrowhawk – one pair in 1922
Water Rail – confirmed breeding by at least one pair in 2007
Moorhen – unsuccessful introduction attempts in late 1930s; wild birds bred
    successfully 1985 and possibly 1986
Collared Dove – single pairs bred 1988, 2000 & 2001; possibly 1985
House Martin – up to six pairs bred successfully 1987 to 1990; two pairs nested
    1991, success unknown
Sedge Warbler – one pair bred 1934 and 1935
Garden Warbler – one pair bred 1934 and possibly 1938
Lesser Whitethroat – one pair bred 2003
Goldcrest – single pairs 1952, 1971, 1978 & 2000 (possibly two pairs in 2000)
Tree Sparrow – several pairs bred 1929 to 1932; one or two pairs bred 1961 to 1963
Greenfinch – single pairs bred 1934, 1938 and 1985
Siskin – one pair bred 1952 and possibly 1999
Hawfinch – bred once before 1909, and in 1927
Reed Bunting – one pair bred 1971

A further 16 species may possibly have bred:

Storm Petrel – occurs around the island during breeding season
Ringed Plover – reportedly bred occasionally in nineteenth century
Dunlin – reportedly nested 1904
Snipe – reportedly bred 1935 and on other previous occasions
Woodcock – may have bred occasionally in nineteenth century
Great Auk – circumstantial evidence only
Turtle Dove – reportedly bred in nineteenth century
Nightjar – may have bred nineteenth century and first half of twentieth century
Swift – suggestions of breeding in nineteenth and twentieth centuries
Sand Martin – reportedly bred nineteenth century and early twentieth century
Grey Wagtail – may have bred nineteenth century
Redstart – may have bred nineteenth century
Blackcap – singing males regularly hold territory into the summer
Red-backed Shrike – may have bred nineteenth/early twentieth century
Jackdaw – stated by one early twentieth century author to be breeding in
    "fair numbers" but no other mention of nesting
Bullfinch – single pairs may have bred 2003 and 2004

Puffins

The slaughter of Lundy's seabirds

In his Lundy Island monograph of 1877, Barnstaple solicitor John Roberts Chanter told of a visit to the island by Mr Cleveland, the then owner, and several of his friends in July 1787. The journal of his visit described the exploitation of seabirds:

"After dinner we walked to view the rocks on the western part of the Island, and saw vast quantities of wild fowl, and the method of taking them in nets, which the inhabitants use for the advantage of their feathers. The nets are just the same as those commonly used for taking rabbits on warrens. They are fixed on the rocks, and sometimes on the ground on sticks in the breeding-places. Every morning and evening the natives watch their nets, and take out the birds that are entangled. They catch in a good season 1,700 or 1,800 dozen, and make one shilling per pound of their feathers. People from the neighbouring coasts are hired to pluck them at twopence per dozen, and pluck about four dozen per day. The birds usually taken are muirrs, of which there are two sorts – parrots [Puffin] and a small kind of gull [Kittiwake]. The parrots are about the size of a teal, with crooked and bright coloured bills, large heads, and beautiful plumage. These birds, it appears, annually forsake the Island when the young birds can fly, and are not seen again till the time returns for depositing their eggs. The natives collect these eggs and send them to the Bristol sugar refineries. The muirrs are the most profitable, twelve of them producing one pound of feathers. After being plucked they are skinned; these skins are boiled in a furnace for the oil they yield, which is used instead of candles, and the flesh is given to the hogs, who feed on it voraciously. At the north part we found the birds so tame that we might shoot a dozen at a shot."

The account also described the netting of birds on Gannets' Rock:

"There is one rock 200 feet high, disjointed from the Island, where innumerable quantities of birds lay their eggs. The inhabitants fix their nets on this rock, and catch vast quantities as they fly backward and forward from the sea to their young. Their method of conveying them when taken is by means of a rope fastened at each end to the Island and rock, on which hangs a basket to a pulley, which is drawn occasionally to and fro with the birds. The people run great hazards in taking them out of their nets and sometimes lose their lives. In 1780, Mr Hole, the tenant farmer, lost his life in this pursuit. He is supposed to have slipped over the rocks with a basket of eggs, as he was found dead on the beach the following morning."

The journal continued:

"The eggs are still taken in considerable numbers by sailors and trespassers, as well as by fishermen from the neighbouring coasts. The collector is let down from above by a rope, and as he traverses the ledges he picks up the eggs and places them in a girdle, or pocket, round his waist. They are frequently offered for sale by the fishermen's children at Ilfracombe, where they are in great demand by visitors for their peculiarity of marking and shape and vividness of colour. On Lundy they are used for cookery purposes, but are not eaten alone, except by the poorer labourers. In 1816, 379 pounds of feathers were plucked by the women, 24 puffins yielding one pound of feathers. But since the present owner's occupation neither birds nor their eggs or feathers have been a source of revenue."

Ninety years after Mr Cleveland's visit, Chanter also wrote:

"The present owner [Rev. H.G. Heaven] discourages the destruction of the birds, but within the last few years the fashion of wearing sea-birds' plumes in ladies' hats has led to a considerable amount of unauthorized destruction of the birds, principally by boats sent to the vicinity of the Island for that purpose; and much wanton slaughter has been committed by visitors shooting them down, as they sit in rows, indiscriminately, old and young, for the mere pleasure of slaughter, and without the probability of obtaining them when shot. This system has led to a scarcity of late in some of the rarer varieties."

Later, Lewis Loyd in his *Lundy, its history and natural history* (1925) quoted an account by Howard Saunders published in 1885 in which it is stated:

"At Clovelly, opposite Lundy Island, there was a regular staff for preparing the plumes; and fishing smacks, with extra boats and crews, used to commence their work of destruction at Lundy Island by daybreak on the 1st of August (when the close time under the Sea Birds Preservation Act expired), continuing this proceeding for upwards of a fortnight. In many cases the wings were torn off the wounded birds before they were dead, the mangled victims being tossed back into the water...On one day 700 birds were sent back to Clovelly, on another 500, and so on; and, allowing for starved nestlings, it is well within the mark to say that at least 9000 of these inoffensive birds were destroyed during the fortnight."

Given that the Sea Birds Preservation Act only came into force in 1869, any efforts made by the Heaven family to discourage the killing of seabirds seem to have had little impact.

Ups and downs

○ Fulmars have become a common nesting species after being unknown a century ago. Lesser Black-backed Gulls are increasing, but Puffins are only just about holding on as a Lundy breeding bird and Kittiwake numbers have also crashed.

○ On one hand, White-tailed Eagle and Osprey have long-since vanished as nesting species and Buzzard has been lost in the last 50 years or so. On the other hand, the Peregrine population has gone from strength to strength and numbers of migrating Ospreys and Marsh Harriers are at an all-time high.

○ There has been a noticeable decline in the number and variety of migrant waders recorded since the 1970s and 1980s, but why this should be so is far from clear.

○ Lundy was secured for the nation through its purchase by the National Trust in 1969 and the large Site of Special Scientific Interest and Marine Nature Reserve are managed with nature conservation as the top priority. What a contrast to the 'seabird slaughter' of centuries past!

○ Records of North American vagrants – both waders and land-birds – peaked in the 1970s and 1980s, but have been fewer and farther between in recent years (see figures opposite). Is this just a temporary and random blip, or are there real changes with underlying explanations we don't yet understand?

○ Lapwing and Curlew have been lost as breeding birds, their decline partly reflecting national trends, but perhaps hastened by over-stocking with domestic sheep in the late 1980s and 1990s.

○ Rhododendron once threatened to overwhelm much of the island but is now on the run, making way for native flora and fauna.

○ The eradication of rats has offered a lifeline to Manx Shearwaters, Puffins and other ground-nesting birds whose eggs and young provided rich pickings for the once ubiquitous rodents.

○ Coverage of the island by birdwatchers is now very much focused on spring and autumn migration periods, whereas the presence of LFS bird wardens in years gone by ensured that birds were well recorded for most of the year. On the other hand, optical equipment and identification skills are more sophisticated than ever before.

○ Several species that would have been considered extreme rarities – and others completely unknown on the island – when LFS recording began in 1947 are now seen regularly, among them Little Egret, Collared Dove, Yellow-browed Warbler and Common Rosefinch.

○ As we gaze into the crystal ball, trying to see what the future holds for the birds of Lundy, one certainty is that climate change will be increasingly important. Migrants may face severe droughts on their African wintering grounds, while seabirds will have to cope with changing water temperatures and consequent shifts in their food supply. On the other hand, generally shorter, milder winters and hotter summers may help some southern European species to spread further north, following the trend set by Cetti's Warbler and Little Egret.

Frequency of North American landbirds in five-year periods, 1947–2005

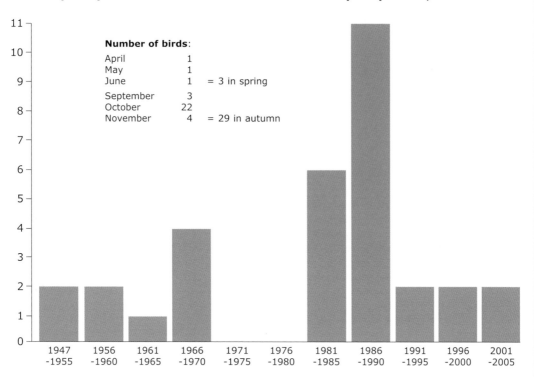

Number of birds:

April	1	
May	1	
June	1	= 3 in spring
September	3	
October	22	
November	4	= 29 in autumn

Frequency of North American waders in five-year periods, 1947–2005

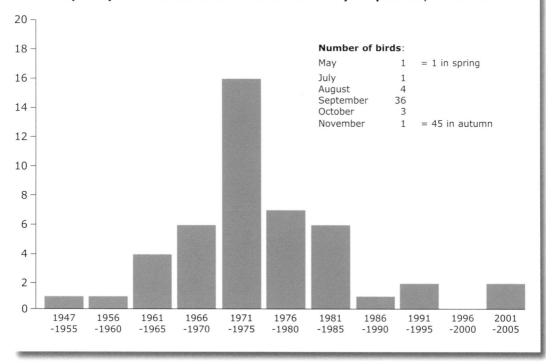

Number of birds:

May	1	= 1 in spring
July	1	
August	4	
September	36	
October	3	
November	1	= 45 in autumn

From ship to shore
– and four suggested bird walks

The crossing

For any birdwatcher, a trip to Lundy starts to get exciting the moment the island boat, the *MS Oldenburg*, departs from either Bideford or Ilfracombe on the North Devon coast. Most birdwatchers choose the peak spring (mid-April/May) or autumn (September/October) migration periods to visit. These are the seasons when the greatest numbers of birds occur, passage migrants mingling with resident species, always with the chance of something rare, sometimes exceptionally so.

From Bideford the high-tide cruise down the estuary of the River Torridge brings the opportunity to look for waders on the fringing saltmarsh – Curlew, Redshank, Dunlin and Oystercatcher, along with the occasional Grey Heron and Shelduck are the most likely to be seen. Little Egrets have become commonplace in recent years; for several autumns evening roosts of up to 80 birds gathered in trees overhanging the estuary on the west bank upstream of the Torridge bridge. As the *Oldenburg* sails past Appledore towards the Bar which guards the entrance to the confluence of the Taw and Torridge estuaries, cast an eye over the Skern, the intertidal area of sand- and mud-flats, shallowly covered at high tide, and the pebble ridge, which fringe Northam Burrows.

From Ilfracombe the ship sails along the North Devon coast to Bull Point before heading out into the open sea. From whichever port of departure, the two-hour sea crossing – in all but the worst weather conditions – is an integral part of the Lundy birding experience. Gannet, Fulmar, Guillemot, Razorbill, Kittiwake and Herring, Great Black-backed and Lesser Black-backed Gulls are the species most often encountered. Much less common are migrating Sandwich, Common, Arctic, Little and Black Terns, all of which tend to favour the waters closer to the mainland. Great and Arctic Skuas are encountered only rarely, mostly in May and September/October. If you are lucky, from mid-April to the end of September the ship may pass close to a raft of Manx Shearwaters resting on the surface, or more likely you will catch sight of them, alternating black and white, as they glide over the water, their wingtips skimming the waves. Storm Petrels sometimes flit past at great speed. Watch out, too, during spring and autumn migration periods for small landbirds: Meadow Pipits, Swallows, martins, Starlings and even the odd Wheatear can sometimes be encountered well out to sea, perhaps heading to or from Lundy.

Voyage over, the adventure begins...

In spring and early summer, the closer you get to the island the greater the number of auks – mainly Guillemots and Razorbills, but always with the possibility of a Puffin, even though they are few and far between these days. As the ship enters the Landing Bay the first Shags can be seen, diving for fish. Oystercatchers, which breed around the island shores, may make themselves heard, *kleeping* angrily at one another in territorial dispute. More times than not, Ravens will glide overhead, 'cronking' and rolling. And the chances are these days that you will see the first Peregrine of your trip whilst still on the boat.

Making the most of limited time

For the birdwatching day-tripper setting foot on Lundy, especially for the first time, the temptation is to try and cover as much of the island as time allows. However, in the brief hours ashore it just isn't feasible to get round all of the good birding spots, let alone appreciate everything else the island has to offer. Better to take your time and enjoy a more leisurely exploration of some of the most promising areas, rather than to circumnavigate the island only to get back to the Landing Bay exhausted, probably having taken in rather little.

Time of year and weather conditions should be used to help you decide. The East Side is more sheltered when the wind is in the west, and vice versa. The West Side is the place to go for breeding seabirds (from April to July), while the vegetated combes of the East Side, especially Millcombe/St John's Valley, St Helen's Copse and Quarter Wall Copse are the best places to look for migrant warblers and flycatchers. Four routes are suggested here as the best options for making the most of a day-trip, or indeed a leisurely birdwatching walk while staying for longer on the island. Each can be easily followed using the map on pages 10 and 11, or the map leaflet produced by the Landmark Trust available either on the *Oldenburg* or from the island shop.

○ **Bird walk 1 – Pondsbury and Jenny's Cove (about 2¹/₂ hours)**

Beach Road (main track from Landing Bay) – lower Millcombe – turn right before ruins of walled gardens and go through small wooden gate – take Lower East Side Path past St Helen's Copse and Quarter Wall Copse to the Terrace – take track northwards past the Quarries – follow track round and up onto main track and cross to Pondsbury [this is roughly the halfway point] – continue to south side of Jenny's Cove – take main West Side path across Ackland's Moor to Old Light – at Old Light turn left along north side of wall and pass Stoneycroft – through High Street gate to the village – Millcombe – Beach Road.

○ **Bird walk 2 – Halfway Wall and the West Side (about 3 hours)**

Beach Road (main track from Landing Bay) – Millcombe – take path to right and behind Millcombe House and walk to top of Millcombe – before field gate turn right and take Upper East Side Path, heading north – go through gate at eastern end of Quarter Wall – pass ruins of Quarry Cottages to Quarry Pond – pass Timekeeper's Cottage and descend to the Terrace – take track northwards past the Quarries – continue to Halfway Wall and walk along either side of wall to the West Side [this is roughly the halfway point] – Jenny's Cove – at south end of Jenny's Cove turn inland towards Pondsbury – at Pondsbury either cross dam or circle around the wetland and head in a south-westerly direction to the western end of Quarter Wall – walk across Ackland's Moor to Old Light – enter South West Field – pass cemetery and follow field boundary wall – turn left through second field gate into Tent Field and take track to village – follow main track south and at junction with track to Castle turn left into St John's Valley – Millcombe – Beach Road.

○ **Bird walk 3 – South End and north to Threequarter Wall (about 3¹/₂ hours)**

Beach Road – stay on main track through Millcombe – pass battlements with view over whole of East Side – stay on main track up through St John's Valley – at junction at top of valley turn left towards Castle – at Castle turn right over Castle Hill – over stile to Benjamin's Chair [don't turn left here!] – follow main track to Rocket Pole Pond – cross South West Field – pass Old Light – cross Ackland's Moor to western end of Quarter Wall – stay on main track to Jenny's Cove – at western end of Halfway Wall cross stile – wander northwards across Middle Park [this is roughly the halfway point] – at Threequarter Wall turn right and walk up to join main track – turn south and pass Tibbett's – through Halfway Wall – stay on main track, looking down onto Pondsbury – turn left at Quarter Wall – at end of Quarter Wall turn right and go through gate – follow Upper East Side Path south to Millcombe – Beach Road.

○ **Bird walk 4 – North End (allow at least 4 hours)**

Beach Road – stay on main track through Millcombe and St John's Valley to village – continue up High Street past shop, museum and farm – go through gate at top of High Street and follow main track north – through gate at Quarter Wall – stay on main track, looking down onto Pondsbury – through Halfway Wall gate into Middle Park – meander across to West Side and head north to Threequarter Wall – cross over stile at western end of Threequarter Wall and follow path along West Side, rejoining main track near Gannets' Combe – continue to North End [this is roughly the halfway point] – descend steps to North Light if time allows – return along main track through Threequarter Wall gate – pass Tibbett's – go through Halfway Wall gate – at Quarter Wall turn left – at end of Quarter Wall turn right and go through gate – follow Upper East Side Path south to Millcombe – Beach Road.

Walks 1 and 2 can comfortably be done inside three hours, walk 3 a little longer, allowing time for short stops to watch birds along the way. Walk 4 is more challenging in terms of both distance and terrain (especially if the descent down to the North Light and the long haul back up the steps are included) and only suitable for fit walkers who have at least four hours ashore and who are willing to spend most of that time walking. It is likely to be most rewarding during the seabird breeding season from April to July. For the best Puffin-watching spot, bear slightly left immediately after crossing Threequarter Wall and, taking care on the rock-strewn grassy slopes which are very steep in this area, look down into the indented bay between St Mark's Stone and St Philip's Stone. If you are very lucky, Puffins may sometimes be seen on the water or outside nesting burrows about halfway up the cliff-face.

Remember that Lundy is a wild place and, even in fine weather, care needs to be taken when walking, especially while on the sidelands, and suitable footwear is strongly recommended. In wet weather, grass and rocks become slippery. Low cloud and fog can quickly obscure paths and tracks. Wind presents its own dangers and can be particularly strong near the tops of cliffs and sidelands. The general rule is be aware at all times of the weather conditions – which on islands can change very quickly – and take no unnecessary risks, especially when walking alone. A hat, sunscreen and water are essentials on hot, sunny days. And if you are on a day-trip, double-check the time you are required to be back at the jetty and keep an eye on your watch – a missed boat can result in one or several nights on the island and unplanned expense!

Finally, don't forget to record your bird sightings, whether of common or unusual species, in the LFS wildlife logbook which is kept in the Tavern. If you have seen a rare bird, you will need to include a good description – preferably with a contact phone number and/or email address – if the record is to be accepted for inclusion in the *LFS Annual Report* and the *Devon Bird Report*. Information in the logbook will tell you how to go about this. If you managed to take a photograph of the bird, this can later be sent to the LFS wildlife warden (warden@lundyisland.co.uk) for inclusion in the logbook.

Enjoy your time on Lundy...and leave nothing but your footprints.

Systematic List

The Systematic List gives full status to 317 category A, B and C species in the the official *British List* (7th edition), as published in July 2006 by the British Ornithologists' Union (BOU). The nomenclature and sequence follow that used in *The British List*. The phrase 'LFS records' is used to indicate sightings since regular bird recording by the Lundy Field Society began in 1947. The information presented has been drawn from LFS logbooks, *LFS Annual Reports, Devon Bird Reports* and, for historical information prior to 1947, a variety of sources listed in the Bibliography. We have considered all records up to 25 August 2007.

Each species account includes the name in most common usage (e.g. Robin), the scientific name (e.g. *Erithacus rubecula*) and, where different, the international English name applied by the BOU (e.g. European Robin) following the recommendations of Gill & Wright (2006). This is followed by a line giving the species' status – see below for an explanation of the main terms used. For British vagrants and nationally scarce migrants, the species' geographic range is given, along with its frequency of occurrence in Britain, using the most recent information available at the time of publication (2005 for vagrants and 2003 for nationally scarce migrants).

A description of the species' occurrence on and relationship with Lundy follows. For all British vagrants and for many nationally scarce migrants and Lundy vagrants, LFS records for the period 1947–2006 are listed in chronological order, beginning with the earliest record. Where known, details such as finding date, length of stay and location are included. An analysis of ringing data arising from ringing controls and recoveries on or away from Lundy is given for species where such information is available.

This is followed by an Appendix (page 276) containing brief accounts of a further 36 species which, for varied reasons, cannot be accorded full status in the Systematic List.

A series of Endnotes (page 293) details discrepancies within and between the various information sources used and explains our conclusions or judgements in these cases.

Explanation of the status line

British vagrant*	Occurrences in Britain exceptionally rare; records must be verified by the *British Birds* Rarities Committee (BBRC). Visit: www.bbrc.org.uk
Nationally scarce migrant*	Occurs annually in small numbers, mainly during spring and autumn migration periods; records must be verified by the Devon Birds Records Committee (DBRC). Visit: www.scarce-migrants.org.uk
Lundy vagrant	A species that falls into neither of the above categories but for which there are fewer than 20 LFS records or fewer than 20 records in total (includes some species that are abundant on the mainland but extreme rarities on Lundy; e.g. Jay, Willow Tit).
Rare	Less than annual but has occurred on 20 occasions or more (e.g. Spotted Redshank).
Uncommon	Occurs annually or almost annually; usually fewer than 10 records per year.
Common	Occurs annually; usually many more than 10 records per year.

The other terms used in the status line are self-explanatory: e.g. *breeding resident; passage migrant; winter visitor*. In some cases 'regular', 'irregular', 'occasional' or 'scarce' are used to further denote the pattern of occurrence of a given species.

*Equivalent to the 'Vagrant' and 'Scarce Migrant' status applied by the BOU in the official *British List*.

Mute Swan *Cygnus olor*

Lundy vagrant.

There are four LFS records:

- **1959** 10 Sep – one on the sea off Jenny's Cove.
- **1976** 30 Jun – three adults, first seen in the Landing Bay, swam past Rat Island towards the North Devon coast.
- **1987** 16 Nov – one in the Landing Bay.
- **1996** 13 Jul – two adults seen in the Landing Bay at 10:00 flew north about 15–20 minutes later and were seen on the sea from the *Oldenburg* about a mile to the east of Lundy at 11:45.

In 1928 the then owner of Lundy, Martin Coles Harman, attempted to introduce a pair of Mute Swans. The following passage from Felix Gade's *My Life on Lundy* (1978) describes what happened:

> "In accordance with Mr Harman's instructions, they were taken straight out to Pondsbury and liberated. In the summer of 1928 there was very little water there, and the swans gave Jim Laramy a really dirty look, paddled proudly through the water, climbed the causeway on the west of the pond, continued down Punchbowl Valley and were never seen on Lundy again."

Bewick's Swan *Cygnus columbianus* [Tundra Swan]

Lundy vagrant.

There is one record of a single bird:

- **1991** 30 Oct – an adult first seen flying south high over the East Side was later watched at close range in South West Field and the Lighthouse Field. It remained until 7 Dec, showing a great affinity for the Lighthouse Field but paying occasional visits to the Tent Field and St Helen's Field. A logbook entry by Andrew Jewels on 4 Nov noted: "Bewick's Swan associating with one of the two white [domestic] greylags in corner of Lighthouse Field. Flew round the field calling in the afternoon when the sheep were rounded up but landed back in its favourite spot almost straight away."

Whooper Swan *Cygnus cygnus*

Lundy vagrant.

Chanter (1871) and Parfitt (1876) listed "Hooper" as an "occasional visitant"; however, it was 1949 before the first twentieth century occurrence. There are 13 records, all except two between late October and the end of December. The Whooper Swans that turn up on Lundy are most likely to be from the large Icelandic breeding population, which winters almost entirely in Britain and Ireland. Whoopers normally remain in family groups during their migratory flights and throughout the winter and this is reflected in the following complete list of island records:

- **1949** Nov – a family party of two adults and four young stayed for about two weeks early in the month, being seen on both land and sea, mostly on the West Side.
- **1962** 25 Nov – two adults on Pondsbury stayed "for some weeks", both eventually dying of starvation, one on 13 Dec and the other on 26 Dec, despite being taken into care.
- **1968** 2 Nov – six, with one remaining for several days, associating with domestic geese.
- **1969** 2 to 26 Oct – one, first seen in the Tent Field and later in the Lighthouse Field.
- **1971** 22 Oct – one on Pondsbury.
- **1978** 29 Oct – one.
- **1979** 22 Dec – six passed by the island heading north-west.
- **1981** 19 Dec – three.[1]
- **2001** 2 & 3 Nov – a family group of two adults and two juveniles was first seen flying up St John's Valley and landing in the Tent Field before moving to Pondsbury.

2002   23 Oct – seven adults on Pondsbury, with three remaining from 24 Oct to 2 Nov and one staying until the end of the year (last seen 30 Dec).

2005   3 & 4 Dec – four adults seen flying over the Old Light and later on Pondsbury.

2007   25 Mar to 5 Apr – one on Pondsbury; also seen in the Lighthouse Field and near the Rocket Pole.

16 & 17 May – one on Pondsbury.

In addition, unidentified swans, most likely either Whooper Swan or Bewick's Swan (*C. columbianus*), have been recorded on five occasions: "about the middle of January 1954" (Davis 1954a), 6 March 1977 (two, pond near Threequarter Wall), 21 & 29 October 1992 (the first flying over the village, the second flying north-east off the East Side and settling briefly on the sea) and 4 March 2002 (one over Pondsbury).

Bean Goose *Anser fabalis*

Lundy vagrant.

Listed by Chanter (1871) and Parfitt (1876) as an "autumn and winter visitant". D'Urban & Mathew (1895) saw a small flock of Bean Geese on Lundy during the hard winter of 1860/61 "where they fed always far out in the middle of one of the stubble-fields…[and] never came near enough to afford a shot". Davis (1954a) and Dymond (1980) list three other early records by Felix Gade: a flock of nine which stayed for three days from 10 December 1932; a flock of 10 present on 22 October 1935; and one which arrived on 7 March 1940, joining the flock of tame geese on the island before being shot in April. There has only been one subsequent record:

1973   6 Dec – a single bird joined the flock of tame geese and remained into the following year (there is no record of its departure date, the original LFS logbook having been lost).

None of the Bean Geese occurring on Lundy has been assigned to one of the two generally recognised subspecies in Europe, *Anser fabalis fabalis* 'Taiga Bean Goose' or *A. f. rossicus* 'Tundra Bean Goose'.

Pink-footed Goose *Anser brachyrhynchus*

Lundy vagrant.

There are two dated pre-LFS records: two birds on 24 January 1940 (F.W. Gade, reported by Palmer 1946) and one in December 1949 (M.C. Harman, reported by Davis 1954a). All six LFS records have been in autumn:

1959   1 Oct – one flew south after circling over the island.

Pink-footed Geese

45

1960   6 to 9 Oct – one.
2 to 9 Nov – two.
1984   23 Sep – one flew in from the south-east and headed north along the East Side.
2004   9 to 29 Oct – a first-year bird in the area of Ackland's Moor and the Airfield.
2006   20 & 21 Oct – a lone individual and then a further six birds flew in from the north along the East Side, the flock of six stopping to rest on Quarry Beach for several minutes. All seven geese eventually joined up later in the day and were watched feeding in the Tillage Field, before roosting in the Brick Field overnight. They were relocated on Pondsbury the following day. On 22 Oct the flock increased to 10, before falling to nine on 27 Oct and to eight on 26 Nov. These eight were last seen on 5 Dec, having visited various parts of the island between Castle Hill and Threequarter Wall during their stay.

White-fronted Goose *Anser albifrons*   [Greater White-fronted Goose]

Lundy vagrant.

Since regular recording by the LFS started in 1947 there have been 19 records involving over 50 individuals (see listing below). Only a few of these have been assigned sub-specifically to either the Russian-breeding race *Anser albifrons albifrons* or the Greenland-breeding race *A. a. flavirostris*, though both have occurred in recent years. Most have been seen in October (earliest date 11 October) and November, but there have been two spring records and a small number of midwinter sightings. Though the majority of records have involved single birds, small flocks of up to 12 have also occurred.

1949   27 Oct – eight.
1953   13 Jan to 19 Mar – one of the race *A. a. albifrons*.
1955   13 & 18 Feb – one, with remains of a dead bird, presumed the same, found on 26 Feb.
1961   Dec – one stayed with the domestic geese from before Christmas into the New Year.[2]
1963   20 Jan – one arrived during hard weather and remained for about a week with the domestic geese.[2]
1973   11 Oct – 12 flew south.
1980   23 Oct – 11.
16 to 29 Nov – one.[3]
1981   15 Oct to 6 Nov – two.
1982   15 Nov – one.
3 Dec – one.
1986   5 to 24 Apr – a flock of four.
1990   2 Nov – a first-year bird flying north up the East Side.
1992   23 to 30 Oct – a colour-ringed bird of the race *A. a. flavirostris*, which had been ringed in Nov 1991 at Wexford Slobs – one of the main wintering grounds for Greenland White-fronts – in south-east Ireland. On 30 Oct it departed to the north with a second White-front that had been calling as it flew along the West Side. It was sighted back at Wexford Slobs on 9 Dec 1992, remaining there until 19 Apr 1993.
1993   10 to 15 May – one of the race *A. a. albifrons* on Pondsbury and elsewhere, mainly in the south of the island, usually keeping company with a Canada Goose *Branta canadensis*.
5 to 7 Nov – one, also of the race *A. a. albifrons*, associating with domestic geese in the Lighthouse Field.
2001   6 Nov – a first-year bird of the race *A. a. flavirostris* found huddled by the Rocket Pole departed to the south. Its arrival coincided with strong north-west winds.
2003   27 & 28 Oct – one seen flying south along the East Side.[4]

Chanter (1871) and Parfitt (1876) listed this species as an "autumn and winter visitant". There are five dated nineteenth-century autumn and winter records in the Heaven Diaries, all relating to shot birds: 16 & 18 October 1877, 15 February 1878, 29 October 1880 and 31 January 1881 (Boyd 1950). One was shot about 1938 and two stayed for several days from 22 December 1939 (F.W. Gade, reported by Davis 1954a). In addition, a flock of 10 unidentified geese flying south on 31 October 1990 were "considered most likely to be White-fronted" (1990 *LFS Annual Report*).

Greylag Goose *Anser anser*

Lundy vagrant.

There are eight records – four in spring, two in autumn and two in late winter – all in LFS years and all of single birds except for two in 1976 and four in 1997. The evident tameness of several of the geese is a strong indicator of captive-bred/feral origin. The records for February/March and October are more likely to have been of genuinely wild birds.

1949   9 to 11 Sep – one "on sea and beach" was captured on the last date; "Its remarkable tameness suggested rather strongly that the bird was an escape" (1949 *LFS Annual Report*).
1964   20 Apr to 16 May – one unringed but very tame bird.
1968   25 Mar – two.
1972   2 May – one on Pondsbury was initially very flighty but later joined up with the tame geese on the island and remained until 6 May.
1976   19 to 26 Feb – two, with one remaining until 2 Mar.[5]
1979   31 Jan and 5 Feb – one.[6]
        17 May to 2 Jun – one.[7]
1997   12 Oct – a group of four flew north over the Church.

Snow Goose *Anser caerulescens*

British vagrant.

Breeds in arctic north-east Siberia, North America and north-west Greenland, migrating to winter in the USA. Occurs almost annually in Britain, mainly in Scotland, and ringing has shown that genuinely wild birds have occurred. However, the species' status is clouded by escapes from captivity.

There is one Lundy record of a single bird. While the date is late for wild geese in Britain, Snow Geese migrate in large numbers through north-east Canada in May, and vagrancy of a wild bird cannot be ruled out.

1986   22 May – one flew north along the East Side, circling upwards when it reached North End.

Canada Goose *Branta canadensis*

Lundy vagrant.

There have been 14 LFS records, all since 1978, with 11 of the sightings from 1990 onwards, reflecting the increasing numbers of feral birds in Britain. It is also noticeable that 10 occurrences have been during the period April to June.

1978   28 Apr – two flew north.
        19 Oct – two moving between the Tillage Field and Barton (St Helen's) Field.
1980   18 Oct – two.
1990   22 May – four flew over Pondsbury.
1993   9 to 15 May – one (later joined by a White-fronted Goose *Anser albifrons*) at Pondsbury and elsewhere in the southern half of the island. An island resident reported that three Canada Geese had arrived "a couple of days previously"; two birds, then one, remaining.
1994   1 May – three on Pondsbury.
1996   20 Jun – a flock of 10 flew south-east off South End.
1997   16 Apr – two on Pondsbury, one staying until 18 Apr.
2001   31 Oct – two flew north over the island.
2003   19 to 23 May – one first seen at Jenny's Cove, then in various locations from Halfway Wall Bay southwards.
        10 Jun – a flock of eight at rest on the Landing Beach.
2007   16 Feb – one on the Airfield.
        21 Apr – one flying north over the Landing Bay.
        19 Jun – one flew over The Rattles.

Listed by Parfitt (1876) and Chanter (1877) as "reported, but not accurately identified" and therefore regarded by Chanter as doubtful. Hendy (1922) wrote of his visit to the island in June 1914: "Mr. Heaven showed me a lady's hat made out of the skin of a Canada Goose shot on the island recently."

Barnacle Goose *Branta leucopsis*

Lundy vagrant.

There have been LFS records in nine years, mainly in October and November:

1959 26 Apr to 5 May – one, mostly on the Airfield.

1966 29 Oct to 2 Nov – six in Middle Park.

1968 Nov – a noticeable influx coincided with occurrences in mainland Devon and Cornwall, those on Lundy being 14 on 2nd, 25 from 3rd to 18th, and nine on 1 Dec.

1973 8 to 21 Jan – a single bird.

1977 21 Nov – three.

1980 18 Oct – four, increasing to 10 on 19th and 12 on 20th; six still present on 21st remained until 25 Oct.

1993 7 & 8 Nov – a flock of six were seen flying over various parts of the island and at times settled in the Rocket Pole and Tent Field area.

2000 11 Oct – a flock of seven flew south over the island.

2002 19 Oct – a flock of five flew down the East Side.

In addition, a flock of eight geese reported feeding at North End on 14 October 1990 were "considered most likely to be Barnacle" (1990 *LFS Annual Report*). The only dated pre-LFS records relate to sightings by Felix Gade: a single bird on 24 April 1941 (reported by Palmer 1946) which stayed for nearly a month, and three seen in flight on 6 September 1944 (1944 *Devon Bird Report*). Gade (1978, p. 184) also mentions "a flock of nineteen Barnacle Geese" but gives no indication of date.

Brent Goose *Branta bernicla*   [Brant Goose]

Lundy vagrant.

There have been 13 LFS records of one to three birds, eight in autumn, four in winter and one in spring. Individuals of both the dark-bellied Russian breeding race *Branta bernicla bernicla* and the light-bellied Canadian Arctic breeding population *B. b. hrota* have occurred, though in some cases the racial identity was not recorded.

1947 15 Sep – one.

1953 25 Nov – one dark-bellied at Pondsbury.

1957 9 to 13 May – one dark-bellied.

1976 3 to 8 Feb – one light-bellied.

1979 12 & 13 Feb – one.

1980 13 to 17 Jan – an immature.

1984 24 Sep – two light-bellied seen flying north-west from North West Point.

1988 19 & 20 Oct – one dark-bellied flying south, low over Halfway Wall, on 19th was seen in Gannets' Bay on 20th.[8]

1989 24 to 29 Nov – one dark-bellied in the Lighthouse Field.

1993 19 Oct – one feeding near the Castle.

1994 16 to 18 Sep – three on Pondsbury.

1999 12 Oct – one light-bellied flew east past the island.[9]

2004 14 to 30 Dec – three dark-bellied birds, initially in the Landing Bay and later mainly in the Lighthouse Field.

Listed by Parfitt (1876) and Chanter (1877) as "reported, but not accurately identified" and therefore regarded by Chanter as doubtful. There are two pre-LFS records: one present from 30 January to March 1933 and one on 1 April 1940 (F.W. Gade, listed in the 1953 *LFS Annual Report* and by Davis 1954a).

Ruddy Shelduck *Tadorna ferruginea*

British vagrant (nineteenth century); regular escape from captivity.

The only Lundy record is of a single bird on 16 September 1944 (Gade 1945). The editors of *British Birds* remarked at the time: "Unfortunately all birds of this species are nowadays under a strong suspicion of being strays but Mr. Gade states that this one was rather shy."

The occurrence of genuine vagrancy to Britain is indeed clouded by escapes from wildfowl collections. No post-1950 British record of Ruddy Shelduck has been accepted as referring unequivocally to a wild individual and most older records are considered to relate to escaped or feral birds. However, an influx to Britain (including North Devon) that occurred in 1892 is considered justification for the species' retention in Category B of *The British List* (Harrop 2002).

Shelduck *Tadorna tadorna*　　　　　　　　[Common Shelduck]

Lundy vagrant.

There are 19 LFS records, involving 30 individuals, including 10 occurrences in April and May. Given that most Shelducks are sedentary within their breeding areas in spring, it is likely that these birds were wandering non-breeding adults or immatures.

<dl>
<dt>1966</dt><dd>28 to 30 Aug – one.</dd>
<dt>1970</dt><dd>31 May – a pair took off from Ladies Beach and flew around Rat Island.</dd>
<dt>1976</dt><dd>23 May – a pair.</dd>
<dt>1982</dt><dd>11 Jan – one.</dd>
<dt>1985</dt><dd>21 to 23 Jan – one.
26 Mar – one.
11 May – a pair.
27 to 29 Aug – one on Pondsbury.</dd>
<dt>1987</dt><dd>11 Jan – one.
8 May – two on Pondsbury.
19 May – two.</dd>
<dt>1991</dt><dd>8 Oct – one just east of Ladies Beach.
23 & 25 Nov – an adult male, on 23rd seen flying down the East Side to Rat Island before flying back north over the village.</dd>
<dt>1997</dt><dd>17 Apr – two.</dd>
<dt>2000</dt><dd>26 Apr – a pair on the southern slopes of Castle Hill.</dd>
<dt>2001</dt><dd>7 May – a pair.
27 May – two.[10]</dd>
<dt>2003</dt><dd>30 Apr – one.</dd>
<dt>2005</dt><dd>26 Sep – three flew north-west over the Airfield and out to sea off the West Side.</dd>
</dl>

Apart from the Heaven Diaries' mention of "dying Sheldrakes" being picked up on 25 January 1881 (Boyd 1950), there does not appear to be any other pre-LFS record of Shelducks on the island.

Shelducks

Wigeon *Anas penelope* [Eurasian Wigeon]

Uncommon passage migrant, mainly in autumn, and occasional winter visitor.

Wigeon have been seen in very small numbers – mainly ones and twos, and mostly on Pondsbury – in 42 of the 60 years of LFS recording to the end of 2006. Unsurprisingly for a species that is primarily a winter visitor in southern England, most occurrences on Lundy have been in the period October (by far the peak month) to February. There are two August records, the earliest being 18 August 1959, and September sightings in 11 years. There are nine records for the period March, April and May (three in each month), with the latest date in spring being 18 May (1983). There have been no occurrences in either June or July.

The maximum counts are a modest six on 14 January 1982 and again on 1 November 2002 (the latter a flock of two males and four females seen flying past Rat Island), eight on 9 April 1968 and a "probable nine" on 26 January 1955.

Listed by Chanter (1871) and Parfitt (1876) as an "autumn and winter visitant". An entry in the Heaven Diaries for 29 November 1879 recorded "wild duck and widgeon many on Pondsbury", while single birds were shot on 1 December 1877 and 7 December 1883 (Boyd 1950).

Gadwall *Anas strepera*

Lundy vagrant.

There are only five records, making this amongst the scarcest of the commoner British wildfowl on Lundy. A reported sighting of a male on 11 January 1985 – coincidentally the year in which written details on sightings of vagrants to Lundy were introduced to make recording more rigorous – was excluded from the *LFS Annual Report* for that year as no description was provided by the observer.

1947 20 & 21 Jul – one, seen by Hugh Boyd, who was appointed LFS warden a year later.
1952 25 to 28 Apr – a pair.
       7 May – two males.
1978 22 Oct – seven on Pondsbury.
1982 3 to 5 Sep – one.

Teal *Anas crecca* [Eurasian Teal]

Uncommon migrant and winter visitor in small numbers; rare in summer.

Listed by Chanter (1871) and Parfitt (1876) as an "autumn and winter visitant". The earliest documented twentieth century record is of one "flushed from a pond" on 3 September 1907 (Oldham 1932). Davis (1954a) reported Teal as "the commonest duck on Lundy", a status that still applies today if the resident flock of feral Mallards is discounted, with occurrences in almost every LFS year. However, there appears to have been a decline in the frequency of sightings in recent years.

Most Teal occur on Pondsbury, with occasional sightings from the other ponds and pools around the island. There have been records in all months, though October to March is the peak period. While numbers are generally very small – typically just ones or twos – a few larger flocks have occurred e.g. 30 on 31 January 1954 and 23 on 1 December 1973. There have been just 13 Teal records (to the end of 2006) for the period May to July, including a juvenile on Pondsbury from 9 to 13 July 1989 and four on 28 July 1999, but there is no suggestion that nesting has ever occurred. A female was present together with a male Green-winged Teal (*A. carolinensis*) on 14 May 2006.

Green-winged Teal *Anas carolinensis*

Nationally scarce migrant.

Breeds in northern areas of North America and winters south as far as Central America, also reaching South America. 605 records for Britain 1958–2003, showing a clear upward trend with an average of over 40 per year 2000–2003. Considered by the BBRC until the end of 1990.

There is one Lundy record, also the most recent addition to the island list:

2006 9 to 14 May – a male on Pondsbury, probably also present on 7 & 8 May.

Mallard *Anas platyrhynchos*

Resident breeding flock of feral origin; unknown numbers of wild birds occur from time to time.

Wild Mallards arriving on Lundy are difficult to distinguish from the resident flock, the origins of which lie in past introductions of domestic birds. Pondsbury, the smaller ponds at Rocket Pole, Quarter Wall and Quarry Pond, the small reservoir pond close to Pigs Paradise (Quarters) and the marshy area in the lower part of St Helen's Field are the main areas used.

"Wild Duck" was listed by Chanter (1871) and Parfitt (1876) as an "autumn and winter visitant". Three pairs of 'ducks' said to have nested in marshy ground near the centre of the island in 1920 and 1921 are most likely to have been Mallard (Loyd 1922). There are no accurate large counts, but "a great many" were seen by Felix Gade on 23 December 1927 (reported by Dymond 1980). That wild birds do reach Lundy is evident from ring-recoveries (see below) and the observations of the earliest LFS wardens before the species was introduced. Davis (1954a) reported Mallard as an irregular visitor, usually in small numbers, with records for all months except September, most occurring in June, July and from November to February.

Mallard

A pinioned pair was introduced in 1957 and hatched three broods in 1958. Breeding continued annually until 1974, by which time the population had died out. Following the escape of around 30 domesticated birds in May 1987, a new feral flock became established and breeding has occurred every year since (up to and including 2007), with broods of ducklings reported regularly between April and July. Numbers have varied between a pre-breeding season low of five (in January 2000) and a post-breeding maximum of 35 (in October 1993).

In 2004 there was an apparent influx of wild birds early in the year when 14 were recorded on 18 February; no other count during the period January to April exceeded seven. Post-breeding numbers reached 24 in July, with up to 19 present from September to the end of the year. In 2005 a female and 10 ducklings were seen on Quarter Wall Pond on 22 April, followed by a female with 12 young on Pondsbury on 12 July, while the highest count of the year was 16 on 14 October. In 2006 a female and 10 ducklings were seen on 17 June 2006 and the annual maximum was 26 on 13 August. In 2007 broods of five and seven respectively were on Pondsbury and around Quarters in late April. Many ducklings fail to reach adulthood, most being taken by predators, including gulls, Peregrine and the occasional Grey Heron.

Forty Mallards have been ringed on Lundy, nine of which have subsequently been recovered. All but one – an adult ringed on 10 May 1966 and found on 24 June 1971 – were found away from the island, and all of these were taken by hunters. Six were recovered on relatively nearby parts of the mainland – three in Devon, and three in South Wales – including a juvenile ringed on 28 July 1958 and shot near St David's, Pembrokeshire more than seven years later in November 1965. There have been two foreign recoveries of Lundy-ringed Mallards, both first-year birds ringed within a day of each another, on 28 and 29 July 1958, and found on 27 July 1959 at Pas-de-Calais, France and on 14 February 1961 at IJsselmeerpolders, The Netherlands, respectively. Four of the movements within Britain were of birds ringed as ducklings on Lundy; clear evidence that Mallards hatched on the island do not necessarily remain as part of the resident flock.

Pintail *Anas acuta* [Northern Pintail]

Lundy vagrant.

There are just three LFS records, and although no location is identified in the one surviving logbook (1977), Pondsbury is clearly the most likely place for this species to occur.

1964 September – a female stayed for a week.
1973 12 Mar to 26 Apr – a male.
1977 19 Sep – a female.

Listed by Chanter (1871) and Parfitt (1876) as an "autumn and winter visitant", there is only one dated occurrence prior to LFS recording: a male that stayed for several days from 15 December 1932 (F.W. Gade, reported by Davis 1954a).

Garganey *Anas querquedula*

Lundy vagrant.

There are eight dated LFS records, all in spring, but five of these were in 1959, part of a significant influx into southern and western England. There have been only two occurrences since.

1958 24 to 31 Mar – a male on Pondsbury.
1959 18 Mar – three, with two staying until 19 Mar.
2 to 5 Apr – two males.
9 Apr – a male.
23 Apr – a male.
26 Apr – a female.
1996 13 May – a male on Pondsbury.
2007 30 Apr – a pair flushed from Quarter Wall Pond flew to Pondsbury.

The only (undated) reference to Garganey prior to the start of LFS recording is given by Gade (1978, p. 184) who stated: "…in addition to teal, there have been mallard, shoveller, garganey and (once) a pintail, on Lundy's ponds."

Shoveler *Anas clypeata* [Northern Shoveler]

Lundy vagrant.

The listing by Chanter (1871) and Parfitt (1876) of Shoveler as an "autumn and winter visitant" contrasts with records during the twentieth century: just one late winter record and four autumn occurrences, with most records (eight) in spring. These include the only two dated pre-LFS records: an entry in the Heaven Diaries of a "Strange Goose" seen on 2 November 1904 that was shot the following day and identified as a "Shoveller Duck" (Boyd 1950), and a pair on 15 March 1929 which remained "well on into April" (F.W. Gade, reported by Davis 1954a).

There are 11 LFS records (to the end of 2006) involving 16 individuals:

1949 31 Mar to 9 Apr – one.
1964 8 to 13 Mar – one.
1967 31 Jul to 18 Aug – one seen on four occasions.
1976 19 to 22 May – two males.
1978 7 Apr – a male.[11]
1984 10 Feb – a pair.
1986 6 May – a female on Pondsbury.
1987 8 May – a male on Pondsbury.
12 Sep – a female on Pondsbury.
1992 24 Apr – a pair on Pondsbury.
2000 5 Jul – three on Pondsbury.

Pochard *Aythya ferina*   [Common Pochard]

Lundy vagrant.

Eight dated LFS records have all been in autumn and winter:

1954 18 to 23 Feb – a male.
1969 9 Sep – three on Pondsbury, followed by two on 11th , one found dead on 12th, then singles on seven dates from 15 Sep to 26 Oct, presumed to relate to the same individual.
1975 18 to 21 Dec – a male.
1981 15 Feb – one.
1982 19 to 21 Sep – one.[12]
1989 2 Jan – a male on Pondsbury.
1992 14 to 29 Oct – a male on Pondsbury.
2003 30 Oct to 1 Nov, and 15 Nov presumed the same – a female or immature on Pondsbury.

The only previous record was of a male on 25 & 27 April 1939 (Perry 1940).

Tufted Duck *Aythya fuligula*

Lundy vagrant.

The first known occurrence was a single bird seen by Felix Gade on 5 April 1938, with subsequent sightings reported by Gade on 30 October 1941 and 22 & 23 October 1943, both lone individuals (Davis 1954a). It was another 20 years before the next sighting and the first LFS record, of which there have been 18 in all (to the end of 2006), involving 27 individuals, mostly single males. The maximum count is five. Most have occurred from April to July, with a peak in May. There are only two winter records.

1963 5 Apr – a female on the sea off Miller's Cake.
1966 18 Mar – a male on Quarter Wall Pond.
1968 20 May – two.
          28 May – five.
1970 16 Jun – one on Quarter Wall Pond.[13]
1972 6 to 8 Jul – a male.
1979 27 Oct – two.
1980 27 & 28 May – a male on Rocket Pole Pond.
1988 5 Jul – a male flew south past the Landing Beach.
1989 13 Sep – a male on Pondsbury.
1991 23 & 24 May – a male on the sea off the East Side, then on Pondsbury.
1993 18 to 25 May – a male, mainly on Pondsbury.
1999 12 to 14 May – a male on Pondsbury.[14]
2000 3 to 6 Jul and 28 Jul to 3 Aug, presumed the same – a male on Pondsbury.
2001 18 to 23 May – a pair on Pondsbury.
2002 12 Dec – a pair on Pondsbury, the male remaining until 16 Dec.
2003 3 to 7 Jul – a male on Pondsbury.[15]
2004 21 Feb – two.

Scaup *Aythya marila*   [Greater Scaup]

Lundy vagrant.

Included by Parfitt (1876) and Chanter (1877) in their lists of species "reported, but not accurately identified". There are five LFS records of single birds, including two midsummer records of males on Pondsbury, most likely birds stopping off en route to moulting sites:

1955 9 Oct – an oiled male, found dead the next day.
1965 5 to 10 May – a female on the Lighthouse Field Pond (this pond has since been filled in).
1981 5 Oct – one.
1994 18 Jul – a male on Pondsbury.
2007 18 to 22 Jul – a male on Pondsbury.

Eiders

Eider *Somateria mollissima* [Common Eider]

Lundy vagrant.

Seen very occasionally on the crossing, generally close to the mainland. There are just seven records from the island itself, and only one since 1979. All have been during November to April, and none of more than two birds together:

1963 25 Apr – one off the North End, then one, presumed the same, seen offshore irregularly until 14 Jun.
1967 7 Nov – a female in the Landing Bay.
1972 12 Mar – an immature male in the Landing Bay.
1978 6 Mar – two females.
22 & 24 Dec – an immature male, and one, presumed the same, on 26 Dec.
1979 29 Apr – two males.[16]
1995/96 19 Dec to 7 Jan – a female in the Landing Bay.

Common Scoter *Melanitta nigra* [Black Scoter]

Uncommon passage visitor.

Listed by Chanter (1871) and Parfitt (1876) as an "occasional visitant". Davis (1954a) noted six records "all since 1939", while Dymond (1980) described Common Scoter as a "very rare visitor", with just 12 island records for the 32 years between 1947 and 1978. However, in the following 28 years, up to and including 2006, there have been more than 30 additional sightings.

The greater number of records in recent years probably reflects more interest among birdwatchers in seawatching (and better optical equipment) rather than any real increase in the number of scoters passing Lundy. This species has been recorded in all months except January. There have been four winter occurrences, all in February. In spring Common Scoters have been seen on 10 days in six different years, extreme dates being 16 March (1949) and 21 May (1999). While non-breeding birds or early-returning migrants have been seen from as early as 25 June (1992) and on six other dates to 15 August (1956), most autumn scoters have occurred from mid-October to late November, with two records into early December. Most sightings involve one or two birds, though maximum counts are 30 on 21 Sep 1980, 61 on 22 October 1991 and 65 on 14 October 2004.

All records considered here are of birds seen from the island itself. However, Common Scoters are occasionally also encountered on the boat crossing, the largest flocks to date being 22 on 8 March 1966 and 36 on 18 September 1992.

Surf Scoter *Melanitta perspicillata*

Nationally scarce migrant.

Breeds in North America, wintering along both Pacific and Atlantic coasts of Canada and the USA. 399 records for Britain 1958–2003, with an average of 16 per year 2000–2003. Considered by the BBRC until the end of 1990.

There is one Lundy record of a single bird:

1956 16 Nov – a female or immature in the Landing Bay.

54

Goldeneye *Bucephala clangula*   [Common Goldeneye]

Lundy vagrant.

Chanter (1871) and Parfitt (1876) listed Goldeneye as an "autumn and winter visitant". However, prior to 1947, when LFS records began, the only dated record is of a single bird on 30 October 1941 (F.W. Gade, reported by Palmer 1946). There have been four further records, three in autumn and one in spring:

1971 20 Apr – two.
1990 25 Nov – a female in the Landing Bay.
1991 28 Oct – a female or immature seen landing on the sea near Rat Island and later on Pondsbury.
2002 9 Oct – a female or immature in the Landing Bay.

Smew *Mergellus albellus*

Lundy vagrant.

A male in the Landing Bay reported by Felix Gade on the somewhat unlikely date of 15 September 1933 is the only Lundy record. No details are available, but the sighting of what is a fairly unmistakable bird was accepted by Davis (1954a) and Dymond (1980).

Red-breasted Merganser *Mergus serrator*

Lundy vagrant.

There have been seven LFS records (listed below) involving a total of 15 birds, all since 1979 and mainly in October. The only previous occurrence was of a dying male on the Lighthouse Field Pond (since in-filled) in very cold weather on 19 December 1938 and found dead on 21st (F.W. Gade, reported by Davis 1954a). The relatively recent increase in records may reflect population growth and range expansion of Red-breasted Mergansers breeding in Britain, as well as the increasing popularity among birdwatchers of seawatching. However, there have been no sightings since 1999 (to spring 2007).

1979 24 Oct – four.
1982 16 to 23 May – a male.
1985 22 to 29 May – a female in the Landing Bay.
1988 22 Oct – five, including one male, flew south-west past Rat Island.
1989 29 & 30 Oct – a female or immature in the Landing Bay.
1991 13 Oct – a female or immature fishing south of Rat Island.
1999 25 Oct – two females flying north.

Goosander *Mergus merganser*   [Common Merganser]

Lundy vagrant.

The only record is of a single male on 17 December 1934 (F.W. Gade, reported by Davis 1954a); also noted in the 1934 report of the Devon Bird Watching & Preservation Society as seen "fishing in the [presumably Landing] bay".

Ruddy Duck *Oxyura jamaicensis*

Lundy vagrant.

On 29 September 1975 four adult males flew in from the north-east along the East Side to the Landing Bay, where they remained until 5 October.[17] Two were still present on 10 October and one was seen on 14 & 21 October. This remains the only island record (to mid-2007).

At the time, this introduced North American diving duck had established a strong feral breeding population in Gloucestershire, Avon and Somerset, from where the Lundy birds probably originated. The species has since spread to colonise many other areas of the UK. In 2005 the European Commission approved funding for conservation action to protect the native European population of the closely related White-headed Duck, which is threatened by the Ruddy Duck's arrival. A five-year programme aims to eradicate the Ruddy Duck from the UK and to provide advice on eradication from the rest of Europe (Defra 2006).

Quail *Coturnix coturnix* [Common Quail]

Rare migrant; bred in the nineteenth century.

There have been 29 LFS records (to the end of 2006), the first in 1953, though in some cases it is difficult to be certain whether sightings within a few days of each other refer to more than one individual. Certainly, most occurrences have involved single birds, but two were present at the same time in May 1970, June 1989 and possibly May 1990. 1989 also saw a notable influx to the island, with a series of records for May and June and another bird in early October – to date, the only autumn sighting on Lundy. Otherwise, occurrences have been less than annual and overwhelmingly in late spring and summer, from the last week of April to the end of July (see table opposite). This reflects the general pattern in Britain, more birds moving further north across Europe in years with favourable weather during spring migration.

1953 27 May – a freshly dead female in the Tillage Field.[18]
1958 23 May to 2 Jun – at least one.
1964 13 May – one.
1965 18 May – one calling at night.
1967 31 May – a male trapped and ringed near Manor Farm Hotel (now Old House).
1970 12 May – one by Quarter Wall.
      16 May – one by Quarter Wall and two by the hut circles at North End.
      31 Jul – one on the east sidelands.
1973 26 May – one at Pondsbury.
1974 5 May – a female by Big St John's.
1976 10 Jul – one.
1983 21 May – one by the main track just north of Threequarter Wall.
1988 24 Apr – one on Castle Hill.
1989 16 to 19 May – a female in the north of the island.
      17 to 19 May – a female by the Upper East Side Path and in the Brick Field on 17th & 18th; one, presumed the same, between the Old (quarry) Hospital and Pondsbury on 19th.
      2 to 3 Jun – two near Quarter Wall.
      5 Jun – one male by the Upper East Side Path.
      29 Jun – one between the Airfield and Quarter Wall.
      3 Oct – one flushed from South West Field and later in the Tent Field.

Quail

1990 9 & 10 May, 16 May and 8 Jun – one, presumed to be the same individual, near Quarter Wall, with possibly a second bird on 10 May.
1991 19 May – one heard calling near the Church.
1994 8 May – one flushed in Millcombe.
12 May – one flushed from a stream gully running into the south side of Jenny's Cove.
1996 17 Jun – one on Ackland's Moor.[19]
2001 7 Jul – one near the Church.
2003 13 May – one flushed from rushes near Quarter Wall.
2005 12 May – one flushed from near the stone crusher in the Tent Field.
2006 8 Jun – one heard calling near Halfway Wall.
12 Jun – one flushed from bracken along the east sidelands.

Quail occurrences, 1953–2006
(spring and summer records in half-month periods;
the long-staying 1990 individual appears in three columns)

Apr 16–30	May 1–15	May 16–31	June 1–15	June 16–30	July 1–15	July 16–31
1	8	11	5	2	2	1

In his diaries the Rev. H.G. Heaven recorded 13 or 14 nests in 1870, but added that five were destroyed by mowing on 12 July; and later that year one was shot on 30 October (Boyd 1950). Heaven communicated much of this information to J. Edmund Harting (1871) who wrote that Lundy is "annually a resort for quail during the periods of migration, but never have they been so numerous there as during the past summer and autumn…When shooting in September and October [Heaven] repeatedly flushed and killed quails, sometimes as many as three brace and a half in one day". Describing the species as a "summer visitor", Chanter (1871) listed Quail (along with Water Rail and Woodcock) as birds "whose appearance on Lundy at the seasons of migration, is generally in such numbers as to be worthy of note". Parfitt (1876) described Quail as an "occasional breeder". D'Urban & Mathew (1895) gave Quail as occurring annually on migration and remarked that "good bags have been obtained in September". Two were seen and heard on 15 June 1937 (F.W. Gade, reported by Davis 1954a).

Red-throated Diver *Gavia stellata*   [Red-throated Loon]

Rare passage migrant and winter visitor.

From the commencement of LFS recording in 1947 to the end of 2006 there were irregular (less than annual) sightings, the majority in February (seven), March (10) and April (eight), with a further four sightings in May, the latest being 23 May (1962). In autumn the species is no more than a vagrant (about 11 records) and is much less frequent than Great Northern Diver. The lone August sighting – a single bird reported on 22nd (1995) – was exceptionally early, given that the only two September records are for 29th (1999) and 30th (1995), the latter from a boat 1.3 kilometres west of the island. Most have been seen from the East Side, both inshore and out to sea, sometimes just flying past. The highest number seen together is three off the North End on 17 March 2006 during very cold weather with strong easterly winds. There are nine records of two birds together, all other sightings being of single birds. Given that Red-throated Diver is the most numerous diver in British waters and that large flocks have been seen in winter from nearby Hartland Point on the North Devon mainland, it is perhaps surprising that not more have been recorded from Lundy.

Chanter (1871) and Parfitt (1876) listed this species as an "autumn and winter visitant", but the only dated occurrences prior to 1947 are of singles on 1 September 1926 (Davis 1954a), 7 April 1939 (Perry 1940) and 13 October 1941 (Davis 1954a).

Black-throated Diver *Gavia arctica*   [Black-throated Loon]

Lundy vagrant.

There are nine records, mainly in March and April, but with two autumn records and a single occurrence in winter. All have been since 1950 and all off the East Side:

- **1951**   1 Nov – an immature "seen at close quarters".
- **1964**   Apr – one off the East Side early in the month.
- **1967**   26 Mar to 28 Apr – one off the East Side on several occasions.
- **1984**   26 Mar – one flew north.
- **1988**   9 Oct – one in the Landing Bay.
- **1990**   31 Jan to 2 Feb – an adult in the Landing Bay and off the Sugar Loaf.
- **1992**   1 to 4 Jan – one in the Landing Bay, with the same or another bird off the South End on 22 Apr.
- **1999**   24 Mar to 9 Apr – one off the East Side, mainly in the Landing Bay area, but as far north as Gannets' Combe.
- **2003**   28 Apr to 5 May – one in the Landing Bay and off the East Side.

Great Northern Diver *Gavia immer*   [Great Northern Loon]

Uncommon passage migrant and winter visitor in small numbers, mainly October to March.

By far the most regularly recorded of the three 'common' British divers in Lundy waters, Great Northern Divers have been seen in all months except July and August, mainly off the East Side. Between 1947 and the end of 2006, the greatest number of records have been in October (28) and November (30). The earliest autumn record is 20 September (1978) and there is only one other September sighting. While most occurrences relate to birds passing through, perhaps staying for a few days, there are occasional longer stays; one individual spent most of the 1975/76 winter fishing around the island, remaining from 19 December to 17 March. There are 10 May records and two in June, the latest being 9 June (1992) and birds in full breeding plumage have been seen from time to time, presumably on their way north to Icelandic breeding grounds.

Most sightings are of single birds, but there have been at least 25 occasions on which two were recorded on the same day, five cases of three birds, and three instances where four birds have been present: 7 January 1981, 25 & 26 October 1999 and 21 January 2004.

One was seen in "late 1860" (D'Urban & Mathew 1895) and the species was listed by Chanter (1871) and Parfitt (1876) as an "autumn and winter visitant", while the Heaven Diaries include an entry for 7 February 1874 reading: "People shot 'Northern Diver' (?) in Bay" (Boyd 1950). There are two dated, pre-LFS twentieth century records: two on 27 September 1927 and 1 on 18 October 1944 (F.W. Gade reported by Davis 1954a).

Little Grebe *Tachybaptus ruficollis*

Lundy vagrant.

This is an example of a species that is relatively common and widespread on the neighbouring English and Welsh mainland but which is an extreme rarity on Lundy. There have been just four records, two of which have involved stranded birds. Listed by Chanter (1871) and Parfitt (1876) as an "occasional visitant", there are, however, no dated records other than those listed below:

- **1949**   15 Oct – a remarkable record of one found alive but "somewhat oiled" in the engine room of the North Light; "After attempts at cleaning it was released on the rocket pond."
- **1963**   6 to 18 Apr – one on Pondsbury.
- **1964**   Aug – an exhausted bird was picked up from the Landing Beach late in the month and ringed and released on Pondsbury.
- **2000**   26 to 28 Jul – an adult on Pondsbury.

Great Crested Grebe *Podiceps cristatus*

Lundy vagrant.

There are five records, one in spring and four in autumn:

1970   3 & 4 Oct – one in the Landing Bay.
1971   11 May – one off Quarry Beach.
1986   28 Sep – one in Lundy Roads.
1999   13 Aug – a juvenile in the Landing Bay.
2003   7 Sep – one in the Landing Bay.

Red-necked Grebe *Podiceps grisegena*

Lundy vagrant.

There are five records, mainly in February and March, and all of single birds, except for the most recent occurrence when up to four were seen in the Landing Bay; sadly, this seems to have been linked with the *Sea Empress* oil spill off Milford Haven, South Wales, in February 1996.

1957   23 to 31 Aug – a first-year bird.
1991   17 to 24 Feb – one, probably a first-year bird, in the Landing Bay.
1993   14 Mar – one off Ladies Beach.
1995   19 to 23 Feb – one in the Landing Bay.
1996   16 Feb – two in the Landing Bay off Ladies Beach, increasing to four on 25 Feb, at least two of which were oiled; two were seen again on 26 Feb, then one on 23 Mar.

Slavonian Grebe *Podiceps auritus*   [Horned Grebe]

Lundy vagrant.

Slavonian Grebes have occurred in 11 years since the start of regular LFS recording (to the end of 2006). All sightings have been between October and April, with most during late winter and early spring, and all have been of single birds, except for April 1947 when up to four were seen off the East Side:

1947   7 to 18 Apr – two in Lundy Roads, constituting the first Lundy record, increased to four on 19 Apr, with one still present on 24 Apr.
1951   1 Nov – one in the Landing Bay (see also Black-necked Grebe 1951).
1955   13 & 14 Oct – one.
1957   20 Mar – one.
1969   27 Oct – one.
1972   22 Dec – one.
1976   27 Apr – one in breeding plumage.
1977   16 Mar – one in winter plumage.
1985   19 Feb to 5 Mar – one seen on four days.[20]
2004   25 Nov – one close inshore off North End.
2005   4 to 6 Feb – one in the Landing Bay.

Parfitt (1876) included "Podiceps auritus The Eared Grebe" (our underlining) in his list of "occasional visitants" but as noted by Davis (1954a) there is confusion about whether this is a correct reference to the occurrence of Slavonian Grebe, or whether Parfitt incorrectly transcribed Chanter's 1871 listing of "Podiceps nigricollis Eared Grebe", the latter presumably intended to refer to Black-necked Grebe. It seems most likely that Parfitt made an error, since Chanter's revised list of "occasional visitants", published in his 1877 monograph, again gives "Eared Grebe Podiceps nigricollis". There are no other pre-LFS references to Slavonian Grebe.

Black-necked Grebe *Podiceps nigricollis*

Lundy vagrant.

Apparently listed by Chanter (1871, 1877) as an "occasional visitant" (but see Slavonian Grebe account for details of confusion surrounding this entry). Palmer (1946) stated that "one in the Ilfracombe Museum was shot on Lundy many years ago". Sightings on two dates in April 1947 and included in the *LFS Annual Report* for that year were discounted by Davis (1954a) as "doubtful" and also excluded by Dymond (1980).[21] Thus there is only one reliable, dated record, and none in the last 50 years:

1951   1 Nov – an adult was present "at the same time" as a Slavonian Grebe; the latter was seen in the Landing Bay, so presumably this is also where the Black-necked Grebe was seen, though there are no surviving details.

Fulmar *Fulmarus glacialis*   [Northern Fulmar]

Common breeder; recorded in all months, mainly from January to September.

Fulmars colonised Britain relatively recently, their southward spread thought to have been encouraged by offal and bycatch from whaling and trawling. In 1878 the British and Irish population numbered just 12 pairs. This had increased to an estimated 69,000 pairs by 1949, about 309,000 pairs in 1969, and 536,500 pairs during the 1985–1988 Seabird Colony Register survey. The latest census (1998–2002) suggests little overall change since then, with approximately 538,000 pairs recorded (Mitchell *et al.* 2004).

Fulmars

On Lundy, Fulmars occur mainly along the West Side, especially in Jenny's Cove, and northwards around the perimeter of the island to Gannets' Rock on the East Side. The island's first Fulmar was seen inshore at the North Landing on 11 June 1922 (Loyd 1922), with regular sightings from the summer of 1935 onwards (Perry 1940). The first record of a bird ashore came in 1939 (Perry 1940) but it was not until 1944 that the species first bred on the island: four pairs nested, but only one egg was laid and later "taken, in ignorance, by a temporary resident" (Harman & Fisher 1944). Davis (1954a) gave the location as Jenny's Cove. This was the first record of nesting in south-west England and it was from Lundy that the species colonised the region. Two pairs nested in 1945 and thereafter the population gradually increased in Jenny's Cove but with a new colony establishing on Gannets' Rock in 1947. These remain the principal nesting areas today, with good numbers also between Battery Point and Needle Rock (26 pairs in 1996), in the Long Roost area, and along the East Side southwards as far as Halfway Wall.

Numbers of breeding Fulmars increased from six pairs to around 25 pairs between 1947 and 1957 (Price 1996). By the early 1970s the population had reached 100 pairs. Counts between 1981 and 1996 suggested that the breeding population had almost doubled over a 20-year period, with the highest ever count, of 203 apparently occupied nests, in 1996. Censuses in 2000 and 2004 indicate a slight downward trend in breeding numbers (see figure).

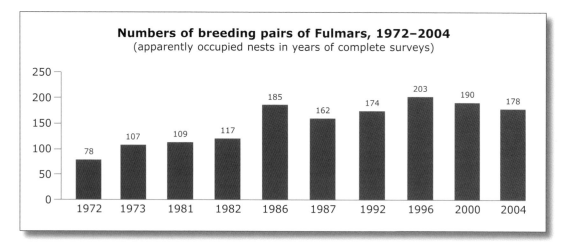

Fulmars occur around Lundy in all months but are infrequent from October to February when they are out in the North Atlantic. Notable counts outside the breeding season include 50 at Gannets' Rock on 20 December 1999, at least 60 at breeding areas on 30 December 1991, 70 on 9 & 11 December 2003, 95 on 18 November of the same year, 100 on 30 January 2007 and more than 100 on 2 February 2005.

A blue-phase Fulmar bred on Gannets' Rock from 1948 to 1958 and the same or another formed one half of a pair that failed to breed successfully in 1966. Another blue-phase bird was seen on 4–5 September 1980.

The School of Psychology, University of Exeter has recently studied the social behaviour of Lundy's Fulmars early in the breeding season, focusing on the approximately 70 pairs nesting on the northern side of Gannets' Rock.

Just one recovery has resulted from the 147 Fulmars ringed up to the end of 2006: a chick ringed on 31 July 1972 was found dead 95 kilometres away at Perranporth on the north coast of Cornwall almost seven years later on 25 June 1979.

Great Shearwater *Puffinus gravis*

Lundy vagrant.

In addition to a record of two birds on 14 April 1939 (Perry 1940), there are two LFS records, one for spring and one in autumn:

1950 20 & 21 Apr – one possibly two on the first date, and two on 21st, seen diving in the vicinity of the Landing Bay.

1974 7 Sep – one off the Battery.

There are also five records of birds seen during the boat crossing: two on 6 September 1950 and singles on 16 July 1966,[22] 2 June 1974, 26 September 1975 and 6 July 1980.[23] In addition, the 2002 *Devon Bird Report* mentions 100 seen on 28 August 2002 on the crossing to Lundy, four miles from Clovelly, with a further eight on 30 August.

Given that the overwhelming majority of Great Shearwaters are seen off UK coasts in late summer and early autumn, the April and June records are highly unusual. Nevertheless, these sightings were accepted for the relevant *LFS Annual Reports* and *Devon Bird Reports* and were included by Dymond (1980). The few surviving details are insufficient to prove that correct identifications were made, but equally it is unknown what additional information may have been made available at the time.

Sooty Shearwater *Puffinus griseus*

Lundy vagrant.

Though recorded annually off the coast of Devon and Cornwall, sometimes in large numbers, Sooty Shearwater appears to be a vagrant in the waters around Lundy, with only three sightings from the island itself:

1970 17 Aug – one close inshore.

1973 26 Sep – one flew past Battery Point.

2006 19 Oct – one 200 metres off the South End.

Sightings on the boat crossing from Bideford or Ilfracombe include one on 17 Aug 1970,[24] one on 13 August 1972,[24] one on 5 August 1973, singles on 11 & 25 September 1979, two on 8 August 1987 and one about four miles from Lundy on 8 October 2002. In addition, there was a remarkable series of records in the late summer of 2002, mainly during crossings from Clovelly; singles were noted on 14, 21, 23 & 24 August, followed by 50+ on 28 August, 20+ on 30 August and four on 4 September.[24]

Manx Shearwater *Puffinus puffinus*

Common breeder and passage migrant; usually seen from late March to September; occasional records in October.

A walk well after nightfall to almost any part of the island's coastline from April to July, particularly on pitch-black nights, can reward the listener with the eerie, ventriloquial calls of Manx Shearwaters as they fly low over the sidelands. (They can sometimes be heard without the need for getting out of bed!) During daylight hours 'Manxies' can be seen offshore a kilometre or more out from the island, and occasionally over the tide races off South End and, especially, North End. They are usually first recorded from mid-March. Rafts of several thousand have been seen close to the island in midsummer (e.g. 8,000 were counted off North End on 4 July 1979) and birds are occasionally observed inshore in October. There are usually no records from November to mid-March – most birds migrate to spend the winter months off the Atlantic coast of South America.

In conservation terms Lundy is perhaps more important for Manx Shearwaters than for any other species. British breeding Manx Shearwaters were estimated at 280,000 to 310,000 pairs for the years 1999 to 2002 (Baker *et al.* 2001), about 90% of the world population. The Pembrokeshire islands of Skomer, Skokholm and Middleholm combined support over 150,000 pairs (JNCC 2001). Given the proximity of Lundy (only 75 kilometres away) and the habitat available on the island – thousands of holes and rabbit burrows – the potential for a sizeable colony is evident, given a predator-free environment. The two questions that have intrigued birdwatchers and conservationists over many years are do Manx Shearwaters breed on Lundy and, if so, in what numbers?

Among the early Lundy writers, Moore (1837) stated that the species bred on the island. Chanter (1871) and Parfitt (1876) listed it as a "summer visitant", the latter describing it as a "constant breeder", while D'Urban & Mathew (1895) reported it as very numerous and breeding. Blathwayt (1900) stated

Manx Shearwaters

that Manx Shearwater was "well known on Lundy" and "probably breeds". Rousham (1908) referred to it as not numerous, but breeding. Cummings (1909) reported hearing but not seeing Manx Shearwaters. Hendy (1922, 1933) thought it probable that breeding took place in 1914, his only visit to the island, but found no nests. Loyd (1922, 1925) reported a "considerable colony numbering perhaps half a hundred pairs" but later thought this to be an overestimate (Southern & Tucker 1944) and reputedly discovered a nesting site containing eggs after "weeks of disappointment". However, none of these authors gave any substantiating details to confirm breeding. Roberts (1903) appears to be the first ornithologist to have documented adults, eggs and young, writing: "Some of the holes that we examined contained a smooth white egg, others a young bird resembling a young Puffin, except for a curious tuft on its head, but in every case we found the parent bird at home." On 20 June 1903 Dr H.B. Elton extracted an egg from "a number of burrows excavated" but apparently without finding any adult or young birds (Southern & Tucker 1944). Harrisson (1932) failed to locate a nest during three "nocturnal attempts" in June 1930 and stated: "It is difficult to believe that there can be a very large number breeding at the present time." Other evidence of breeding was provided by Felix Gade who found young shearwaters, evidently making their way down to the sea, in Millcombe in both 1934 and 1935; and also through the reports of lighthouse keepers at the North Light who found both young birds and eggs laid in holes among granite boulders (Southern & Tucker 1944).

Even until relatively recently very little was known about the population on Lundy, in particular whether the birds coming ashore on the island were actually breeding; nesting was suspected for many years but without conclusive evidence. Perry (1940) estimated 1,000 pairs to be nesting around the island in 1939. Southern & Tucker (1944) began their paper by stating that the species' status on Lundy "has long been problematical" and concluded that while the colony had been present for many years, there was no evidence that it had ever been large (in 1942 they found only one chick in 19 burrows examined on Puffin Slope). They also thought it possible that the Lundy colony was continually plundered by rats. Davis (1954a) stated that there were several small colonies but considered that many birds that came ashore were pre-breeding adults from the Pembrokeshire colonies (e.g. Skokholm, Skomer), a finding subsequently backed up by ringing studies. Dymond (1980) suggested a probable breeding population of between 100 and 1,000 pairs. Studies by the Department of Zoology of University College, Cardiff between 1976 and 1981 revealed a strong preference for the sidelands on the East Side from White Beach north to North East Point, and on the West Side from Pilot's Quay to north of the Old Light; together, nine sites in these areas accounted for 95% of calling birds. The study concluded that the population of Manx Shearwaters on Lundy may be between 1,000 and 10,000 breeding pairs (Thomas 1981).

More recent survey work has shown that estimates based on calling birds are unreliable; non-breeders are responsible for most of the calling, while nesting birds fly in straight and silently to land and enter burrows (Tony Taylor, personal communication). Extensive surveys in late August and early September from 1979 to 1983 near the Old Light and in Halfway Wall Bay found no shearwaters at all, when adults feeding chicks, or the emergence of young from burrows, would have been expected. This suggested that any successful breeding was on an insignificant scale (Taylor 1985). Taylor also concluded that while breeding was continually attempted, it was almost totally unsuccessful as a result of predation by rats. Based on offshore counts of about 200 at dusk early in the breeding season, and the tendency for individuals to incubate for about six days before being relieved by their mate, Taylor suggested a maximum population of about 1,200 pairs attempting to breed. Further studies in 1987, focused mainly on a 50 square metre sloping patch of short turf between Old Light and The Battery, produced evidence of nesting birds, but none was successful (Taylor 1989). This reinforced the idea that attempts by shearwaters to breed largely resulted in failure because of predation by rats – a possibility that had been raised in the pages of *British Birds* in the 1940s (Southern & Tucker 1944; Perry 1945). Taylor also postulated that the Lundy population must be sustained by immigration, probably from the South Wales colonies – several birds ringed on Skomer have subsequently been controlled on Lundy. A sample census using tape playback in 2000 estimated there may be 300–400 occupied burrows, while a comprehensive, island-wide follow-up survey of over 7,000 burrows in mid-May 2001 produced a revised estimate of 166 breeding pairs (Price & Booker 2001).

So, the most likely answers to those intriguing questions are that shearwaters have bred through the years, but largely unsuccessfully on account of the large numbers of Brown and Black Rats on the island, and that the population, according to several studies over a period of 60 years, has numbered anything between 100 and 10,000 pairs. This huge variation in published estimates bears witness to the difficulty of surveying a species that only comes ashore at night and which may spend days on end either deep in a burrow incubating the single egg, or feeding far out at sea.

The results of the 2000 study suggested that, with continuing predation by rats at the time, Manx Shearwaters were maintaining only a tenuous hold as a breeding species on Lundy. It was for this reason that the Seabird Recovery Project was initiated in 2001 as a joint venture of English Nature (now Natural England), the Landmark Trust, the National Trust and the Royal Society for the Protection of Birds, centred around a rat eradication programme. Over the winters of 2002/03 and 2003/04 the entire island was covered with a 50-metre grid of 2,100 poison bait stations (Appleton *et al.* 2003). This appears to have been successful, with no signs of rats since February 2004, although monitoring continued until the final detailed check in January/February 2006 when the island was declared rat free. Monitoring will continue in perpetuity around the jetty. Attention is now being focused on long-term monitoring of the seabird populations, in particular Manx Shearwaters. Given that young shearwaters do not reach breeding maturity until 5–8 years of age when they return to nest, measurable change in the breeding population will take many years. However, the signs appear promising as birds were found bringing food to burrows in July 2004, and at least 10 different chicks were seen outside burrows on five nights in September – confirmation at last of successful breeding on Lundy. There was further breeding success in 2005 (11 large chicks found outside burrows between 27 August and 9 September) and in 2006 (23 juveniles found in the colony below Old Light on 12 & 13 September; the RSPB estimated 30–40 breeding pairs with at least 30 young fledged).

Offshore counts in July and August in recent years have recorded 5,000 or more shearwaters, with "huge numbers" – estimated to be at least 50,000 – seen on 13 July 2004.

Extreme early and late dates are 20 January (in both 2004 and 2007; five seen on the latter date) and 26 October (2006 – a single bird). While the late January records appear exceptional, Wernham *et al.* (2002) report winter sightings from the Bay of Biscay. Could global warming also be prompting changes to the species' migration pattern?

By the end of 2006, 1,162 shearwaters had been ringed on Lundy. Controls and recoveries indicate regular movements between Lundy and the Welsh breeding colonies on Skomer and Skokholm, and to a lesser extent between Lundy and Bardsey off the Llyn Peninsula in North Wales, and Annet in the Isles of Scilly. Lundy-ringed birds have been found at Ravenglass, Cumbria (1), Angelsey (1), the Llyn Peninsula (1), the South Wales coast from Pembrokeshire (including Skomer and Skokholm) to Glamorgan (15), the North Devon coast (3), the Cornish coast (4), the south coast of Devon (1), the Isles of Scilly (3) and the French coast (2). Amongst these birds, one ringed on Lundy on 23 July 1992 was controlled on Annet on 30 June 1993, caught again on Annet on 12 August 1997 and found dead at Whiteford Burrows, Llanmadoc, Gower (South Wales) on 4 August 1998. The longest-lived Lundy bird to date is an adult ringed on 16 July 1987 and found dead at Chapel Porth, Cornwall, 15 years later on 8 August 2002.

Balearic Shearwater (Mediterranean Shearwater) *Puffinus mauretanicus*

Lundy vagrant.

There are seven Lundy records involving up to 15 birds:

1959 16 Jul – one flew past Rat Island "about 600 yards" offshore.
2005 19 Oct – one was seen from the Ugly flying south.
20 Oct – one flew south past the Landing Bay.
21 Oct – three were seen moving south off the Landing Bay at different times.
2006 7 Oct – five off the East Side; two still present the following day.
25 Oct – one off the East Side.
7 & 8 Nov – at least three off the East Side.

The 1956 *LFS Annual Report* states that a "probable" Balearic Shearwater was seen half-a-mile off the North End on 2 August that year.

Observations during the boat crossing include two seen from the *Lerina* on the passage to Bideford on 6 September 1950 and one on 8 August 1987. In addition, the 2002 *Devon Bird Report* mentions four records of Balearic Shearwaters seen during the Lundy crossing, with a peak count of six on 30 August that year. In 2005 two were seen on the crossing in July, with a single bird in October (2005 *Devon Bird Report*).

Storm Petrel *Hydrobates pelagicus*   [European Storm Petrel]

Uncommon spring migrant that possibly breeds; recorded on the island at night in small numbers in the breeding season and seen occasionally offshore during daytime in summer and autumn.

Daytime sightings from the island are infrequent and usually involve very small numbers. However, in line with this species' common name, rough weather can bring significant arrivals of 'stormies' seeking more sheltered waters in which to rest and feed. Following severe westerly gales, about 25 were in the Landing Bay on 28 May 1972 (accompanied by two Leach's Petrels), with at least 12 remaining on 29th. There was an even bigger influx the following year, again associated with severe westerly gales, when about 70 Storm Petrels were seen in Lundy Roads on 7 August, with around 15 still present on 8th. More recently, larger numbers seen from the island have included up to 15 off the East Side from 22 to 25 June 1998, 20 on 4 August of the same year, 20 from 27 to 29 June 1995 and 20 on 16 June 2007. The earliest spring sighting from the island itself is of two on 29 April 2003 and the latest autumn record is of two in Lundy Roads on 30 October 1952.

Although listed by Chanter (1871) and Parfitt (1876) as a "summer visitant" (Parfitt adding "occasional visitant"), and by Blathwayt (1900) as a possible nesting species, breeding on Lundy has yet to be proven, but there is strong circumstantial evidence. Dymond (1980) referred to records of single birds found dead during the summer months, the characteristic musky smell detected at three sites in 1958, and the frequent night-time visits by petrels to the west sidelands (from May to August) in the 1970s (e.g. 10 at Pilot's Quay on the night of 28 July 1976). Since the mid-1980s, ringing studies using tape lures of Storm Petrel calls suggest that nocturnal visits to the island – at least to inshore waters – are routine; 29 birds were caught and ringed on the nights of 19–22 July 1986 alone, while 57 were captured in June 1996. One bird caught ashore on 26 July 1991 and two on 23 July 1992, without the use of tape lures, strengthen the likelihood that the species does nest on Lundy. The strongest suggestion to date came on 27 August 2005 when one of three birds caught had a brood patch. This indicated that the individual concerned had probably attempted to breed in 2005, though not necessarily on Lundy. The eradication of rats from the island (see the species account for Manx Shearwater, page 64) can only enhance the chances of successful breeding.

Between April and October, Storm Petrels are sometimes encountered during the boat crossing to or from the North Devon mainland, higher counts including eight on 11 June 1979, 10 on both 17 April 1950 and 31 October 1972, 12 on 25 July 1954, and 15 on 15 August 1967. In addition, the 1953 *LFS Annual Report* states that "R.M. Lockley saw several hundreds to the north whilst crossing from Lundy to Tenby [South Wales], July 5th". The latest date for a Storm Petrel seen during the crossing is 3 November 2000.[25]

By the end of 2006, 232 Storm Petrels had been ringed on Lundy, with nine subsequently controlled elsewhere, including at: Gwennap Head, Pendeen Watch (2) and Pendeen Lighthouse (Cornwall); St Martins (Isles of Scilly); Portland Bill (Dorset); Strumble Head (Dyfed, 2); and Calf of Man (Isle of Man). A further 12 Storm Petrels controlled on Lundy, mostly since 1995, had been ringed as full-grown birds at: Bardsey Island (North Wales); Sanda Island (Kintyre, Strathclyde); Loop Head (Co. Clare, Ireland); Sheepland (Ardglass, Co. Down, Northern Ireland); Copeland (Co. Down, Northern Ireland); Gugh and Burnt Island (Isles of Scilly); St Alban's Head (Dorset); Pendeen Watch (2) and Rumps Point (Cornwall); and from just across the water at Hartland Point (Devon). Taken together, these 21 movements to/from Lundy show that the Storm Petrels visiting the island during the summer also visit sites distributed around a broad sweep of the English Channel, Western Approaches and Irish Sea coasts, including known breeding colonies.

Storm Petrels

Leach's Petrel *Oceanodroma leucorhoa*   [Leach's Storm Petrel]

Lundy vagrant.

There are two LFS records, both associated with westerly gales:

1972   28 May – at least two in the Landing Bay with Storm Petrels after westerly gales.

1998   27 Oct – two in the vicinity of the Landing Bay and Rat Island during westerly gales.

In addition, the 1971 *LFS Annual Report* states: "On 24th January, six petrels seen at Jenny's Cove were believed to be of this species."[26] The only previous occurrence was of one found dead on 2 June 1928 (F.W. Gade, reported by Davis 1954a).

Gannet *Morus bassanus*   [Northern Gannet]

Common offshore from spring to autumn; less frequent in winter; formerly bred.

Gannets can be seen offshore virtually daily from April to early November. With luck, individuals, small groups and occasionally larger flocks can be observed diving repeatedly in the same area of water to feed on densely packed shoals of fish, perhaps accompanied by porpoises or dolphins – a truly spectacular sight, especially through binoculars or a telescope. Gannets may be seen anywhere around the island, but sitting quietly and scanning the sea off either the North End or South End is probably the best bet. At times, especially in calm conditions when the clear, shallow waters make for good fishing, they can also be encountered close inshore along the East Side and in the Landing Bay.

Sightings are much less frequent from mid-November to March and are probably highly dependent on prevailing weather at a time of year when most Gannets are normally well out to sea (Wernham *et al.* 2002), though observer coverage is also very patchy in winter.

The highest numbers have usually been seen in late summer and autumn as birds disperse from the UK's 21 breeding colonies, which together hold up to 70% of the world population. These include the huge colony on the nearby (in Gannet terms) Welsh island of Grassholm, about 80 kilometres to the north-west of Lundy. Grassholm was once owned, like Lundy, by Martin Coles Harman. Mr Harman gave Grassholm to the RSPB in 1947 so that the gannetry might be protected. The Grassholm colony grew from just 12 pairs in 1872 to 300 pairs in 1905, 15,500 pairs in 1964 and more than 32,000 pairs in 2004 (the most recent RSPB estimate). It is interesting to speculate whether the Grassholm gannetry would have developed in such spectacular fashion had the Lundy colony, whose sorry history is related below, survived unpersecuted.

Peak Lundy Gannet counts to date (end of 2006) are of 300 on 24 October 1994, 30 September 1999 and 25 October 2005, 400 passing the island on 1 September 1977, 440 on 24 October 2004 and 450 on 21 October 2005. During the 20-year period 1987 to 2006 there were at least a further nine instances of 200 or more seen in a day: 22 February 1990 (250), 2 & 10 October 1997 (200), 16 July 2005 (200), 15 & 16 August 2005 (250), 19 August 2005 (200), 19 October 2005 (200) and 28 October 2005 (227). However, recording of Gannets in the LFS logbook has been very inconsistent during this period, with frequent use of ticks instead of actual numbers seen and this makes it difficult to draw firm conclusions. Nevertheless, there is some suggestion that spring sightings are more numerous now than 20 years ago, while many of the highest counts on record are from recent years, perhaps reflecting the overall upward trend in the UK breeding population, not least the growth of the Grassholm gannetry. The series of high counts from July to October 2005 is particularly notable.

Parfitt (1876) described Gannet as a "summer visitant" and "constant breeder". Chanter (1871) listed it as a "summer visitant" and stated "Gannets appear at one time to have been very plentiful", adding: "They are continually referred to in the old record as constituting one of the chief sources of the riches and revenue of the island. Gannet Rock and Cove were so called from the hosts of birds that made it their headquarters, but they have decreased much of late years." In his monograph of 1877 Chanter amended the conclusion to read "but they, as well as the other sea-birds, are perceptibly and rapidly decreasing in numbers, from the incessant and reckless robbers of their nests during the breeding season, principally by the crews of pilot and tug-boats".

Until the island was deserted by Gannets in the first years of the twentieth century, Lundy was the species' only nesting site in England, and the UK's most southerly breeding colony. Writing in 1934, Morrey Salmon & Lockley stated: "…there is evidence of the existence of this gannetry in the year 1274. There are however, large gaps in the history of the Lundy Gannets. Gurney [author of The Gannet, 1912], in spite of exhaustive researches for his book was quite unable to trace any record of Gannets there between 1631 and 1830…Gurney mentioned another reference to them in 1839, and subsequently the existence of the colony appears to have been widely known." Roberts (1903) stated that when Edward II [1284–1327] "gave the island to Despenser, the Gannet Stone figures as a 'certain rock, with two places near it, where Gannets settle and breed worth in ordinary years sixty-six shillings and eight pence'."

During the nineteenth century the colony was originally established on Gannets' Rock, where 15 pairs nested in 1883 but no young were reared then or subsequently. By 1892 the colony had been abandoned, the remaining birds moving to nest on North West Point (D'Urban & Mathew 1895). Here 16 pairs nested in 1887, rising to almost 70 in 1889 but dropping back to 30 in 1893 (Blathwayt 1900, Morrey Salmon & Lockley 1934). Persecution, which continued throughout the nineteenth century, and disturbance, especially from the building of the North Lighthouse in 1896–1897, saw the colony dwindle to three or four pairs in 1900 (Blathwayt 1900), seven pairs in 1901 (Jourdain 1922), and five pairs in 1903 that nested in a cove below the lighthouse, though all five eggs laid were taken (Gurney 1913). There are no definite records of nesting birds thereafter, though in 1904 the Society for the Protection of Birds (now RSPB) had a 'watcher' (i.e. a warden) on the island throughout the breeding season. The Society stated that "the difficulties have been considerable; but the Coastguard and Trinity House authorities expressed their willingness to cooperate…and it is hoped that the people of Lundy will in every way support the efforts made to preserve one of the great natural attractions of their island" (Society for the Protection of Birds 1904). In 1922 one bird attempted to build a nest just north of Gannets' Rock (Loyd 1925) but eventually left shortly after 24 May when "after continuous fogs" they were "disturbed, there can be no manner of doubt, by the north-end fog-horns". North Light keeper Robert Hall thought that a pair may have nested in 1927 (Harrisson 1932). An attempt to re-establish a colony was made in 1938 when 20 eggs from the gannetry on Grassholm were placed in the nests of Cormorants and Shags. Whether the eggs hatched successfully is not known, but plans to restore Gannets in succeeding years were thwarted by the outbreak of World War II.

A stuffed Gannet on display in the small island museum bears a label reading "Gannet shot on Lundy 1870. Present by Taunton Museum" and stands as sad testimony to former persecution. It is to be hoped that with the continuing success of the Grassholm gannetry this species might one day return to breed on Lundy, though that would mean coping with inevitable disturbance from visiting light aircraft, helicopters and large numbers of well-meaning visitors on foot. Any prospective colonists will also have to watch out for some of Lundy's incumbent avian residents, as the following cautionary tale, related to us by Tony Taylor, demonstrates: "In July 2004 an adult Gannet gliding north along the West Side and level with the Old Light was stooped on from behind by a juvenile Peregrine. Just before contact the Peregrine pulled out. At the same time the Gannet finally noticed it and took violent evasive action, the result of which was that it completely lost control and cartwheeled downwards, only just avoiding rocks below. The way it flew out to sea suggested it would not be back any time soon!"

Cormorant *Phalacrocorax carbo*   [Great Cormorant]

Uncommon but regular spring and autumn migrant; formerly bred.

Cormorants have been recorded in every month but it is during the spring and autumn migration periods that they are most frequently encountered, usually flying over the island or low over inshore waters. Small flocks of up to 20 or so birds often fly northwards past Lundy between mid-March and late May each year (e.g. 23 on 30 March 1997); four reported on 13 June 1986 were exceptionally late. Southward movements of sometimes 20 or more are recorded from early August to the end of October. Occasional midsummer and winter sightings are mostly of immature birds. It is likely that many of the birds seen on Lundy are moving to or from the largest Welsh breeding colony on St Margaret's Island off the Pembrokeshire coast near Tenby, which in 2004 held 189 nests.

One was seen fishing in Rocket Pole Pond on 9 June 1954. More recently, there is a suggestion that Cormorants may have emptied the pond of fish altogether! Highest counts since regular recording began in 1947 are of 41 birds flying north on 3 April 1975, 44 on 12 April 1982, 51 moving south on 26 September 1999 and five flocks totalling 84 birds on 23 March 1998.

Listed by Chanter (1871) and Parfitt (1876) as "resident all the year", the latter adding "and breed there", which they once did in small numbers. Loyd (1922) found about twelve pairs in 1922, while 16 pairs in 1932 (H. Davies, reported by Davis 1954a) is the highest count on record. The species declined in the late 1940s and last nested in 1959, a single pair above Quarry Beach raising four young. Nests were usually situated on Gannets' Rock, though occasionally on the adjacent cliff of the main island. One pair nested at Shutter Point (South West Point) in 1875 (Heaven Diaries 1870–1905, reported by Boyd 1950) and two above Quarry Beach in 1939 (Perry 1940).

Forty-six Cormorants, all nestlings, were ringed on Lundy between 1948 and 1959, of which 13 were subsequently recovered – see table. These indicated that some of the birds that survived their first winter (several were found dead in Cornwall and South Devon a few months after fledging) migrated to the Atlantic coasts of France and Spain, as do birds from current breeding colonies in Ireland, south-west England and southern Wales (Wernham *et al.* 2002).

Movements of Cormorants ringed as nestlings on Lundy

Date ringed on Lundy	Place found	Date recovered	Speculation about date/place of finding
13 Jul 1948	Sennen Cove, Cornwall	19 Sep 1948	Post-juvenile dispersal/ on autumn migration
02 Jul 1949	Exmouth, South Devon	26 Oct 1949	Post-juvenile dispersal/ on autumn migration
02 Jul 1949	Lannion, Cotes-d'Armor, **France**	05 Nov 1949	Post-juvenile dispersal/ on autumn migration
30 Jun 1950	Sarzeau, Morbihan, **France**	15 Jan 1952	In wintering area
08 Jul 1952	Bude, Cornwall	21 Sep 1952	Post-juvenile dispersal/ on autumn migration
24 Jul 1952	River Fowey, Cornwall	25 Dec 1952	In wintering area
26 Jun 1953	Ste Marie du Mont, Manche, **France**	07 Sep 1953	Post-juvenile dispersal/ on autumn migration
26 Jun 1953	Erme Estuary, South Devon	09 Jun 1957	In summering area
25 Jul 1955	Sada, La Coruña, Galicia, **Spain**	09 Nov 1961	In wintering area
18 Jun 1957	Devon (location unknown)	24 May 1960	Late spring migrant
18 Jun 1957	Devon (location unknown)	16 Jun 1959	Late spring migrant
27 Jun 1958	Lanildut, Finistère, **France**	21 Sep 1958	Post-juvenile dispersal/ on autumn migration
27 Jun 1958	Devon (location unknown)	21 Apr 1960	On spring migration

Shag *Phalacrocorax aristotelis* [European Shag]

Common breeder; uncommon from October to February.

For much of the year, Shags are often the first bird encountered on arriving in the Landing Bay and can be seen from virtually any cliff-top vantage point. They nest mainly in narrow clefts or underneath large rocks on the lower sections of cliffs around most of the island, with the main concentrations along the West Side at Goat Island, near Pyramid Rock and St Mark's Stone, and on the East Side around Tibbett's Point and below the quarries. Outside the breeding season they gather in small flocks on rocky outcrops close to open water, especially on Mouse Island (next to Rat Island), Great Shutter Rock, and at North West Point.

Listed by Chanter (1871) and Parfitt (1876) as "resident all the year", the latter adding "and breed there". Numbers of breeding Shags have fluctuated considerably over the years, from a low of 12 or 13 pairs in 1922 and 1923 (Loyd 1922, 1925), to a maximum of 132 pairs in 1956 (see figure opposite for complete counts since 1939). The size of individual colonies also varies year on year, unsuccessful pairs often choosing a new site in the following year. An exceptionally late breeding record in 2004 involved an adult feeding young still in the nest on 23 September. The highest count outside the breeding season is 50 on 29 September 1987 and 5 September 1999. Most birds have usually left the island by October – though 40 were present on 8 November 2006 – and return in March, with a few staying through the winter months.

Barbara Snow (née Whitaker) conducted detailed research into the breeding biology and breeding-season behaviour of Lundy's Shags during her time as LFS warden in the mid-1950s. The results of this work were published in two major papers: in *Ibis*, journal of the British Ornithologists' Union (Snow 1960), and in *British Birds* (Snow 1963). She noted that the first breeding birds returned in the second or third week of February, with further arrivals during the remainder of February and well into March. The total number of nests varied from 123 (in 1954) to 131 (in 1957). The average date of laying of the first egg (1954–1957) was 29 April and the average number of young fledged each year (1955–1957) was 215. Both adults and juveniles began leaving the island three to four weeks after the young had fledged, most departing between mid-August and mid-September. Some birds present during late September and October were thought to have been passage migrants. Ringing recoveries at that time suggested that most Lundy Shags wintered on the south coast of Cornwall and Devon and the north-west coast of France. Of 140 recoveries analysed, 71% were in these areas and nearly all the remainder in the vicinity of the Bristol Channel.

More recently, Lundy Shags have been studied by the University of Exeter as part of research into the diving patterns of shag and cormorant species in south-west England and New Zealand (Lea *et al.* 1996).

By the end of 2006 a total of 1,187 Shags had been ringed on Lundy, 1,028 of them between 1947 and 1967. There have now been 211 recoveries, which reinforce the pattern described by Barbara Snow, though it must be kept in mind that few Shags have been ringed on Lundy in the last 30 or 40 years, so any recent changes in distribution outside the breeding season would not be evident.

There are 47 controls/recoveries of Lundy birds along the north-west French coast: 33 of these from the *département* of Finistére, 10 from Côtes d'Armor (formerly Côtes-du-Nord) and singles from Manche, Morbihan, Ille et Vilaine and Seine Maritime. Birds ringed as chicks on Lundy have also been found along the coasts of Cornwall (88, plus one from the Isles of Scilly), Devon (33), Glamorgan (8),

Shag

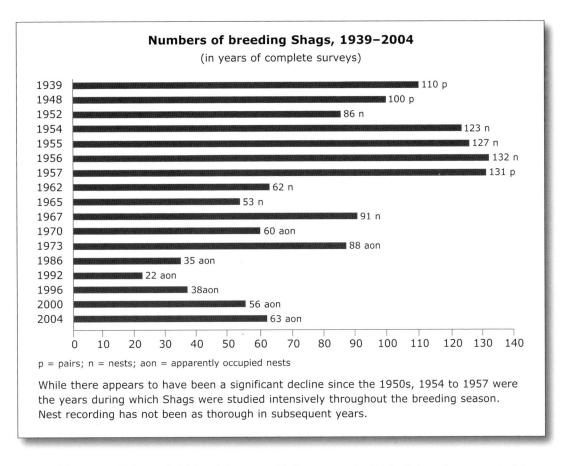

Numbers of breeding Shags, 1939–2004
(in years of complete surveys)

1939	110 p
1948	100 p
1952	86 n
1954	123 n
1955	127 n
1956	132 n
1957	131 p
1962	62 n
1965	53 n
1967	91 n
1970	60 aon
1973	88 aon
1986	35 aon
1992	22 aon
1996	38 aon
2000	56 aon
2004	63 aon

p = pairs; n = nests; aon = apparently occupied nests

While there appears to have been a significant decline since the 1950s, 1954 to 1957 were the years during which Shags were studied intensively throughout the breeding season. Nest recording has not been as thorough in subsequent years.

Dorset (7), Gwynedd (6), Dyfed (5) and Somerset (3). One or two individuals have been reported from each of Avon, Gloucestershire, Cambridgeshire, Essex and Kent, as well as from the Irish counties of Cork and Wexford. Four birds ringed as nestlings in 1957 were recovered as part of a widespread inland 'wreck' of immature Shags in eastern England in late 1957 and early 1958, including birds ringed at other breeding colonies around the British coast. The most intriguing movement of a Lundy-bred Shag, and by far the longest distance travelled, is of a nestling ringed on 3 July 1948 and shot at Esbjerg, Jutland, Denmark, on 22 September the same year. A chick ringed on 12 July 1972 and found dead at Lizard Point, Cornwall almost 14 years later on 11 April 1986 is the longest-surviving of the Shags recovered away from the island.

Wernham *et al.* (2002) showed that immatures, especially those in their first and second winters, disperse much further than adults and have a much greater tendency to occur inland. Many older birds remain throughout the year within 50–100 kilometres of their breeding colonies.

Bittern *Botaurus stellaris* [Eurasian Bittern]

Lundy vagrant.

Listed by Chanter (1871) and Parfitt (1876) as an "occasional visitant", there is just one dated record referring to a single bird:

1930 23 & 24 Sep – an immature seen on 23rd was picked up in an exhausted state the following day and released after being examined (F.W. Gade, reported by Davis 1954a); Davis stated: "Mr Gade has shown me a photograph of this bird."

Little Bittern *Ixobrychus minutus*

British vagrant.

Breeds in continental Europe, especially in central and southern regions, as well as farther afield in parts of Africa, Asia and Australia. European breeders migrate to wintering grounds in sub-Saharan Africa. 218 records for Britain 1950–2005.

There is one Lundy record of a single bird:

1976   2 Apr – a female, flushed three times near Quarter Wall.

Night Heron *Nycticorax nycticorax*   [Black-crowned Night Heron]

Nationally scarce migrant.

Breeds in southern and central Europe and parts of Africa, the Americas and Asia. European birds winter in sub-Saharan Africa. 441 records for Britain 1958–2003, with an average of eight per year 2000–2003. Considered by the BBRC until the end of 2001.

There are three Lundy records, all of single birds:

1975   15 Apr – a first-year bird flew north cross the Landing Bay mobbed by gulls and landed below the rhododendrons, subsequently making two more flights before returning to the cliffs.

1976   28 May to 1 Jun – a first-year bird frequented the South End ponds and Millcombe.

1990   16 Mar – an adult seen on several occasions, mainly around the pond in Millcombe, last seen flying towards South Light.

Little Egret *Egretta garzetta*

Lundy vagrant.

In line with the recent rapid colonisation of southern Britain, occurrences of Little Egrets on Lundy have increased significantly since 1989, with 19 records involving at least 24 individuals, and are perhaps to be expected even more regularly in future. Prior to 1989, the year of the first major post-breeding influx to Britain, there had been just two occurrences on the island. Half the records have fallen within a period of just a few weeks in spring, from late April to mid-June. There have been two midwinter sightings (both in January), with the remainder in autumn, from late July to early November.

1957   22 to 26 Apr – an adult male in breeding plumage was seen flying in from the south. It landed on Pondsbury but to escape mobbing gulls moved to small pools in the north of the island. It was found dead on the last date but can still be seen, mounted in a glass case, in the Tavern.

1984   6 May – one.

1989   19 Sep – one in flight near Quarry Bay and the same or another around Rat Island on 23 Sep.

1993   11 Oct – one flew north over Quarter Wall.

1995   16 & 17 Jan – one in fields around the village.[27]

1996   6 May – one flew north past Jenny's Cove.

   30 May – one, Rat Island.

2000   25 Jul to 3 Aug – an immature, mainly around Rat Island but also seen at Rocket Pole Pond.

2001   12 Aug – two in the Landing Bay and around the South End, one remaining until 16 Aug.[28]

2002   2 Jan – one in St John's Valley and later roosting in rhododendrons.

   16 May – three flying south off the west coast.[29]

2004   26 Apr – one watched from the Ugly, flying towards the mainland off Rat Island.

   24 May – an adult in breeding plumage flushed from Pondsbury and later seen flying over Tibbett's.

   19 Oct – one flying west near the Castle.

   5 Nov – one.

2005   29 Aug – three, with one present on 30 Aug.
2006   10 & 11 May – one.
           17 Jun – one fishing in Quarry Pond.
2007   30 May – one flying south over Quarry Beach.

Grey Heron *Ardea cinerea*

Uncommon visitor; recorded throughout the year but most regular during late summer and early autumn.

Listed by Chanter (1871) and Parfitt (1876) as an "occasional visitant", Grey Herons have been recorded in every year since LFS records began. The entry in the first *LFS Annual Report*, for 1947, reads, "occasional visitor to the various ponds, remaining for a few days at a time in July and August". This

Grey Heron

general pattern remains valid and although there are now records for every month of the year, by far the greatest number of occurrences have been in July and August, indicative of post-breeding dispersal. There were sightings in every month of 1975, while in 2003 regular sightings of at least one bird from 9 March to 31 October could have involved a long-staying individual. Grey Herons are usually seen singly on Lundy, but there have been occasional reports of two or more birds, with peak counts being nine seen by Felix Gade on one day in July 1940 (Davis 1954a), 10 on 16 July 1973, and four groups totalling 16 flying north on 25 July 1975.[30] While rock pools around the shoreline presumably provide good feeding opportunities, most of the freshwater ponds on the island plateau contain little in the way of food for a hungry heron and there are many records of individuals found either dead or dying. For example, on 7 March 2000 an exhausted bird caught in the Landing Bay was fed and sent to the RSPCA on the mainland.

The 2003 *Devon Bird Report* contains the following behavioural note:

> "One on Lundy...on 16 Jun flying N along the coast was mobbed by successive parties of nesting gulls, especially the Great Black-backed Gulls. It continued to circle laboriously in uninterrupted flapping mode to a height of 150m while heading NE out to sea, and at this height was evading each gull attack. Eventually maintaining this height it returned to the coast and passed S again without a single gull causing even the slightest commotion."

Purple Heron *Ardea purpurea*

Nationally scarce migrant.

Breeds in wetlands of southern and eastern Europe, and parts of Africa and Asia. European breeders winter in sub-Saharan Africa. 762 records for Britain 1958–2003, with an average of 18 per year 2000–2003. Considered by the BBRC until the end of 1982.

There are four Lundy records, all in spring, typical of the pattern of British records generally:

1970   19 Apr – an adult near Threequarter Wall and later at Pondsbury (one of an influx of nearly 30 Purple Herons into Britain and Ireland in April and May 1970).
1978   24 & 28 Apr – one first seen flying over the Airfield and taking refuge from mobbing gulls in a gorse thicket.

1987 29 May to 4 Jun – an adult, first seen at Quarter Wall Pond, reportedly with a wriggling frog in its bill (though neither frogs nor toads are known to occur on Lundy), moved to the Brick Field and was seen later in the northern part of Ackland's Moor.[31]

1994 4 to 10 May – an immature seen on many occasions, either in flight mobbed by gulls or at various of the island's ponds. The bird grew steadily weaker and was found dead at Rocket Pole Pond on the last date. Unconfirmed sightings suggest the possibility that it had been present since 22 Apr, though the following entry by K. Wimbush in the LFS logbook for 4 May clearly indicates a new arrival:

"Seen attempting to enter island via Millcombe at 12.10hrs, but it was prevented from doing so by a number of gulls and ravens. The bird was forced along the east side of the island and made numerous attempts…during the next $2^{1}/_{2}$ hrs or so, but was continuously thwarted by the attentions of harrying gulls and ravens. The bird went into rhododendron cover for $1^{1}/_{2}$ hrs as it was completely exhausted before making other attempts."

White Stork *Ciconia ciconia*

Nationally scarce migrant.

Breeds in continental Europe, especially in south-western and eastern regions, migrating to wintering grounds in sub-Saharan Africa. 682 records for Britain 1958–2003, with an average of 34 per year 2000–2003. Considered by the BBRC until the end of 1982.

White Stork

Lundy's only record is of a single bird in spring:

1992 20 Apr – first seen from St John's Valley flying northwards along the East Side at approximately 15:00, then very shortly afterwards over Tibbett's and later over the village on three occasions before eventually leaving to the south around 17:00.

Glossy Ibis *Plegadis falcinellus*

British vagrant.

Breeds in parts of south-eastern Europe, Africa, Asia, Australia and eastern USA. European birds are mainly trans-Saharan migrants. 91 records for Britain 1950–2005. Spring records are suggestive of birds overshooting their breeding grounds on return migration.

Though not mentioned in his original 1871 listing, Chanter added this species to his 1877 revision, in the category "occasional visitant". While occurrences in Britain were much more frequent in the nineteenth century than in the twentieth century, there is only one dated record:

1987 21 May – one first seen circling over the Church flew towards the Old Light, turned east and disappeared from view.

A significant influx of Glossy Ibises to the UK in April/May 2007 reached the North Devon mainland, but none was recorded on Lundy.

Spoonbill *Platalea leucorodia*　　　　　　　　　　　[Eurasian Spoonbill]

Lundy vagrant.

In recent years, small numbers have wintered regularly on the Taw & Torridge Estuary, North Devon. There is one Lundy record of a single bird:

2002 19 Oct – one seen flying towards the Devon coast, "at least a couple of miles" offshore (Steve Cooper, personal communication). This record appears in the 2002 *Devon Bird Report*.

Honey Buzzard *Pernis apivorus*   [European Honey-buzzard]

Lundy vagrant.

Breeds widely in continental Europe and winters in sub-Saharan Africa. There is a small breeding population in the UK, estimated at 50–60 pairs; also occurs as a passage migrant. 4,187 records for Britain 1986–2003, more than half of these in 2000.

There are six Lundy records, all since 1975:

1975 27 Jul – one flew across Ackland's Moor and out to sea.

1981 5 Oct – one, seen from Millcombe high to the east moving away southwards.

1983 28 Sep – one flying south.[32]

1987 24 Oct – an immature bird flew south over the island.

2004 23 May – one seen flying steadily north over Quarter Wall at around 11:00 was seen soaring over the East Side about an hour later before flying off to the north; the same or another bird was reported on 24 May but the record was rejected for lack of a description.

2006 27 Apr – one being mobbed by gulls and Ravens over South End was quickly driven off to the south.

Black Kite *Milvus migrans*

Nationally scarce migrant.

Breeds widely in southern, central and eastern Europe, wintering in sub-Saharan Africa. Most UK sightings are in spring, when migrants moving north are liable to overshoot their continental breeding grounds. 355 records for Britain 1950–2005. Considered by the BBRC until the end of 2005.

Three Lundy records have all been in spring and all since 1984:[33]

1984 20 Apr – one seen arriving from the east, being mobbed by gulls over the Landing Bay, seen subsequently over the Ugly before circling out of sight above Tibbett's.

1989 10 May – one ranged widely over the island before soaring over South Light and drifting off southwards.

2001 24 May – one flew in off the sea at the South End and continued north.[34]

Black Kite

Red Kite *Milvus milvus*

Lundy vagrant.

Red Kites breed fairly widely in continental Europe and are migratory in the northern part of their range. As a result of successful re-establishment, the British breeding population has grown significantly since the mid-1980s, numbering about 800 pairs in 2006. While sightings in mainland Devon have increased, the species remains extremely rare on Lundy.

Listed by Chanter (1871) and Parfitt (1876) as an "occasional visitant". Three flew over the island on 28 April 1929 (F.W. Gade, reported by Harrisson 1932). There are six LFS records, all except one in spring, though possibly involving only four individuals:

1971 6 Oct – one near Quarter Wall being mobbed by a Raven.

1997 22 Mar – one soaring over the Landing Bay and Castle being mobbed by gulls.

2002   15 Apr – one flew west along the south coast, from Rat Island towards the Rocket Pole, before dropping below the observer's line of sight.
5 May – one in various parts of the island.
12 May – one "obligingly soared over the island while the DBWPS boat trip circumnavigated on 12 May" (2002 *Devon Bird Report*).
The 2002 *LFS Annual Report* notes: "It is not clear if these [sightings] refer to different birds or to one long-staying individual." An unconfirmed report of a Red Kite seen over the North Light on 3 Jun may suggest the latter.

2004   22 May – one flying north over the island.

White-tailed Eagle *Haliaeetus albicilla*

Formerly bred; no twentieth or twenty-first century occurrences.

The British breeding population was hunted to extinction in the early twentieth century, with the last native individual shot in Shetland in 1918 (Forrester & Andrews 2007). However, a painstaking reintroduction programme, using birds of Scandinavian origin, began in Scotland in 1975 and a small but increasing population has since become established on the west coast. On the continent, White-tailed Eagles nest around Scandinavian and Baltic coasts and in the wetlands of eastern Europe, some moving south-west in winter, occasionally reaching Britain.

Chanter (1871), Parfitt (1876) and D'Urban & Mathew (1895) listed White-tailed Eagle as an occasional visitor to Lundy that was also believed to have bred in the early part of the nineteenth century. A specimen in Ilfracombe Museum is documented as having been shot on the island in about 1880. Harting (1901) also recorded this species as formerly nesting.

With the Scottish population now numbering up to 300 birds (including around 35 breeding pairs), reintroduction programmes beginning in south-west Ireland and eastern Scotland in 2007, and consultations under way for possible reintroductions to North Wales and the east coast of England, there is a glimmer of hope that White-tailed Eagles may one day return to Lundy.

Marsh Harrier *Circus aeruginosus*   [Western Marsh Harrier]

Formerly a Lundy vagrant, now a rare passage migrant, mainly in spring.

In line with recent growth of the British population, which the RSPB estimated at 360 breeding females in 2005, representing an increase of more than 130% over 10 years, there has been a dramatic rise in the number of records on Lundy. Of 24 occurrences since LFS records began in 1947, half of these have been since 1995. As can be seen from the summary table opposite, the great majority of sightings (over 80%) have been in spring, between late April and the end of May, with a noticeable peak in the first half of May. The handful of late summer and early autumn sightings are confined to a six-week period between early August and mid-September.

1958   30 Apr – one near Pondsbury.
1972   9 May – a female or immature.
1973   12 Sep – an immature.
1982   9 & 10 May – one.
1986   17 May – a female in the vicinity of Pondsbury.
1989   24 Apr – an adult female around the south of the island.
8 May – an immature, probably female.
9 May – an immature, probably male.
11 & 12 May – an immature, possibly female, roosted overnight near Tibbett's.
14 & 15 May – an immature female.
1992   5 May – a female that came in off the sea at North End drifted south and was later seen quartering over Ackland's Moor.

Marsh Harrier

1994 1 May – a female soared over the north of the island and left to the north-west.
1995 22 & 23 May – a female hunting over various parts of the island.
6 Aug – a male at Quarter Wall.
1997 27 Aug – a male.[35]
1999 26 Apr – one off the West Side leaving to the north-west.
5 Sep – an immature off the West Side departed to the south-west.
2000 12 May – an immature male between Acklands Moor and Tibbett's.
2001 2 May – a female or immature near Quarter Wall.
2003 26 May – one, considered to be a second-year male, soaring over Pondsbury before moving off south.
2004 24 Apr – a female in the Quarter Wall and Tibbett's area.
25 Apr – a female with different markings from that seen the previous day seen flying south.
2 May – a third female seen at Pondsbury.
2005 15 May – a female was watched hunting between Pondsbury and Halfway Wall.

Both Chanter (1871) and Parfitt (1876) listed Marsh Harrier as an "occasional visitant", but the only dated pre-LFS records are of one, possibly two birds on 15 October 1944 (N.V. Allen, 1944 *Devon Bird Report*) and one on 1 November 1944 (F.W. Gade, reported by Davis 1954a).

Marsh Harrier occurrences, 1947–2006					
(arrival dates in spring and autumn by half-month periods)					
Apr 16–30	**May** 1–15	**May** 16–31	**August** 1–15	**August** 16–31	**September** 1–15
5	12	3	1	1	2

Hen Harrier *Circus cyaneus* [Northern Harrier]

Uncommon spring and autumn migrant; rare winter visitor.

The tracts of moorland and rough grassland on the island plateau, especially between Quarter Wall and Halfway Wall, are the best areas to scan for quartering Hen Harriers, which turn up fairly regularly during migration periods, sometimes staying for several days, occasionally much longer.

The earliest Lundy record is of a male feeding on starving Fieldfares during the severe winter of 1860/61 (D'Urban & Mathew 1895), while Chanter (1871) and Parfitt (1876) listed the species as an "occasional visitor". There are only two dated records prior to the LFS era, both of birds seen by Felix Gade: one on 26 August 1934, which stayed for a week, and a pair on 24 April 1937 (Davis 1954a). The first LFS record, of an adult male, occurred on 13 November 1951. Excluding three sightings of birds presumed but not certain to be Hen Harriers, there were just 11 sightings in the period covered by Dymond (1980), these occurring between 1951 and 1978. Since then there have been at least a further 56 records (to the end of 2006), with 1983 and 2000 the only blank years. All records are of single birds with the exception of four occasions on which two birds were seen on the same day: 24 April 1937, 6 November 1963, 5 October 1999 and 15 November 2003.

Most sightings are of spring or autumn migrants, May (15 occurrences) and October (24 occurrences) being the peak months. The British breeding population is only partially migratory, with first-year birds from Wales and the Scottish Highlands being most likely to undertake long-distance movements, while older birds from these areas, as well as birds of all ages from south-west Scotland and Ireland, generally remain close to the breeding grounds. Ringing and wing-tagging has shown that first-year males from the Scottish Highlands pass through south-west England en route for wintering areas in France and Spain. Furthermore, it is thought that most Hen Harriers wintering in southern Britain are of continental origin (Wernham *et al.* 2002). Taking these findings together, it seems likely that birds from both British and continental populations pass through Lundy, though – as yet – there is no proof of this.

The earliest of the 22 spring records is of a ringtail seen on 17 March 1966, while the latest spring occurrence is of a female on 25 May 1991. Perhaps the most unusual spring record is of one seen bathing in a puddle on a track on 2 April 2005. There are no confirmed June or July sightings, though a harrier seen on 11 June 1985 may have been of this species.

The earlier of the two August records that we have been able to substantiate is of a female seen on 29 August 1967[36] and there are just four occurrences in September. By far the greatest number of autumn Hen Harriers have occurred in October and November, with 24 and 12 new arrivals, respectively. Birds arriving in October may occasionally remain on the island for several weeks, lingering into November and, on three occasions, into December. The latter include regular sightings from 24 October to 23 December 2003, and from 20 October to 15 December 2004 that were thought to relate to long-staying individuals. There are only two post-December winter occurrences, singles on 20 January 2004 and 25 February 1978.

Montagu's Harrier *Circus pygargus*

Lundy vagrant.

Though listed by Chanter (1871) and Parfitt (1876) as an "occasional visitor", it was not until 14 May 1937 that the first twentieth century sighting – of a single male – was made, attributed in the 1937 *Devon Bird Report* to "J.W.S".

Of 14 LFS records, 10 have been in spring and four in autumn, all single birds and mostly females or juveniles. There were four instances in the 1960s and 1970s of birds staying on the island for periods ranging from a few days to several weeks.

There has been only one Lundy record in the 10 years up to and including 2006, perhaps reflecting the decline of Montagu's Harrier as a breeding species in Britain. Following the loss of the small population that nested regularly on the Devon mainland until the late 1970s, it is highly probable that most, if not all, of the birds occurring on Lundy are now migrants from continental breeding areas.

1948 24 Aug – a juvenile.
1950 12 Aug – a juvenile.
1958 12 Sep – an immature at Pondsbury.
1960 10 May – a male.
1961 10 Apr – a female.
1962 7 to 12 May – a female over the Tillage Field.
1974 17 to 24 May – a female hunting over the south of the island, followed by a female in primary moult, presumed the same individual, at Gannets' Combe on 9 Jun.
1976 6 to 19 May – a female, seen daily, mainly hunting between Quarter Wall and Pondsbury, followed by a female, presumed the same, on 23 & 24 May.
1977 27 Apr to 2 May – a male.
1989 15 May – a male seen in flight near Quarter Wall.
1992 4 May – a female seen several times hunting between Ackland's Moor and Pondsbury.
1993 1 Jun – a female flew in off the sea into lower Millcombe, over the Ugly and then north along the East Side.
1996 3 Sep – a ringtail, probably an adult female, hunting in the Pondsbury area.
2004 26 Apr – a male flew south-east across the Airfield.

Goshawk *Accipiter gentilis* [Northern Goshawk]

Lundy vagrant.

There are six Lundy records, all but one in spring, but none since 1991:

1951 17 to 18 Apr – an immature.
1977 1 to 5 May – an immature female.
1979 21, 22 & 25 May – a female, first seen flying north along the East Side and subsequently in the area between Halfway Wall and Tibbett's Point.
1980 4 Apr – one.
1988 22 Oct – an adult male seen over Millcombe, then stooping towards the north.
1991 5 to 9 May – an adult female sighted on several occasions was possibly still present on 15 May. It was first seen as it flew along the wall between South West Field and the Lighthouse Field, then being mobbed by Lapwings over Ackland's Moor. Later during its stay the bird ranged widely from the Landing Bay north to Tibbett's.

Sparrowhawk *Accipiter nisus* [Eurasian Sparrowhawk]

Common spring and autumn migrant in small numbers; has bred at least once.

Most Sparrowhawk sightings tend to be on the East Side, where there is plenty of cover and a ready supply of small birds available for this supreme woodland hunter. However, chance encounters can occur just about anywhere on the island, from the cliffs of the West Side to the drystone walls of the plateau that are often used as cover for ambushing an unwary pipit, finch or Wheatear.

Sparrowhawk was listed by Chanter (1871) and Parfitt (1876) as an "occasional visitant". One pair bred at the extreme north-west corner of the island in 1922 – about as far away from trees as it is possible to get on Lundy – and may have done so in other years around that time (Loyd 1925). There is always the possibility of future breeding attempts, though these are likely to be sporadic at best.

Nowadays this species is regular, in small numbers, during both spring and autumn migration periods. Occurrences have reflected the overall changes in the British breeding population, which crashed as a result of pesticide poisoning during the 1950s and 1960s. There were regular records from Lundy until 1955, then a sharp decline, such that by the mid-1960s sightings were less than annual. Following the banning of the most harmful chemicals, numbers recovered quickly in the 1970s and 1980s and Sparrowhawks are now seen every year. While there are also records for every month (1985 brought the first January and December sightings since LFS recording began in 1947), most pass through from late March to mid-May and again from mid-August to mid-November. Spring passage peaks in April, while the more extended autumn passage is usually strongest in October (e.g. there were sightings on 23 days in October 2002, with two birds present on six of these days). During both migration seasons, individuals may linger for several days or even a few weeks. The maximum seen on any one day in spring is three on 3 May 1992, while the maximum daily count in autumn – also three birds – has occurred on five occasions, all since 1980, most recently on 10 & 15 October 2005.

Fifteen Sparrowhawks had been ringed by the end of 2006, but there are no controls or recoveries involving the island.

Buzzard *Buteo buteo* [Common Buzzard]

Uncommon visitor; formerly a breeding resident.

By far the most frequently seen bird of prey on the nearby North Devon mainland, Buzzards are scarce on Lundy, with odd ones and twos turning up from time to time, sometimes passing high over the island, on other occasions stopping off for a few days, occasionally longer. Watching a Buzzard soaring over the sidelands is an impressive spectacle and one that used to be much commoner.

Buzzard

Chanter (1871) and Parfitt (1876) listed Buzzard as "an occasional visitant". Parfitt's assertion that this species was also an "occasional breeder" was quoted by D'Urban & Mathew (1895), giving a firm impression that the species bred in the second half of the nineteenth century. Crespi (1888), Davenport (1897), Blathwayt (1900), Cummings (1909) and Ross & Rousham (1909) all mentioned Buzzard as "resident", "seen daily", "common" or words to similar effect. Hendy (1922, 1933) reported at least two, perhaps three nesting pairs in 1914, including a "cliff-nest with two partly fledged young". Loyd (1925) stated that in 1922 two or three pairs nested and that early in that year "a male was killed by a farm-hand with a stick, in the act, with its mate, of devouring a chicken". In 1923 Loyd noted "a marked increase… and no fewer than four lots of young". Gade (1978) referred to Buzzards as "a common sight" in the late 1920s; he located two nests on the West Side and one on the East Side in 1927, and four successful pairs in 1930. Wynne-Edwards & Harrisson (1932) also quoted four pairs in their "census of land-feeding birds" in 1930. N.V. Allen recorded "6 at least, possibly 8" Buzzards on the island in October 1944 (1944 *Devon Bird Report*).

Davis (1954a) assessed that in the 40 or so years up to 1954, between one and five (perhaps six) pairs bred annually. In 1955 there was no evidence of breeding. From 1956 to 1965, a pair attempted to breed each year but although eggs were laid in several years there is no evidence that any hatched, and no young were reared. One bird stayed throughout 1966 but none occurred between 1967 and 1970. Since then there have been records in most years, usually of single birds, though two – the maximum daily count – have been recorded on nine occasions (most often in April). There are sightings for every month and most, if not all of the Buzzards reaching Lundy are likely to be those wandering or dispersing from the adjacent mainland, given that British breeding birds are largely sedentary (Wernham *et al.* 2002). In 2001 there were reports on many days from 8 June to 4 November, perhaps all referring to the same long-staying individual. Of two birds recorded on 18 October 1989, one drowned off Ladies' Beach on 21 October.

Whatever the reasons for the disappearance of Buzzards from Lundy as a resident breeder, their fortunes do not seem to be directly tied to those of rabbits – a major food source – of which there has generally been a plentiful supply on the island. In 1955, the year in which Buzzards appear to have ceased breeding on Lundy after a successful run of four decades, there were also very few breeding attempts elsewhere in southern Britain. On the mainland this was due in part to a widespread outbreak of myxomatosis that decimated rabbit numbers across the country, as well as pesticide poisoning that was beginning to affect birds of prey populations at that time. However, the disease did not reach Lundy until 1983, probably through deliberate introduction (Parsons 1984) at a time when the rabbit population was estimated at 60,000. While there have been further myxomatosis outbreaks on the island, notably in 1992, 1996 and 2006, and rabbit haemorrhagic disease (RHD) has also been recorded, rabbit numbers have usually recovered quickly afterwards. Even so, rabbits were almost wiped out in 2006 and the former rabbit 'cities' such as that on the west side of Castle Hill were reduced to eerily-empty 'dropping-free' slopes. The likelihood is that rabbit numbers will continue to show a pattern of 'boom and bust', meaning that any potential Buzzard colonists on Lundy would face an uncertain future.

Seven Buzzards – all nestlings – were ringed between 1951 and 1953, but there have been no controls or recoveries involving the island.

Rough-legged Buzzard *Buteo lagopus*   [Roughleg]

Lundy vagrant.

Breeds in northern regions of Scandinavia, Finland and Russia, migrating to wintering grounds mainly in central and eastern Europe. 1,211 records for Britain 1974–2003, with an average of 35 per year 2000–2003.

There are records in five years, involving a total of six birds, mostly autumn migrants passing through in October/November. However, one bird stayed for ten months from summer 1988 to spring 1989 and was joined by a second during the autumn and early winter of 1988. This constitutes a highly unusual record not only for Lundy but also nationally.

1959 29 Nov – one in Millcombe, flew off southwards on 30 Nov.

1981 15 to 20 Oct – one, joined by a second on 17 Oct.

1988 15 Jul – the presence of a Rough-legged Buzzard, thought to be a sub-adult female, was first confirmed on this date, but undocumented reports suggest it may have been on Lundy since early June. There were further sightings from 12 to 18 Jul, 29 Aug and 4 Sep, with virtually daily sightings from mid-September to the end of the year. Throughout its stay this bird was generally seen in the vicinity of Tibbett's Point, Brazen Ward and Threequarter Wall Bay. Remarkably, on 10 Oct it was joined by a second individual, thought to be a first-winter male, which also remained to the end of the year, the two birds usually being seen together in the northern third of the island, with occasional forays further south. On 31 Dec both buzzards were watched soaring over Halfway Wall Bay, but this proved to be the final sighting of the 'male'.

1989 Of the two birds present at the end of 1988, the presumed female remained until 11 May.

1997 22 to 31 Oct – a first-year bird seen frequently, mainly along the East Side.

Osprey *Pandion haliaetus*

Rare passage migrant; bred in the nineteenth century.

Records of this spectacular raptor have become more frequent on Lundy in line with the expansion of the British breeding population to around 200 pairs in 2006 (RSPB estimate); two-thirds of the 17 LFS records have been since 1990. Eleven sightings have been made during spring migration (from March to June), with six in autumn (July to October). The peak months are May (eight records) and September (three), while the earliest and latest dates are 20 March (1986) and 27 October (2001). The overwhelming majority of records refer to migrating individuals that over-fly the island, passing through in a matter of moments. There are a few cases of birds breaking their journey for several hours to rest or feed, but only one known instance (May 1992) of an individual remaining for more than a day. The following is a listing of all LFS records up to 30 June 2007:

1974 18 Jul – one flew in from the south-east at midday, circled over the East Side for five minutes before gaining height and moving off north.

1978 17 May – one seen flying north along the West Side off Jenny's Cove.
6 Sep – one.[37]

1980 7 Sep – one flew over the Landing Bay being harried by a Raven.

1984 17 May – one flew north-west.

1986 20 Mar – one flew north off Shutter Rock.

1991 15 June – one perched in Millcombe being mobbed by crows had possibly been present since 12 June.

1992 8 May – one mobbed by gulls at North End.
19 to 24 May – one.[38] Presumably the same bird was seen flying west, carrying a fish, at Northam Burrows, on the North Devon mainland, on 19 May and from *MS Oldenburg* on the return crossing from Lundy on the same date.

1995 8 May – one flew north over Pondsbury.

1997 23 Sep – one flew north along the West Side.[39]

1999 26 Apr – one flew over Millcombe.

2001 27 Oct – one flew south over the Landing Bay, then north across Millcombe.

2003 2 May – one circled over Quarry Bay, then moved off north.

2006 18 Oct – a first-year bird off the East Side ranging from St Helen's Combe north to Tibbett's Point and seen attempting to fish in the waters off St Helen's.

2007 1 May – one soared north-east over the Church, Millcombe and along the East Side before being lost to view.
4 May – one, presumed different to the 1 May bird, flew north from the Castle, along the East Side and over the Terrace, rapidly being lost to view.
(2007 records subject to acceptance by the Devon Birds Records Committee.)

The Rev. H.G. Heaven stated that a pair bred regularly in the Gannets' Combe area until 1838 when the male was shot by a Bristol Channel pilot "and the female never returned" (Palmer 1946). Gosse (1865) reported Osprey as "not unfrequently seen fishing around the rocks". Chanter (1871) stated "the Osprey used to be frequently seen" but included it in his list of "occasional visitants", as did Parfitt (1876).

Kestrel *Falco tinnunculus* [Common Kestrel]

Common visitor in small numbers, mainly in spring and autumn; breeds occasionally.

Kestrels can be seen on Lundy in every month of the year anywhere over the island plateau and on or over the cliffs and sidelands.

Listed by Chanter (1871) and Parfitt (1876) as "resident all the year", Parfitt adding "and breed there". Blathwayt (1900) wrote "I noticed Kestrels were fairly common" (in May 1900). Two pairs were reported in 1922 (Loyd 1922), 1927 and 1930 (Harrisson 1932). In total, they are known to have bred in at least 20 years during the twentieth century, involving mostly one or two pairs in any one year, except for the period 1957 to 1959 when up to three pairs may have nested annually using cliff sites below Benjamin's Chair, near the Sugar Loaf, close to the Old Light and perhaps in Jenny's Cove. Breeding may have been attempted in at least 11 other years – including 2004 given that birds were present through the summer and two juveniles were seen in late August – but there has been no confirmation of breeding since 1982.

Swelling the ranks of any resident birds, Kestrels also pass through Lundy during both spring and autumn migration periods; movements in autumn being more marked than those in spring. As many as 20 were estimated on 2 September 1951. Since the early 1980s, maximum daily counts in autumn have been of four or five birds, rarely of six or more. Exceptionally, 12 birds were recorded on 6 October 1989.

Kestrel

Quite why Kestrels do not appear to breed regularly is something of a mystery. Potential nest sites are plentiful and food, too, is seemingly in abundant supply, ranging from Pygmy Shrews and small birds to invertebrates (especially Dor Beetles) and insects. Wynne-Edwards & Harrisson (1932) observed Kestrels feeding largely on beetles, "with an occasional pigmy shrew", while a brood of four young Kestrels ringed by Tony Taylor in an old Raven's nest in Jenny's Cove in 1978 was surrounded by the wings of many fledgling Starlings and nothing else. In late autumn Kestrels are remarkably adept at catching migrant passerines, perhaps picking off tired individuals. The increase in Peregrine numbers in recent years may be one reason why Kestrels have become scarce as a breeding bird.

Twenty-four Kestrels had been ringed up to the end of 2006, with just one recovery: a first-year bird ringed on 16 September 1986 was found dead 94 kilometres away at Plymouth Hoe, Devon, 107 days later on 1 January 1987.

Red-footed Falcon *Falco vespertinus*

Nationally scarce migrant.

Breeds in eastern Europe, migrating to sub-Saharan wintering grounds. 698 records for Britain 1950–2005. Considered by the BBRC until the end of 2005.

There are seven Lundy records of single birds, four in late spring and three in autumn:[40]

1972 16 Oct – an immature seen flying along the top of the sidelands at South End alighted on a fence-post near the Church before moving off north past Stoneycroft.

1975 27 & 28 Aug – a first-year male was seen in the vicinity of the Airfield.

1977 1 & 2 June – an adult male.[41]

1978 30 May – an adult female.

1985 6 Sep – a second-year female seen between Halfway Wall and Threequarter Wall.

1992 19 to 24 May – a female ranged widely over the island north of Quarter Wall, but was usually to be found around the quarries early and late in the day.

2003 30 May – a first-summer male was watched feeding in the Gannets' Combe area, frequently alighting on the ground, before moving off to the south.

Merlin *Falco columbarius*

Common passage migrant and winter visitor in small numbers; very rare in summer.

Merlins are most often encountered in areas of rough grassland or moorland on the island plateau where they feed mainly on small birds, especially Meadow Pipits. They are particularly active at dawn and dusk often being seen around the farm and village hunting for birds leaving the island or going to roost.

Chanter (1871) and Parfitt (1876) listed Merlin as an "occasional visitant", while D'Urban & Mathew (1895) stated that it was an occasional winter visitor. Nowadays, Merlins are seen every year during spring and autumn migration and usually also in winter. Spring passage occurs mostly in March and April, though there is also a good scattering of May records and there have been exceptionally late occurrences in June and even into July: on 10 June 2002 (a male), 19 & 20 June 1991 (another male), 6 July 1980 (a female)[42] and 19 July 2002. Particularly in June, these are likely to be itinerant non-breeding birds or failed breeders. Records are much more frequent during autumn migration, which extends from late summer onwards, though most are seen between mid-September and the end of November, with a distinct peak in October. The Merlins passing through Lundy, whether in spring or in autumn, are likely to include birds from both the British and Icelandic breeding populations (Wernham *et al.* 2002).

Most sightings involve single birds, though up to four have been seen in one day (e.g. 7 October 1984, 17 October 1989 and 18 October 2006). There are regular winter records, but the sparse coverage by birdwatchers at this time of year makes it difficult to assess whether Merlins typically remain on the island throughout the winter and, if so, how many. In 2004/05 there were sightings on 38 days between early November and late March, with records on 27 days during the corresponding period for 2005/06.

Two anecdotes stand out: the first involving a Merlin that was taken by a pair of Peregrines on 30 October 2004. The other instance was on 18 October 2006 when we watched an apparently tired first-winter female Merlin sitting on heather by the main track near Gannets' Combe. We were able to approach to within 30 metres, when she suddenly flew directly towards us, veering at the last moment to catch and eat a passing Red Admiral.

Three Merlins had been ringed on Lundy by the end of 2006, but there are no controls or recoveries involving the island.

Hobby *Falco subbuteo*   [Eurasian Hobby]

Uncommon spring and autumn migrant.

Sightings of this strikingly marked migrant falcon can occur anywhere over the island plateau or sidelands and tend to be brief but exciting!

Listed in the nineteenth century as an "occasional visitant" (Chanter 1871, Parfitt 1876) or as occurring on Lundy "in the spring" (D'Urban & Mathew 1895), the first twentieth century record was of one reported by Felix Gade on 10 March 1936, still the earliest spring date. The first LFS record was of two Hobbies together on 29 March 1948, though the *LFS Annual Report* for that year stresses the "exceptionally early date" and the fact that the observers had to rely on shape and structure, seeing the birds against the light. Since then there have been sightings in most years and in all but two years from 1972 up to and including 2007; only 1973 and 1981 were blank.

Records are spread more or less evenly between spring (at least 69 occurrences) and autumn (over 50). Spring passage occurs primarily in April and May, with August and September the peak months in autumn. The latest spring date is 13 June (1994), while autumn extremes are 24 July (1972) and 8 November (2004). A count of two Hobbies on one day has been recorded on four occasions (29 March 1948, 25 & 28 July 1972 and 13 May 1991) and there are three instances of a daily count of three birds (3 May 1992 and 2 & 6 May 1994). The longest-staying individual was a juvenile seen from 3 to 12 October 1998.

As stated by Davis (1954a), the record of a Hobby on 14 December 1931 must be considered doubtful in view of the extraordinary date. However, there are comparable winter records in Europe including one bird which stayed on the Isles of Scilly from autumn 1947 to January 1948 (Robinson 2003).

Gyr Falcon *Falco rusticolus* [Gyrfalcon]

British vagrant.

Breeds in northern Scandinavia, Iceland, Greenland, and northernmost parts of Russia and North America, moving south in winter. 146 records for Britain 1950–2005.

Gyr Falcon

Listed by Chanter (1871) and Parfitt (1876) as an "occasional visitant", one was shot in the month of November in the mid-nineteenth century and sent to Bristol Museum (D'Urban & Mathew 1895). Another shot on 21 March 1903 went to the Royal Albert Memorial Museum, Exeter (Loyd 1925). One seen on 3 March 1937 was found dead near Constable Rock two or three weeks later (Gade 1978; F.W. Gade, reported by Palmer 1946).

There are three LFS records, all in March or April:

1972 19, 21 & 22 March – an immature of the white Greenland race (*F. r. candicans*) first seen just south of Halfway Wall and later near The Cheeses. It was relocated on 21st soaring back and forth over Brazen Ward and during the day was seen over much of the East Side and the plateau. The falcon was glimpsed briefly at North End on the last day. A similar white phase bird at Trevone, Cornwall, on 26 March 1972 and / or one on Bryher, Isles of Scilly, from 6 to 10 May could possibly have been the individual seen on Lundy (Smith *et al.* 1973).

1986 11 & 12 Apr – an immature white-phase bird first seen in Middle Park and at Threequarter Wall the following day.[43] The bird was probably the same one seen at Berry Head in South Devon from 31 March to 9 April.

1996 20 Apr – one white-phase bird seen flying over all parts of the island, from the Landing Bay north to the Devil's Slide. It was seen to catch and eat a Wheatear (*Oenanthe oenanthe*) at Threequarter Wall.

The logbook entry by LFS warden Nick Dymond for 19 March 1972 reads:

"Just south of Halfway Wall a superb Greenland Falcon got up less than 100 yards in front of me; it flew low to the north out of sight. An hour later, with Jane and Arthur Strick, it was located under a screaming hoard of Herring Gulls near the Cheeses. We watched it on the ground at about 70 yards for 20 minutes or so. We had flushed it off a freshly killed rabbit. Largely white, head, breast, thighs, neck etc, with grey freckled wings and mantle, and light brown barring on the tail. Size was considerably larger than a Peregrine."

Peregrine *Falco peregrinus* [Peregrine Falcon]

Breeds; recorded in all months in recent years.

Peregrines have a distinguished historical link with Lundy and remain one of the island's ornithological highlights. Today they can be encountered relatively easily on the island, whether sitting regally on a rocky outcrop, circling patiently high over the island plateau or in high-speed pursuit of prey on the sidelands, though this has not always been the case.

Lundy has the claim to fame of being the earliest known (or at least the first documented) nesting site in Britain, with records dating back to the thirteenth century. At that time, trained Peregrines were highly valued for their ability to catch birds for sport and for the pot; thus, in 1243 Henry III gave

Peregrine

falcons from the Lundy eyrie to his cleric Ade de Eston (Gurney 1921). Lundy is again mentioned in 1274 in the Crown Jurors' assessment of the island as "the esteemed Peregrine eyrie" (Ratcliffe 1993). Lundy birds were especially prized for falconry. Strangely, however, it was only eyasses (chicks) taken from one particular eyrie which carried this reputation; a status which persisted into the twentieth century. Indeed, in 1937, the falconer Colonel Gilbert Blaine stated that since the time of Elizabeth I (sixteenth century) about four out of five birds from one Lundy eyrie have always been found to be the best falcons in any falconer's experience (Ratcliffe 1993). Blaine himself secured eyasses from this traditional eyrie in at least 14 seasons between 1900 and 1924 (Upton 1980), so had first-hand experience of the prowess of Lundy birds. It seems probable that the pre-nineteenth century population was one to two pairs. Gosse (1865) wrote that one of the farm labourers on the island "shewed me a pair of well-grown birds which he had reared from the nest; they were in excellent health and condition, and in full plumage. The nest had been rifled by a boy let down from above for the purpose...The fellow was in the habit of feeding his pets with the flesh of the puffins and guillemots, which his dog would catch for him in any desired quantity". Chanter (1871) and Parfitt (1876) listed the species as "resident all the year", the latter adding "and breed there". D'Urban & Mathew (1895) stated that Peregrines deserted the island for a time in the nineteenth century due to persecution; though they did not specifically state the reason why, the Victorian pastime of egg-collecting may well have contributed.

There are breeding records of one pair, and often two, in 23 years between 1875 and 1938, and breeding probably occurred in most if not all of the intervening years. Blathwayt (1900) "discovered the eyrie of a pair of Peregrines by accidentally startling the Falcon from the face of a steep cliff. Another pair had, I think, established themselves at the opposite end of the island near the Shutter Rock". Felix Gade mentions three young taken in 1935 by the falconer Harry Savory in what was the last recorded brood going to falconry; while Gade himself had one from a brood of three in 1930. In 1938 one pair was thought to have bred successfully. With the advent of World War II, Peregrines and their nest sites in Devon and Cornwall were ruthlessly targeted to the point of virtual elimination under the 1940 *Destruction of Peregrine Order*, due to the threat posed to pigeons carrying messages of military importance. However, their status on Lundy remains something of a mystery during this period. Certainly Peregrines were seen between 1939 and 1944, and while no breeding was recorded, no mention was made of any birds being destroyed under the 1940 Order. Perhaps news of Lundy's famous falcons was deliberately kept quiet during those years.

Although birds were recorded in most of the post-war years up to 1949, it was only in 1950 that successful breeding was again confirmed when two young were reared. It is worth noting this was at a time when the Devon (and south-west England) population was low and still recovering following the effects of the 1940 Order. Although nesting took place up to 1960, young birds were only reared in 1953 (two), 1955 (three) and 1960 (two). There then followed the well-documented and disastrous crash in the UK population due to the build-up of toxic organochlorine insecticide residues (Ratcliffe 1993). Lundy also featured in the pesticide story when, in June 1963, a tiercel (male Peregrine) was found dead at its Lundy eyrie. Subsequent analysis of this bird's liver showed it contained a cocktail of DDE, dieldrin, heptachlor and BHC (lindane); these combined levels were considered by scientists to constitute a lethal dose. Although depressing news, this Lundy bird helped in providing vital evidence of direct adult mortality attributable to these compounds. The indirect effects of DDE and DDT also later came to light as causing greatly reduced breeding success through eggshell thinning and consequent egg breakages. During this period, sightings of adults became increasingly sporadic and none was recorded from 1968 to 1971 (apart from a falconer's escape in 1969). During the crash a remnant Devon population of one or two pairs just held on, on the adjacent North Devon coast, and from here the south-west England population slowly began to recover. Lundy was re-occupied fairly early on, with up to two birds seen in 1973 and 1974, but it was not until 1975 that a pair of adult Peregrines was again holding territory at the traditional site – much to the delight of birdwatchers in the know at the time. Although Peregrines now had full legal protection, details of their status on Lundy during this critical time were not published because of the threats posed by egg-collectors, pigeon fanciers and rogue falconers. Successful breeding finally resumed in 1976, with one pair producing a total of four fledged young between 1976 and 1980, and another producing at least seven young between 1978 and 1980.

Despite the presence of two pairs, there then appeared to be no successful breeding until 1983 when one pair reared two young, followed by one youngster in 1984. Records up until 1991 are sketchy but usually two pairs were present with young produced in at least 1987 and 1990 (one). In 1991 Lundy was covered as part of the BTO National Census of Peregrines, which found there were now three territories occupied by adult pairs. At the time this represented the highest recorded level on the island. During the next few years the Devon Peregrine Group monitored the population, witnessing a rise to four pairs in 1997 and five pairs in 2001. The next BTO National Census in 2002 found six territory-holding pairs and another occupied by a single adult. However, breeding success was variable through this period, with sometimes only one successful pair; the exceptions being 1997, 2000 and 2001, with at least two pairs successfully rearing five, seven and five young respectively. In 2002 breeding success was very poor with only one successful pair (fledging two young) despite the increased population. An interesting recent observation was an adult with aylmeri (leather anklets), indicating a falconer's escape, paired and holding territory for at least two seasons (Mark Darlaston, personal communication).

With the current relatively high population, food is an interesting issue, perhaps raising more questions than answers. Peregrines being opportunist hunters, Lundy's strategic position must ensure a plentiful supply of both spring and autumn migrants, no doubt supplemented by lost feral pigeons and the occasional rarity. During early summer, breeding seabirds seem to provide most food – a male was once seen to carry a Razorbill to its eyrie. An account of two eyasses taken for falconry in 1933 (Hornby 1943) describes the climber descending to find "four nestlings amid a litter of Puffins' paddles, Guillemots' heads, and pigeons' legs" – a time when Lundy had Puffins in numbers. Once the auks have departed the cliffs, prey selection seems poorly documented, though there is potentially a wide selection of species migrating south from midsummer onwards through autumn. Most juvenile Peregrines are likely to have left the island by autumn, but whether some adults also leave in winter when food is scarce is not clear.

A very dark juvenile seen on 1 & 2 October 1953 was thought possibly to have belonged to the North American race *F. p. anatum* (*LFS Annual Report* 1953, p5), though separation of races in the field is now regarded as unreliable.

Ten Peregrines have been ringed on Lundy, with just a single recovery: a bird ringed as a nestling on 31 May 1953 was recovered on 17 March 1958 near the coastal village of Termonfeckin, Co. Louth, eastern Ireland. While juveniles and non-breeding adults can turn up almost anywhere (Wernham *et al.* 2002), established breeders are virtually sedentary in their nesting territories throughout the year, and it therefore seems likely that this bird, in its fifth year and of breeding age, had established a territory on the Irish Sea coast.

Water Rail *Rallus aquaticus*

Common passage migrant in small numbers; occasional winter visitor; first confirmed breeding 2007.

Water Rails prefer wet, well-vegetated areas that provide good cover. On Lundy these are found on the East Side, especially in lower Millcombe, though you are more likely to hear the characteristic pig-like squeals rather then see the birds themselves.

LFS records show that small numbers occur regularly in autumn, the earliest date being 3 August (1953). Movements typically peak in October, when daily counts have reached a maximum of six, for example on 20 October 2005. Up to five or six have overwintered in some years, and very small numbers occur on spring passage, mainly in March and the first half of April. One bird flew into – and was killed by – a barbed-wire fence near Quarter Wall trap on 30 March 2000. May records of Water Rail are highly unusual, having occurred in only four years (1990, 2003, 2005 and 2007), the latest of these being 29 May (2005) – but see box opposite.

The 1994 *LFS Annual Report* noted a decline in recent years and, until 2003, this was particularly evident in the relative dearth of spring records. An apparent improvement in autumn numbers was noticed in 2001, and in 2002 between one and three birds were recorded on 44 days between 4 September and 12 November, with sightings on all but four days in October (though these could have been a few long-staying individuals rather than many different birds passing through). Hints of an improvement in the species' fortunes continued in 2004 and 2005, with birds present on many days from mid-September to late November of both years.

Water Rail

Chanter (1871) and Parfit (1876) listed Water Rail as "resident all the year", the latter adding that breeding had occurred on the island, although he provided no evidence for this statement. The Heaven Diaries recorded five being shot: two in October 1872 and three in January 1878 (Boyd 1950). On 25 October 1880 the Heavens recorded "2 Water Rail having Homeric combat by stream by drawing room for long time with shouts and screams of conflict (like warring rabbits) – then one fled". Harrisson (1932) reported Felix Gade telling him that an overwintering bird in 1926/27 became "so tame that it would enter the house for food".

Forty-one birds had been ringed on Lundy by the end of 2006, but there are no controls or recoveries involving the island. The paucity of ringing recoveries nationally means that the pattern of movements and migration of this species remains largely unknown, though the British breeding population is thought to be largely resident and augmented in winter by continental birds (Wernham *et al.* 2002).

Water Rails...a new breeding species for the island in 2007

In the first week of May 2007 a Water Rail was seen and heard around Quarter Wall Pond and the nearby rushy margin of the Brick Field and another heard calling at night from the campsite. This was followed by the first-ever June record for the island when one was heard calling in the early hours of 12 June from the rushes around the reservoir pond, close to Quarters (Pigs Paradise). The 'observer', Andy Jayne, reported the call not to be the familiar squealing but the much softer call that the species makes during the breeding season. This was followed in July by the first records of summering birds, with birds heard calling in lower Millcombe and around Pondsbury in mid-month. Confirmation that Water Rails bred on Lundy – possibly for the very first time – came in late August when a chick was found in lower Millcombe (see www.lundybirds.org.uk). Given the signs of increasing numbers in both autumn and spring in recent years, and now the first evidence of breeding on the island, it is tempting to speculate that the almost exclusively ground-dwelling Water Rail may have benefited from the eradication of rats. The question now is: did more than one pair breed in 2007?

Spotted Crake *Porzana porzana*

Lundy vagrant.

Widespread breeding species in continental Europe, migrating to wintering grounds around the Mediterranean and in sub-Saharan Africa. 1,125 records for Britain 1986–2003, with an average of 65 per year 2000–2003. Breeds sporadically in the UK in small numbers.

Historically, this species was listed as an occasional visitor by Chanter (1871), Parfitt (1876) and D'Urban & Mathew (1895), and one was mentioned in the Heaven Diaries on 17 May 1887 (Boyd 1950). Since the first twentieth century occurrence in 1967 there have been confirmed records of Spotted Crakes on Lundy in a further seven years, though there have been several additional sightings of unidentified crakes that may well refer to this species. All of the accepted records, given below, have been between 30 April and 29 May in spring (four records), and between 5 September and 10 October in autumn (five records).

1967	11 May – one near the Terrace trap.
1978	30 Apr – one.
	5 Sep – one.
1980	27 to 29 May – one at Pondsbury.
1986	2 Oct – one caught and ringed in Millcombe was seen again on 12 Oct.
1991	17 & 18 May – one at Rocket Pole Pond.
1995	19 to 21 Sep – one, thought to be a first-year bird, at Pondsbury.
1998	28 to 30 Sep – one at Pondsbury.
2006	10 Oct – one found in a very weak condition on the path to Quarry Beach later died.

Little Crake *Porzana parva*

British vagrant.

Breeds in wetlands of continental Europe, particularly central and eastern regions, wintering in sub-Saharan Africa. Recorded in Britain less than annually; the number of records has declined in recent decades. 39 records for Britain 1950–2005.

There is one (rather astonishing) Lundy record of a single bird:

1983 17 Apr – a female found wandering around Puffin Slope.

A crake in the walled gardens of Millcombe from 12 to 14 September 1952 was identified as a Little Crake and listed as such in the 1952 *LFS Annual Report*. However, a review of pre-1958 records by the BBRC decided that the description provided at the time was insufficient to exclude Baillon's Crake (*P. pusilla*) and the record was therefore rejected (2001 *Devon Bird Report*, p. 171).

Baillon's Crake *Porzana pusilla*

British vagrant.

Breeds in wetlands of southern, central and eastern Europe. Probably winters in sub-Saharan Africa. Though formerly more regular, there were only 16 British records between 1950 and 2005, most of these in spring.

There is one Lundy record of a single bird:

1995 15 & 16 May – a male around the pond in lower Millcombe.

Corncrake *Crex crex*   [Corn Crake]

Lundy vagrant; formerly a regular migrant that bred until at least 1928.

The pattern of Corncrake occurrences on Lundy reflects the species' long-term decline and eventual disappearance during the twentieth century as a breeding species across virtually the whole of Britain and much of Ireland. It seems likely that breeding on the island was regular in the nineteenth century, for the 'Land Rail', as it was then commonly known, was listed by both Chanter (1871) and Parfitt (1876) as a "summer visitant", Parfitt adding "constant breeder". Blathwayt (1900) recorded Corncrake during his visit in May 1900. The last nest was found in 1928 but a final suspected breeding attempt was made in 1935 (F.W. Gade, reported by Davis 1954a).

Corncrake

Thereafter, Corncrakes continued to be recorded annually in small but gradually declining numbers from 1947 to 1960, and in most subsequent years to 1979, especially in spring. However, there have been just 11 occurrences since then, all but two in September/October (see below).

With 'Corncrake-friendly' grassland management helping the surviving UK breeding population – found mainly in the Hebrides – to increase from 488 calling males in 1993 to more than 1,100 in 2005 (UK Biodiversity Partnership 2006), and a new project to reintroduce the species to suitable habitat in England, it will be fascinating to see if this mysterious and elusive bird is seen more frequently on Lundy in the future.

All accepted Corncrake records for the 30-year period 1977 to 2006:

1977 8 Apr – one.
1979 7 Sep – one.
1982 7 Sep – one.
1984 25 & 26 Jun – one.
8 Oct – the remains of a freshly dead bird were found.
1986 3 Oct – one.
1987 8 Oct – one near Quarter Wall.
1989 6 May – one caught at Quarter Wall was ringed and released at Brambles.
1999 27 Sep – one at Pondsbury.
2000 13 Oct – one in Millcombe.
2003 22 to 29 Sep – one in lower Millcombe. This long-staying individual remained in the same restricted area around the stream below Windy Corner and showed itself very well, sometimes seen together with a Water Rail.
2004 16 Sep – one in lower Millcombe.
2006 9 Sep – the remains of one found on the Lower East Side Path, possibly the result of a Peregrine kill.

Moorhen *Gallinula chloropus* [Common Moorhen]

Rare visitor; has bred.

Listed by Chanter (1871) and Parfitt (1876) as an "occasional visitant". Loyd (1925) stated "a pair used to haunt wet ground in the south-east combe, and others two ponds on the top of the island" at some time prior to 1922. Felix Gade saw one on two occasions in 1931 and one on 15 February 1936.

Unsuccessful efforts were made to introduce the species in 1937 and 1938: "The attempt to introduce adult birds had failed and so moorhens' eggs were set under the bantams, but only three out of a dozen hatched and they simply hid themselves away in dark corners and soon died" (Gade 1978).

Excluding the two years when Moorhens are known to have bred on the island (see below), there have been 29 LFS records in 23 years, up to and including 2006, involving between 27 and 29 individuals. They have been recorded in every month, with most sightings in May (nine) and October (eight), indicative of spring and autumn movements.

The first confirmed breeding took place in 1985 when a pair was seen with chicks on Pondsbury on 12 July, while two adults and two juveniles were present in late August. In 1986, observations of single birds were made in January, May, June and July, with up to three in August and September and four in October. Since the August records included juveniles, it is assumed that breeding was successful for the second year running. There have been subsequent sightings in 1988, 1990, 1999, 2002, 2003, 2004 and 2006, all during the months February to May or October, but with no further sign of nesting.

Although Pondsbury is the most likely place to find a Moorhen on Lundy, they have been encountered at a variety of other sites, including the High Street, the Terrace, St Helen's Field and Millcombe, where one bird stayed from 15 December 1973 to about 25 January 1974. An immature bird was found dead at South Light on 30 October 1971.

Only one Moorhen has ever been ringed on Lundy, a bird caught in a newly erected 'crake' trap on 3 April 1967; there are no controls or recoveries involving the island.

Coot *Fulica atra* [Common Coot]

Lundy vagrant.

There are six pre-LFS records, five of which were made by Felix Gade: one stayed from 23 December 1927 to 8 January 1928; one on 11 December 1932; another, or possibly the same bird, on 28 January 1933; one on 3 March 1941; and a juvenile on 27 October 1941. In addition, Perry (1940) recorded one from 21 to 23 March 1939.

There have been four LFS records since:

1951 15 Dec – one seen in the Manor Farm Hotel garden, found dying the next day.
1957 10 Oct – one in St Helen's Combe.
1966 13 Aug – one, found dead next day.
1984 7 Oct – one north of the Landing Bay.

A Coot sitting on the sea was seen from *MS Oldenburg* about half way between Lundy and Bideford on 28 May 1991 (1991 *Devon Bird Report*).[44]

Oystercatcher *Haematopus ostralegus* [Eurasian Oystercatcher]

Common breeder and passage migrant; recorded throughout the year but scarcer in late autumn and winter.

Oystercatchers occur all round the island, feeding, roosting and breeding on rocky outcrops close to high-tide lines, only very occasionally appearing on top of the island. Their loud *kleep-kleep-kleep* calls are one of the most familiar sounds on Lundy in spring and early summer as the birds busily defend breeding territories, nests and chicks.

This species is severely under-recorded on the island, no doubt reflecting the fact that many suitable nesting and feeding areas are extremely difficult to see or reach. While there is little firm information on breeding numbers, Oystercatchers nest annually, their population having fluctuated over the years between eight pairs and Perry's 1939 count of 22 pairs (Perry 1940). In reporting 14 breeding pairs in 1930, Wynne-Edwards & Harrisson (1932) estimated that this equated to one pair for every 900 yards of the island's coastline. Complete counts of territory-holding pairs have been made in just seven years – see table.

Barbara Whitaker (1956b), LFS warden from 1954 to 1958, described the requirements for Oystercatcher nest sites on Lundy:

> "East side. A comparatively flat area free of anything but short vegetation, and with adequate food supplies (especially limpets) close by. Such sites are comparatively rare

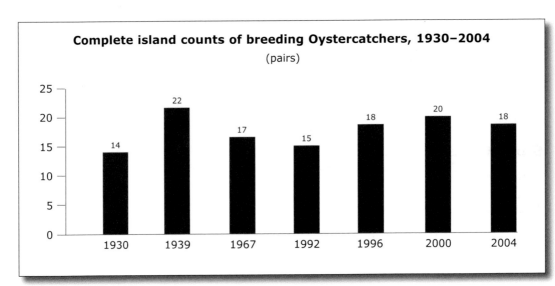

Complete island counts of breeding Oystercatchers, 1930–2004

(pairs)

Oystercatcher

due to heavy vegetation often growing down close to sea-level, steep cliffs and few beaches.

West side. A fairly flat area in the thrift zone backed by a comparatively gentle slope of short vegetation up which the parents and young chicks can walk and feed. Such areas are found at S. [of] Pilots Quay, Dead Cow Point, The Pyramid and N. of St John's Stone. Nests are usually located in all these places. These requirements for nest sites and feeding areas probably account for the rather small breeding numbers on Lundy."

Most Oystercatchers have left the island by late September, after which small numbers occur during the winter in most years. Seventeen birds were counted along the West Side on 24 January 2007 during a national BTO winter shorebird survey. The highest counts are of 40 birds on 17 February 1994, over 40 between 10 & 20 April 1971 – the latter figure probably including a mix of both breeding pairs and non-breeding/passage birds – and 51 on 9 May 2007, including a non-breeding flock of 37 birds flying along the East Side. A flock of 21 birds were seen feeding on top of the island on 27 July 1977.

Chanter (1871) and Parfitt (1876) listed this species as "resident all the year", the latter adding "and breed there". In his 1877 monograph, Chanter also referred to Oystercatchers being "nearly exterminated" by the crews of pilot and tugboats as "being much prized for eating".

British breeding Oystercatchers are partial migrants, some staying close to nesting areas while most move south in winter (Wernham *et al.* 2002). There have been just two recoveries from the 37 birds ringed on Lundy to the end of 2006, both found on Atlantic-coast wintering grounds: a nestling ringed on 19 June 1963 recovered 427 kilometres from Lundy near Morbihan, southern Brittany, France, on 4 January 1967; and a nestling ringed on 24 June 1963 recovered near La Coruña, Galicia, north-west Spain, on 9 February 1966, a movement of 998 kilometres.

Stone Curlew *Burhinus oedicnemus*   [Eurasian Stone-curlew]

Lundy vagrant.

The only LFS record is of a single bird seen on the ground and in flight near North East Point on 10 April 1997. There are three earlier records: 15 March 1938 (F.W. Gade, reported by Davis 1954a), 20 May 1939 (Perry 1940) and 19 October 1939 (F.W. Gade, reported by Davis 1954a). With intensive conservation efforts helping the British breeding population to recover from 168 pairs in 1991 to over 300 pairs in 2005 (RSPB estimates), there is every chance that occasional migrants will occur on Lundy in future, particularly when birds are moving north from their wintering grounds in spring.

Collared Pratincole *Glareola pratincola*

British vagrant.

Breeds in southern Europe, western Asia and parts of Africa. European birds migrate south to sub-Saharan wintering grounds. 63 records for Britain 1950–2005.

The only pre-LFS record is a bird seen by Charles Robertson, a shepherd, on 21 February and 14 March 1945 (Gade 1946). Gade states that Robertson "first saw the bird on the wing, hawking up and down a combe on the east side of the island and momentarily took it for some kind of swallow, but immediately realised it was too large and differently coloured. He watched it for ten minutes or more and was able to note the buff throat and ring of black edging it and the swallow-like tail. He had no notion what kind of bird it was, but told his wife about it on returning home, and she looked it up in Coward's *Birds of the British Isles*. Immediately he saw the illustration of the Pratincole he said "That's the bird". On the second occasion, the bird, probably the same one, was on the ground by a small pond, but took wing immediately and, after hawking along a streamlet for a turn or two, made off to sea in a south-westerly direction. He was quite definite that the underside of the wing was not black, showing that it was not a Black-winged Pratincole (*Glareola nordmanni*)".

There has since been one further record of an unidentified pratincole species:

1987 1 May – while walking on the Airfield, Mary Gade saw an unfamiliar bird being flushed by two Peregrines and pursued by them in the direction of the village. Moments later, observers in and around Millcombe and St John's Valley saw a pratincole being chased by two Peregrines over Millcombe and towards the South End. They noted the wader-like structure and flight, deeply forked tail, clear white rump and superlative aerobatic skills in out-manoeuvring repeated stoops by the Peregrines. In spite of extensive searching the bird could not be relocated. Most British pratincole sightings, especially in spring, are of Collared Pratincole but the views of this bird were insufficient for conclusive identification. The record was accepted by the BBRC as either Collared or Black-winged Pratincole.

An entry in the 1962 *LFS Annual Report* states that on 26 April a strange bird was seen in the region of Quarter Wall by a group of students from Bristol University and, separately, by R. Carden, the assistant warden. Both parties independently identified the bird as a pratincole. Though also included in the 1962 *Devon Bird Report*, it seems the record was never submitted to the BBRC (there is no trace of acceptance or rejection) and was excluded by Dymond (1980).

Little Ringed Plover *Charadrius dubius*

Lundy vagrant.

Although this species is relatively scarce in south-west Britain, it is perhaps surprising that none was recorded on Lundy until 1998. Remarkably, the second occurrence came just two years later.

1998 8 May – one at the Rocket Pole.
2000 8 Apr – one in South West Field.

Ringed Plover *Charadrius hiaticula*   [Common Ringed Plover]

Uncommon spring and autumn migrant in small numbers; occasional winter records.

Closely grazed turf and rocky pools on the island plateau are the favoured habitats of Ringed Plover on Lundy, although the plaintive flight call can be heard anywhere over the island, sometimes at night. This species has been recorded annually since LFS records began in 1947.

During spring migration most occur in April and May, usually in ones and twos, extreme dates being 15 February (2006) and 24 June (1997). The highest spring count is of 10 on 31 May 1991. Ringed Plovers are seen more frequently in autumn, particularly during August and September, when most records are of one to six birds. Higher counts have been seven at Pondsbury on 10 & 11 September 1989,[45] 10 on 25 August 1978 and 12 on 24 August 1973. In addition, at least 30 were reported flying over the island at night on 12 September 1956. The latest autumn record is of a single bird on 21 November (2002). There are no December records and the highest winter count is of two birds on 30 January 1996.

Chanter (1871) and Parfitt (1876) listed "Ring Dotterel" – an old name for this species – as a "summer visitant", Parfitt adding "occasional breeder". This latter assertion was quoted by D'Urban & Mathew (1895) but there is no corroborating evidence provided. Oldham (1932) recorded "odd birds passing" between 28 August and 4 September 1907. Alexander *et al.* (1945) reported one on top of the island at North End on 5 July 1942 and added: "There is just a possibility that the species bred, as two young ones were repeatedly seen at the N. end in September."

Three Ringed Plovers have been ringed on Lundy (to the end of 2006), but there are no controls or recoveries involving the island. Birds passing through western Britain are known to include migrants from breeding grounds in arctic Canada, Greenland, Iceland and Fennoscandia (Wernham *et al.* 2002).

Dotterel *Charadrius morinellus* [Eurasian Dotterel]

Uncommon but virtually annual spring and autumn migrant in small numbers.

Although this is a bird that is a delight to see at any time of year, there is little to compare with close-up views of a 'trip' (small flock) of Dotterels in breeding plumage as they stop off on Lundy to feed in late spring, en route from Moroccan wintering grounds to mountain-top nesting sites in Scotland (Wernham *et al.* 2002). Areas of rough, extensively grazed grassland on the island plateau – such as South West Field, Ackland's Moor, the Airfield and Middle Park – are the best places to look, especially in fine, settled weather. Individuals and small groups sometimes associate loosely with passage Golden Plovers, sharing similar feeding habitats and behaviour.

Dotterels were possibly overlooked in the past – being discreet in their behaviour and surprisingly difficult to pick out – and there is no mention of them until Felix Gade encountered one on 12 May 1937 (reported by Davis 1954a). The only other pre-LFS record was of a single bird on 9 & 10 September 1942 seen "on the high barren area at the north end of the island" by Alexander & Radford (1942), who also wrote that "Mr F.W. Gade informs us that he has twice seen single Dotterels on Lundy in spring" (one of these presumably the 1937 individual mentioned above). There followed LFS records in 1947, 1949 and 1951, and – somewhat remarkably given the paucity of historical sightings – Dotterels have occurred almost annually since 1955 during spring and autumn migration.

Most spring records involve from one to six birds, some of which have remained for several days. The extreme spring passage dates are 13 April (1982) and 6 June (1996), but by far the majority of birds pass through during May. Apart from the above-mentioned 1996 occurrence, there is only one other June record. Peak spring counts are seven (five females and two males) on 6 May 1990,[46] eight on 14 April 1949 and a trip of 10 in South West Field on 25 April 1999. During southward migration in autumn, Dotterels are most frequent in September, with records in 25 years since 1947 making it the peak month of the year. The earliest and latest autumn dates are 7 August (1966) and 22 October (1981), other than one exceptionally late bird seen and heard in flight on 20 November 2003. While most autumn occurrences involve from one to three birds, mostly juveniles, six were present on 23 August 1984 and at least 18 different individuals were believed to have passed through in September 1973.

The following is a complete list of Dotterel records for the 10 years 1997–2006 (there were no sightings in 2006):

1997 29 Aug – an adult in the Brick Field.
1998 11 May – one female.
       1 Sep – a juvenile at North End.
       2 Oct – one.
1999 25 Apr – 10 in South West Field.
       30 Apr – one on the Airfield.
       23 Aug – a juvenile at North End.
2000 4 & 5 May – a male and female between the Airfield and Quarter Wall.
2001 11 May – five.
2002 26 May – one.
       21 to 24 Sep – one.

2003 29 Apr – two.

13 & 14 Oct – one.

20 Nov – one over Millcombe and South End then flew north along the East Side.

2004 25 Apr – three females and two males in Middle Park.

3 May – a male and female.

28 & 30 Aug – a juvenile in South West Field.

27 & 28 Sep – two seen in flight on 27th were in Middle Park the following day.

2005 19 May – one in Middle Park.

Six Dotterels had been ringed on Lundy by the end of 2006, but there are no controls or recoveries involving the island.

Golden Plover *Pluvialis apricaria*   [European Golden Plover]

Common spring and autumn migrant in small numbers; irregular winter visitor.

Not many spring or autumn weeks are spent on Lundy without encountering a Golden Plover, as often as not heard without being seen – the plaintive, far-carrying flight call easy to pick up but very hard to locate overhead. Even when on the ground, the birds can be difficult to spot as they merge with their favoured moorland or rough grassland habitat, especially in autumn.

Numbers of Golden Plovers on Lundy vary considerably from year to year. Overall since LFS records began, they have been most abundant in spring. However, in line with the general decline in waders on the island in recent years, spring numbers have fallen, in spite of higher than average counts of between 15 and 26 birds from 26 to 30 April 2000. The average autumn peak appears to have changed little – see table.

A prolonged spring migration begins in early March, with occasional records extending into June in some years. Peak numbers pass through in late March and April. By far the highest count is 200 on 25 March 1955, but this is exceptional, the next two spring maxima being 80 on 24 March 1962 and 66 in early April 1966. June records have occurred in at least 19 LFS years, the latest being one on 30 June 1954 – most likely a non-breeding bird or an early-returning failed breeder.

There are July records in at least nine years, but the main autumn migration generally picks up from mid-August, peaks in September and runs through to October, with occasional sightings in November in some years. The highest count is 41 birds on 26 October 1960.

Single birds or small flocks are seen in most winters, most probably resulting from movements induced by cold weather elsewhere. The three highest counts are 40 on 22 February 1985, 85 on 29 December 2000 and about 100 birds on 14 January 1955.

D'Urban & Mathew (1895) wrote of "imitating their whistling call-note" to decoy Golden Plovers within gunshot and "by employing this artifice" to have "obtained them in the winter on Lundy Island". Chanter (1871) and Parfitt (1876) listed the species as an "autumn and winter visitant", while Blathwayt (1900) recorded seeing Golden Plover in breeding plumage during his visit to Lundy in May 1900.

Lapwings and (right) Golden Plovers

Spring and autumn maxima of Golden Plovers					
(based on LFS records since 1947)					
Spring average					
1947–1960	1961–1970	1971–1980	1981–1990	1991–2000	2001–2005
34	31	11	8	8	3
Autumn average					
1947–1960	1961–1970	1971–1980	1981–1990	1991–2000	2001–2005
17	15	18	14	8	14

Three Golden Plovers had been ringed on Lundy by the end of 2006, but there are no controls or recoveries involving the island. The birds passing through Lundy are likely to belong to both the Icelandic and British & Irish breeding populations. Those of Icelandic origin winter mainly in Ireland (Wernham *et al.* 2002).

Grey Plover *Pluvialis squatarola*

Rare spring and autumn passage migrant and winter visitor.

Given that Grey Plovers favour estuaries and sandy shores, they are much scarcer on Lundy than the closely related Golden Plover, even though Greys are common passage migrants and winter visitors on the mainland coasts of North Devon and South Wales.

Listed by Chanter (1871) and Parfitt (1876) as an "occasional visitant", the only precisely dated pre-LFS records were two flocks seen by Felix Gade during cold weather: 40 to 50 on 5 March 1938 and 24 on 5 February 1939 (Davis 1954a). While the dates and numbers would seem more consistent with the pattern of Golden Plover occurrences on the island, there is no evidence that an error was made. Other records of single birds were made in April 1928, April 1930, October 1938 and March 1939 (Davis 1954a).

The first LFS record occurred on 3 September 1953, since when there have been 22 further autumn sightings, mostly in the second half of September and the first half of October. Early and late autumn dates are 3 July (2005) and 18 October (1976). Of 12 spring records, most have occurred from mid-April to mid-May, extreme dates being 21 March (1998) and 7 June (1967) – the only records for these two months. In addition to Gade's winter records, there are three other winter sightings: singles on 10 January 1971 and 30 November 2005, and two birds on 2 December 2005 – the only occurrences for each of these three months. All records are of single birds apart from two on four occasions and seven on 12 August 1959.

Lapwing *Vanellus vanellus*   [Northern Lapwing]

Major decline in recent years; now an uncommon migrant. Formerly a common breeder and spring and autumn passage migrant and occasional winter visitor.

Ackland's Moor, the Airfield and other short grassland areas on the island plateau are the most favoured stopping-off places for migrating Lapwings in spring and autumn. Sadly, the drawn-out *pee-wit* calls and energetic acrobatic displays of breeding birds are no longer part of the Lundy birdwatching experience.

Listed by Chanter (1871) as a "summer visitant" and described as a "frequent breeder" by Parfitt (1876), Lapwings are known to have bred in 1888 (Heaven Diaries 1870–1905; Crespi 1888). Wynne-Edwards & Harrisson (1932) reported that "the lapwing has formed a small colony on Pondsbury since 1927". Two pairs nested in 1929 (F.W. Gade, reported by Davis 1954a) and three pairs bred in 1930 (Wynne-Edwards & Harrisson 1932). From then until the end of the 1960s between three and 18 pairs bred annually; Perry (1940) reported 10 pairs nesting in 1939. Numbers increased in the 1970s, with a maximum of at least 40 breeding pairs in 1973, falling to about 10 pairs in the mid-1980s, followed by a steady decline through the 1990s (though 12 pairs were recorded on 1 June 1991[47]), until the last confirmed breeding took place in 2000 when a single pair hatched four young.

Regrettably, breeding Lapwings were under-recorded in the LFS logbook in most years after the peak year of 1973, so the decline of the breeding population is hard to trace in detail. However, it seems that 1999 was probably the first year for many decades when Lapwings failed to breed on the island – only one adult was seen in spring. There may be several reasons for the decline, not least the overall crash of the British breeding population linked to the intensification of agriculture. However, overgrazing in some years, together with an increase in human disturbance (through growing numbers of visitors) may have accelerated the demise of the Lapwing as a breeding species on Lundy. Gulls, Ravens and Carrion Crows – and probably rats, too – have had an adverse impact on both hatching and fledging success. For example, it was noted in the 1967 *LFS Annual Report* that, where Lapwings bred singly, the main predation came from Carrion Crows; only three young reached maturity from 20 breeding pairs that year.

Numbers of spring passage migrants were formerly masked by the return of breeding birds in early March, with at least 30 or more individuals seen regularly in spring up to 1990. Since 1996, spring maxima have been six birds or fewer. Once numerous as an autumn migrant – 400 birds were logged on 24 October 1958 – counts have fallen sharply in recent years, reaching doubles figures on only eight days during the 10 years 1997 to 2006, with a high of 30 on 8 November 2000. Maximum winter counts are 200 on 20 February 1955, 7 & 8 February 1976 and 21 January 1985, and 300 on 27 January 1979. More recently, 62 Lawings were counted on 30 December 2000, but the highest winter count since then is of just 20 birds on 20 December 2006.

If Lapwings are to return to breed on Lundy in the future, it will be important to maintain areas of suitable nesting habitat through appropriate grassland management; the recent reduction of grazing pressure on Ackland's Moor is a welcome step. If Lapwings did attempt to breed again, it would also be important to minimise human disturbance, since adults are easily put up from eggs and chicks, leaving them vulnerable to predation. Some consideration would also need to be given to controlling the high numbers of Carrion Crows, which spend much of their 'loafing' time in the vicinity of the Lapwing's former main breeding area on Ackland's Moor and the Airfield.

British breeding Lapwings are partial migrants, some staying close to nesting areas while others move west and south to Ireland and continental Europe (Wernham *et al.* 2002). Of 211 Lapwings ringed on Lundy, just one has been recovered away from the island: a chick ringed on 20 May 1991 was found

Lapwings

98

dead on a farm at Crantock near Newquay, Cornwall, on 8 January 1997. A Lapwing found dead on Lundy on 29 June 1978 had been ringed on the island as a nestling five years earlier on 26 June 1973. Birds of continental origin may occur on Lundy from time to time as passage or winter visitors.

Knot *Calidris canutus*   [Red Knot]

Rare spring migrant and uncommon autumn migrant.

Listed by Chanter (1871) and Parfitt (1876) as an "occasional visitant", the first twentieth century record of a Knot was a single bird in Middle Park on 16 April 1952. There have been just five subsequent spring sightings, the earliest being 20 March (1998) and the latest involving two birds on 14 May (1971). There have been 25 autumn records, all occurring in either August or September, extreme dates being 12 August (1991) and 30 September (1983); as would be expected, many of these have involved juvenile birds. While Dymond (1980) stated that a party of four birds stayed from 1 to 15 September 1967, careful reading of the *LFS Annual Report* for that year shows that the four birds did not necessarily occur together: "Four birds were recorded between 1st–15th September, three of which were trapped and ringed". Unfortunately, the original data for 1967 no longer exist, so it is not possible to check the exact circumstances. All other records have been of single birds, except for two on three occasions: 16 September 1964, 14 May 1971 and 3 September 1988.

Three Knots had been ringed on Lundy by the end of 2006, but there are no controls or recoveries involving the island. Most birds occurring on Lundy are likely to be of the race *C. c. islandica* which breeds in arctic Canada and Greenland, migrating through Iceland to winter in western Europe (Wernham *et al.* 2002).

Sanderling *Calidris alba*

Rare migrant, mainly in autumn; has occurred in winter.

Given the absence of their preferred sandy shoreline habitat, most Sanderlings on Lundy have been found on short grassland, marshy areas and pond edges on the island plateau, although they have occasionally turned up on the Landing Beach. Most sightings have been in autumn, with at least 26 records to the end of 2006, many of these involving juveniles. Extreme dates are 25 July (2000) – the only record for this month – and 29 September (1990). In spring there have been just 10 occurrences, all in May, including one found dead and plucked by a predator at North End on 16 May 1998. In addition, a flock of seven was seen during the boat crossing on 7 May 2000 (2000 *Devon Bird Report*). Most occurrences on the island itself are of ones and twos, with the two highest daily counts both falling in 1977: four on 15 May and eight on 29 August.

The only winter record is of three birds on 23 February 1985.

Writing in the 1934 report of the Devon Bird Watching & Preservation Society, Felix Gade stated that "several visited the island between May 24th and 31st, and again on Sept. 13th", noting these as the first records for the island. There appear to be no earlier references.

Semipalmated Sandpiper *Calidris pusilla*

British vagrant.

Breeds on the tundra of arctic North America and north-east Siberia, migrating to winter in South and Central America and the West Indies. 77 records for Britain 1950–2005.

There are five Lundy records, all of single birds in autumn, and most during a short period from late August to early September:

1966 8 Sep – one, mist-netted and ringed, was the first for Devon. A Least Sandpiper (*C. minutilla*), another vagrant from North America, was trapped at the same time.

1980 5 & 6 Sep – a juvenile first seen on the marshy area close to the Rocket Pole was seen the next day at Quarter Wall Pond where it allowed observers to approach to within less than half a metre.[48]

1982 22 to 25 Aug – a juvenile at Quarter Wall Pond.

1983 3 & 4 Sep – a juvenile.

1994 9 & 10 Oct – a juvenile, watched at close range, by a small stream in South West Field and near the Rocket Pole.

Little Stint *Calidris minuta*

Uncommon autumn migrant; two spring records.

Little Stints stopping off on migration tend to favour the limited areas of open mud and short grassland around the margins of pools, ponds and flushes on the island plateau.

Although listed by Chanter (1871) and Parfitt (1876) as an "occasional visitant", the first dated Lundy record was not until a single bird was seen on 31 August 1956. Of some 37 subsequent sightings to the end of 2006, two-thirds have occurred in September, mainly in the second half of the month. Early and late autumn dates are 3 August (1995) and 13 October (1962) – the latter one of only two October records. The first spring occurrence was as recently as 1991 when a summer-plumaged bird stayed from 29 to 31 May. The only subsequent spring record is of one on 13 May 1997. The highest count is eight on 26 September 1957.

Six Little Stints had been ringed on Lundy by the end of 2006, but there are no controls or recoveries involving the island.

Temminck's Stint *Calidris temminckii*

Nationally scarce migrant.

Breeds in northern Scandinavia and Russia and migrates to wintering grounds in the Mediterranean basin, Middle East and Asia. 3,293 records for Britain 1968–2003, with an average of 112 per year 2000–2003.

There is one Lundy record:

1992 27 & 28 May – a single bird first seen in South West Field in a wet flush between the Old Light and the Rocket Pole, later seen at Pondsbury and Rocket Pole Pond. It eventually returned to the original site, where it was still present the following day.

Least Sandpiper *Calidris minutilla*

British vagrant.

Breeds in sub-arctic Canada and the USA, migrating to winter from southern USA south to Brazil and Chile. 28 records for Britain 1950–2005.

There are two Lundy records, both of single birds and both occurring within a week of each other in 1966; these were the first Least Sandpipers to be ringed in Britain:

1966 8 Sep – one seen in company with a Semipalmated Sandpiper (*C. pusilla*) in the Lighthouse Field and close to the Church was mist-netted and ringed.

14 & 15 Sep – one caught at night (by dazzling) on 14th and ringed.[49]

A record published in the 1957 *LFS Annual Report* and 1957 *Devon Bird Report* of a Least Sandpiper at Pondsbury from 24 to 26 September 1957[50] was originally accepted by the BBRC, but later rejected on the basis of insufficient plumage detail (2001 *Devon Bird Report*, p. 171).

White-rumped Sandpiper *Calidris fuscicollis*

Nationally scarce migrant.

Breeds in north Alaska, arctic Canada and north-east Siberia, migrating to winter in South America. 390 records for Britain 1950–2005. Considered by the BBRC until the end of 2005.

There is one Lundy record of a single bird in late autumn:

2002 10 Nov – a first-winter bird watched at close range feeding in a damp flush on the cliff edge in South West Field.

Baird's Sandpiper

Baird's Sandpiper *Calidris bairdii*

British vagrant.

Breeds in the high Arctic of north-east Siberia, Alaska, Canada and Greenland, migrating to winter in South America. 195 British records 1950–2005.

There are two Lundy records, both of single birds in autumn:

1974 6 to 13 Sep – one on the Airfield and near Threequarter Wall.

1989 19 & 20 Sep – a juvenile at Pondsbury.

Pectoral Sandpiper *Calidris melanotos*

Lundy vagrant.

Breeds in parts of Siberia, Alaska and Canada, wintering mainly in southern South America. 2,159 records for Britain 1968–2003, with an average of 103 per year 2000–2003. Considered by the BBRC until the end of 1962. Regarded by the BOU as a passage migrant rather than a nationally scarce migrant.

Following the first Lundy record, a single bird on 12 October 1950, there have been sightings in 13 subsequent years (to the end of 2006), bringing the total to at least 19 individuals. Most records have been of single birds, with two present on three occasions. All except one have been between 30 July and 12 October, with most occurring in September. The only spring occurrence was in May 1978. Following records in nine of the 16 years between 1970 and 1985, there was a 19-year gap until the most recent occurrence in 2004.

Fraser & Rogers (2004) gave the three best years in recent times for Pectoral Sandpipers in Britain as 2003 (170 records), 1999 (132) and 1984 (130) – years in which none occurred on Lundy. Annual averages by decade in this period were 70 records (1980–1989), 57 (1990–1999) and 103 (2000–2003). It may be that the dearth of sightings on Lundy in recent years is due to fewer observers in August and September, a reduction in the appearance and extent of small temporary wetlands (such as the marsh near Rocket Pole) or perhaps a combination of the two. Increased disturbance from higher numbers of visitors is another possible factor.

All records are given:

1950 12 Oct – one feeding on the edge of a small pool on the Airfield.

1961 31 Aug to 2 Sep – one frequented Quarter Wall Pond and was also seen at Pondsbury and in Punchbowl Valley.

1962 2 to 8 Sep – one.

1967 24 Sep – one on a small temporary pool north of Quarter Wall.

1970 16 to 24 Sep – one or two birds seen on seven days in Middle Park (often at the spring-fed wetland below Tibbett's) and the pond near Threequarter Wall. Both birds were trapped and ringed on 17 Sep.[51]

1971 30 Jul – one with a Dunlin at Quarter Wall Pond.
16 Aug – two just north of Threequarter Wall, with one staying until 23 Aug also being seen at the Rocket Pole.

1973 2 to 4 Sep – one, trapped and ringed on 2 Sep.

1974 2 Sep – one.
1976 2 to 6 Oct – one.
1977 14 to 24 Sep – one.
1978 31 May – one.[52]
1982 19 & 22 to 24 Sep – one, increasing to two on 25, 27 & 28 Sep, and dropping back to one again on 29 Sep. Both birds were trapped and ringed, on 19 & 25 Sep respectively.[53]
1985 20 Aug – one together with a Turnstone on the main track north of Quarter Wall.[54]
      19 to 27 Sep – one, caught and ringed; the same or another was reported from 2 to 4 Oct.[55]
2004 21 to 23 Sep – a first-year bird feeding on the Airfield and in the Brick Field, and at Quarter Wall Pond on the last date.[56]

A record of a single bird on 10 October 1960 was published in the 1959/60 *LFS Annual Report* and 1960 *Devon Bird Report* (the latter incorrectly stating 10 September), but appears not to have been submitted to the BBRC as there is no trace of its acceptance or rejection in any BBRC report.

Curlew Sandpiper *Calidris ferruginea*

Lundy vagrant.

A pair in summer plumage was shot by Mr Spencer Heaven "one year" in June, presumably in the second half of the nineteenth century (reported by Davis 1954a). Parfitt (1876) listed the species as an "occasional visitant". One was seen in August or September 1927 (T.G. Longstaff, reported by Davis 1954a) and Perry (1940) reported one on 19 May 1939. Given the relative scarcity of Curlew Sandpipers in western Britain, it is unsurprising that this species has occurred on Lundy in only 12 years since LFS records began in 1947 and that all except two of the 15 records during this period have been of single birds. There are only two spring records; all other occurrences have been in the period mid-August to late October, with most in September:

1957 28 Sep – one.
1959 13 May – one "flying with Whimbrel on the Airfield".
1966 28 Oct – two with a flock of Golden Plover.
1967 16 Sep to 4 Oct – one on the Airfield, usually with Golden Plovers.
1973 20 Sep – one flying east over the island.
1974 18 Aug – one in the Tent Field.
      27 Aug – one "in the Reservoir in Lighthouse Field", presumably either the now in-filled pond in the Lighthouse Field, or the reservoir pond next to Quarters.
      8 Sep – one flew from the Tent Field out over South End and towards Great Shutter Rock.
1982 19 to 22 Sep – one, caught and ringed on 19th.
1985 1 to 5 Oct – a juvenile, caught and ringed on 1st.
      19 Oct – one.
1988 9 Sep – a juvenile in flight over Halfway Wall.
1991 13 Sep – two at North End.
1995 15 May – one.[57]
2004 16 & 18 Aug – one at Pondsbury.

Purple Sandpiper *Calidris maritima*

Uncommon spring and autumn migrant; occasional winter visitor.

As with Turnstone, Purple Sandpipers are probably much overlooked on account of their excellent camouflage and preference for largely inaccessible and inhospitable rocky areas in the intertidal spray zone. However, in severe weather they have sometimes been found sheltering with other waders on the island plateau; for example, on 14 October 1976 one was seen feeding in a puddle outside the Church during hurricane-force winds and driving rain! Under more normal conditions it is always worth keeping a careful eye open at favoured wader sites, such as the rocky platform below North West Point, particularly from October to April.

Although listed by Chanter (1871) and Parfitt (1876) as an "occasional visitant", Purple Sandpipers were rarely recorded during the first half of the twentieth century. Gade regarded the species as a winter visitor (Perry 1940), recording four in winter 1928 (Davis 1954a) and finding a dead bird on 6 January 1931 (Harrisson 1932) – the only fully dated pre-LFS record. The first LFS sightings were four on 12 May 1949 and one on 21 September of the same year. Between 1947 and 1980, 'Purps' were recorded in 19 different years. In the period since then, however – up to and including 2006 – they have been seen annually with the sole exception of 1997.

Small numbers migrate through Lundy in both spring and autumn, records for autumn passage slightly outnumbering those during spring migration. Early in the year there is inevitably a degree of seasonal overlap that makes it impossible to separate late winter visitors from true spring migrants. However, most spring occurrences are in March and April and the latest spring date is 24 May (1964). With the exception of a single bird present on the unusual date of 17 July 1983, the earliest autumn date is 5 August (1992). Very small numbers have been seen later on in August and during September, but most autumn records are in October and November.

Dymond (1980) listed only three midwinter records between 1931 and 1978, but there have been almost 30 winter sightings (December to February) subsequently (to the end of 2006). At all times of year instances of more than two in a day are unusual; the three highest counts are six on both 25 October 1988 and 18 November 2006, and eight on 2 January 1988.

Dunlin *Calidris alpina*

Common spring and autumn migrant in small numbers; very rare in winter; said to have bred on one occasion.

Dunlin is by far the commonest of the many small waders in the genus *Calidris* that have been seen on Lundy and is the first species to rule out if something more unusual is suspected. Dunlins have occurred in all months of the year, but are most regular during spring and autumn migration periods when they turn up around the ponds, pools and wet flushes of the plateau and west sidelands. Others simply fly over, being given away by their calls – at night as well as during the day. Breeding-plumaged adults are seen from time to time in spring and early summer, whereas many of the late summer and autumn birds are more soberly marked juveniles. Freshly arrived from remote northern breeding grounds and perhaps never having encountered human beings before, these individuals are often extremely tame, feeding unconcernedly within a few feet of their sometimes astonished observers.

Dunlin

103

Spring movements take place mostly in late April and May, the earliest date being 10 March (1953) and the latest a single bird on 25 June (1950), though the latter is just as likely to have been an early-returning non/failed breeder. Numbers are usually fewer than 10 but reached 18 on 17 May 1991, 22 on 6 & 7 May 1972[58] and 24 on 11 May 1949. Return passage has started as early as 5 July (1989) but most pass through in August and September, with a few in October and odd ones in November. They were reported as "abundant" in September 1931 but the highest daily count in autumn since the late 1940s is 16 on 22 October 1978. Sightings are more frequent in some years than in others; for example, in 1993 – one of the better years – Dunlins were noted on 31 days between 19 July and 31 October, mainly single birds but with up to four in August and seven in early October. There are 14 winter records, two in December (1990 and 2005), three in January (1991, 2004 and 2006) and nine in February.

Listed by Chanter (1871) and Parfitt (1876) as an "occasional visitant", Dunlins are said to have nested on Lundy in 1904, Loyd (1922) referring to the auction of a clutch of eggs "from the collection of Major W.H. Milburn sold…on January 11th, 1922…catalogued as having been taken on Lundy, June 1st, 1904".

Of 82 Dunlins ringed on Lundy to the end of 2006 there have been two subsequent controls: a full-grown bird ringed on Lundy on 8 September 1972 was controlled at Skjaoholmen, Nesseby, in the county of Finnmark, northernmost Norway, on 23 July 1974; and an adult ringed on Lundy on 10 May 1989 was controlled – most likely during its southward migration – at Butterwick, on The Wash, Lincolnshire, on 20 July 1997, still going strong at more than nine years old.

Three races of Dunlin are generally considered to occur in Britain (Wernham *et al.* 2002): *C. a. alpina* breeds in northern Fennoscandia and western Siberia, wintering in western Europe; *C. a. schinzii* breeds mainly in Iceland and south-east Greenland (with small populations in Britain, Ireland and southern Norway), wintering mainly in West Africa; and *C. a. arctica* which breeds in north-east Greenland, also wintering in West Africa. It is probable that birds of all three races occur on Lundy on migration, but those in winter are almost certainly *alpina*. Likewise, the individual controlled in the far north of Norway seems most likely to have belonged to *alpina*. The bird controlled in Lincolnshire could also have been *alpina* given that The Wash is known to be an important moulting area for this race, but the location and timing mean that other races, especially *schinzii*, cannot be excluded.

Buff-breasted Sandpiper *Tryngites subruficollis*

Nationally scarce migrant.

Breeds in north-east Siberia and along the arctic coast of North America, wintering in southern South America. 629 British records 1958–2003, with an average of 15 per year 2000–2003. Considered by the BBRC until the end of 1982.

Chanter (1871) and Parfitt (1876) listed Buff-breasted Sandpiper as an "occasional visitant", presumably on the strength of one shot by S. De B. Heaven in 1858 (D'Urban & Mathew 1985). There are 13 LFS records for seven years between 1959 and 1983, involving up to 17 individuals, all between early September and early October:

1959 24 Sep – one mist-netted and ringed in St Helen's Field; found dead, apparently killed by a cat, on 28 Sep.[59]

1965 27 & 28 Sep – two seen near the Airfield.[60]

1973 2 Sep – two in Middle Park.

7 Sep – one in Middle Park.

19 Sep – two in Middle Park.

All three records, totalling five birds, were accepted by the BBRC.

1974 6 Sep – one on the Airfield.

7 Sep – one on the Airfield.

14 to 16 Sep – a juvenile in Middle Park and on the Airfield.

Based on plumage differences, these were accepted by the BBRC as three different birds.

1975 8 Sep – one on the Airfield.

29 Sep to 5 Oct – one, also on the Airfield.

1977 5 to 11 Sep – two.
          15 to 25 Sep – one, trapped and ringed on 17th.
1983 4 to 7 Sep – one.

A record of a single bird from 24 to 29 September 1985 was published in the relevant *LFS Annual Reports* but appears not to have been submitted to the Devon Birds Records Committee and is therefore discounted here.

Ruff *Philomachus pugnax*

Rare passage migrant; has occurred in late winter.

The earliest dated record of a Ruff on Lundy is one seen by H.H. Davis and Felix Gade on 11 September 1937 (reported by Davis 1954a). Since the start of regular LFS recording in 1947 there have been sightings in 19 years, the first of these in 1956 and the most recent, of a single bird on 16 August 2007, being the first since June 1992.

Most Ruffs have been seen in autumn, early and late dates being 29 July (1977) and 10 October (1972). A flock of nine – four males and five females – landed on the Airfield on 9 September 1958, a year when an unusually large movement of Ruff was recorded along the west coast of the UK (1958 *LFS Annual Report*). There are 10 late-winter and spring sightings between 2 February (1976) and 3 June (1992), mostly of single birds but with three on 11 March 1973 and four – three females and a male – from 12 to 15 March 1973.

South-west England is on the fringe of the Ruff's European range and Lundy offers very limited suitable habitat, so this is a species that is bound to occur infrequently and in small numbers. Nevertheless, the paucity of records during the last 20 years means that Ruff is perhaps heading for the status of Lundy vagrant, rather than rare migrant.

Jack Snipe *Lymnocryptes minimus*

Uncommon migrant and winter visitor, mainly late September to March.

Usually flushed from ditches, wet flushes and other areas of rushes or damp, tussocky grassland on the island plateau, particularly around Pondsbury and Punchbowl Valley, Jack Snipe are one of the most difficult birds to survey given their propensity for sitting tight until almost trodden on.

Chanter (1871) and Parfitt (1876) listed Jack Snipe as an "autumn and winter visitant", while the Heaven diaries recorded single birds shot in October (twice), November and January, between 1887 and 1905 (Boyd 1950). Other early twentieth century records were singles on 4 September 1927 (Harrisson 1932) and 28 August 1929 (F.W. Gade, reported by Davis 1954a).

Jack Snipe

105

Jack Snipe have been recorded in all but eight LFS years from 1947 to the end of 2006 (the blank years being 1951, 1961, 1963, 1964, 1968, 1969, 1971 and 2005). They have occurred in all months except June and July, the great majority in October. Though mostly encountered singly, with rarely more than two seen in a day, peak counts have been six on 26 February 1976 and 9 October 1990, and 11 on 3 October 1989 (coinciding with peak Common Snipe numbers for that year). Following one pre-LFS record of a single Jack Snipe on 28 August 1928 (Davis 1954a) there have been a further seven August records, all of isolated individuals, the earliest being 4 August 1995. Migration is more noticeable in September (more than 20 LFS records) but reaches a peak in October (over 50 LFS records). Small numbers have been seen throughout the period November to February, presumably including a mix of late migrants and overwintering birds. The main spring migration occurs in late March and early April. Singles on 5 May 2000 and 21 May 1979 – the only May occurrences – were both exceptionally late records for this time of year.

This species' breeding range extends from northern Fennoscandia across Siberia, some migrating to spend the winter as far south as sub-Saharan Africa. Ringing has shown that birds moving through Britain occur outside the breeding season in France, Iberia and North Africa (Wernham *et al.* 2002). Eleven Jack Snipe had been ringed on Lundy by the end of 2006, but there are no controls or recoveries involving the island.

Snipe *Gallinago gallinago* [Common Snipe]

Common passage migrant and winter visitor; may formerly have bred.

Although recorded in all months of the year, Snipe are most often encountered from mid-autumn through to early spring, typically calling in flight as they twist and tower away from their would-be observers when flushed from ground cover on the island plateau. Most are seen between Quarter Wall and Halfway Wall, especially around Pondsbury, but odd ones and twos can turn up almost anywhere. Eight were seen flying west during the boat crossing on 26 August 1982.

Nowadays, most sightings involve only one or two individuals, although there are occasional counts of 10 or more; for example, 15 on 17 February 2004 and 16 on 26 October 2001, but Snipe formerly occurred in far greater numbers on the island. While the most recent daily count of more than 20 Snipe was 25 on 9 February 1991, such numbers were relatively commonplace in earlier decades, with 41 on 29 December 1981, 45 on 25 January 1955, 48 on 23 March 1962 and 50 on 13 January 1982 being among the highest counts. Even these exceptional numbers by today's standards were eclipsed by the "very conservative" estimate of at least 100 in early January 1963 during severe winter weather (LFS 1962), and 113 counted on 18 January 1985. Perhaps coincidentally, 1985 was also the year of the highest-known autumn count: a flock of 30 Snipe, presumed migrants, were seen in flight on 1 November 1985.

The decline in frequency and overall numbers of Snipe on Lundy may be linked to decreases in the UK breeding population; surveys in England and Wales revealed a 62% decrease in the number of breeding birds in wet meadows between 1982 and 2002 (Baillie *et al.* 2007). There is also anecdotal evidence, including our own observations, to suggest that the island has tended to be drier in recent years, perhaps being less attractive to Snipe.

The Heaven Diaries mentioned birds shot frequently in autumn and winter (Boyd 1950). Chanter (1871) and Parfitt (1876) listed Snipe as "resident all the year", Parfitt adding "and breed there" but without giving any substantiating details. Wynne-Edwards & Harrisson (1932) described the species as an irregular breeder, listing a pair as probably breeding in the Middle Park area in 1930, a year in which drumming was reportedly heard in May (Harrisson 1932). In 1935 Dr F.R. Elliston Wright found a chick in Gannets' Combe "which he considered to be a young Snipe" (Davis 1954a), but the wording of this report suggests an element of doubt.

Thirty Snipe had been ringed on Lundy by the end of 2006, but there are no controls or recoveries involving the island. Given that birds from Icelandic and continental breeding populations are known to pass through Britain in large numbers, in addition to those from the British and Irish breeding grounds (Wernham *et al.* 2002), it is likely that Snipe seen on Lundy have quite varied origins.

Woodcock *Scolopax rusticola* [Eurasian Woodcock]

Common passage migrant and winter visitor in small numbers, mainly October to March.

Woodcocks tuck themselves away in rough grassland or bracken on the plateau and sidelands, and flushing one from almost under your feet is invariably sudden and exciting – if sometimes heart-stopping too! Early-rising bird ringers have also reported Woodcocks in Millcombe before dawn, flying into or flushed out of the woods, or sometimes visiting the wet areas to feed along the stream.

Most sightings are made in late autumn and winter, usually involving from one to three birds seen on any one day, and only very rarely more than five – the last such instance being six on 3 November 2001. An exceptional 30 were counted on 20 January 1985, while by far the highest count to date occurred during the bitterly cold winter of 1962/63 when more than 100 Woodcocks were thought to be present at the beginning of January 1963 (LFS 1962).

This species is rare in spring and has been recorded in April in only eight years, the most recent being 26 April 2007, which is also the latest spring date. The earliest autumn date is 20 August (1970), the next being 24 September (1995).

Woodcocks were apparently far more numerous in the nineteenth and early twentieth centuries. D'Urban & Mathew (1895) mentioned "great numbers" resorting to the island in very severe weather in the winter of 1860, during which 93 "cock and snipe" were shot in a single day, mainly Woodcock. Chanter (1871), who listed Woodcock as an "autumn and winter visitant", wrote: "Should the winter be exceptionally severe, and especially should there be a heavy fall of snow, large flights of woodcock seek a more genial climate in Lundy…They find shelter in the little valleys, in the boggy ground formed by the streams, and in the steep cleaves on the eastern side." Parfitt (1876) also listed Woodcock as an "autumn and winter visitant" but added "occasional breeder [?]". The Rev. H.G. Heaven recorded the species as early as August and as late as May (Heaven 1870–1905). Mapleton-Bree (1932) stated that as a boy he "was told by a neighbour…that in former years he had enjoyed very good Woodcock shooting on Lundy in the month of November. He said…the fact of their being found there at this season in numbers was sufficiently well known to west-country sportsmen to make it worth their while to make a trip over…It would seem that the Woodcock has altered its line of migration in this particular district since those days".

Of 10 Woodcocks ringed on Lundy by the end of 2006, two have been recovered. An adult ringed on 31 October 1951 was found near Aalesund, Norway on 11 October two years later – a distance of 1,387 kilometres from Lundy. An adult male ringed on 20 October 1987 was shot in the Vologda oblast (region) of western Russia on 30 April 1988 having moved nearly 3,000 kilometres. These suggest that many of the Woodcocks reaching Lundy in autumn are from breeding grounds in north-east Europe, fitting well with the statement by Wernham *et al.* (2002) that "the populations of Russia and Fennoscandia are migratory, wintering throughout western and southern Europe, but particularly France, Spain, Britain, Ireland and Italy, while those of northwestern Europe are largely sedentary".

Woodcock

107

Black-tailed Godwit *Limosa limosa*

Rare passage migrant; one winter record.

Although listed by Chanter (1871) and Parfitt (1876) as an "occasional visitant", there are no documented occurrences until the first LFS record on 27 May 1952. There have since been 28 further sightings (to the end of 2006). While eight of eleven spring records have been in May, the earliest is of a single bird that frequented a small pool on the Airfield from 19 March to 2 April 1967; the latest spring sighting is also of a single bird, from 29 to 31 May 1957. There are no June records.

Of 17 autumn sightings, nine have been in July – the earliest being on 2 July (1986) – making this the peak month for 'autumn' migration. There are three records in both August and September, and two in October, the latest being 8 October (1975). Most records are of single birds, with two on four occasions and three on 31 August 1959.

The only winter record concerns a party of six found sheltering on the north-west sidelands on 5 February 1973.[61]

Given Lundy's west-coast location, it is likely that many of the Black-tailed Godwits seen over the years have belonged to the Icelandic breeding population *L. l. islandica*, which winters mainly in Britain, Ireland and north-west France (Wernham *et al.* 2002).

Bar-tailed Godwit *Limosa lapponica*

Rare passage migrant; has occurred in winter.

Chanter (1871) and Parfitt (1876) listed Bar-tailed Godwit as an "occasional visitant". There are just three dated occurrences – all of single birds in the 1930s (Davis 1954a) – prior to the first LFS record of one on Rat Island on 19 August 1948. In the years since, there have been about 26 records during spring, extreme dates being 18 April (1980) and 22 June (1959). Of some 23 'autumn' records, the earliest date is 1 July (1981), although as with many other waders it is impossible to distinguish precisely between late-moving spring migrants and early-returning non/failed breeders. The latest date in autumn is 31 October (1971), while the only winter records are of one that stayed for several days from 22 February 1938, a flock of 24 on 20 January 1984 and two birds on 18 & 24 January 1985.

Occurrences during either spring or autumn passage rarely involve more than one or two birds, but a flock of about 30 landed briefly between Pondsbury and the Old Light on 31 October 1971, and 22 were seen flying south over the island on 6 September 1973. The highest spring count is 13 on 27 April 1984. The most recent occurrences have been of single birds on 30 August 1999 (flying over) and 30 April 2007 (on Rat Island), the latter individual probably also present on the West Side on 28 April.

One Bar-tailed Godwit has been ringed on Lundy (in 1979), but there are no controls or recoveries involving the island. Bar-tailed Godwits are true globetrotters, breeding on the Arctic tundra from northern Fennoscandia across Siberia, and wintering as far south as South Africa and New Zealand, though those passing through Lundy are likely to winter in Britain & Ireland, elsewhere in western Europe, or West Africa (Wernham *et al.* 2002).

Whimbrel *Numenius phaeopus*

Common spring and autumn migrant in small numbers; declining.

The Whimbrel's far-carrying, whistling flight call is often the first indication that birds are around – it is also one of the iconic sounds of spring on Lundy. Birds stopping off to rest and feed on the island during migration often frequent heather moorland and the fields on the plateau, as well as grassy cliff edges and rocky shores. Along with Oystercatcher, Whimbrel is probably the most commonly seen and heard wader in spring. The main migration period runs from the end of April to mid-May, late stragglers overlapping with early-returning migrants. Maximum counts have exceeded 30 in 13 years since systematic recording began in 1947. One hundred and five birds on 4 May 1967 is by far the largest number ever seen, followed by 60 on 7 May 1974. The earliest spring record is of a single bird in Lametry Bay on the unusually early dates of 23 February and 12 March 1992.[62]

Overall numbers have declined considerably since the 1970s, the spring peak at one time averaging 20 birds per day. Since 1990 the maximum daily counts have been of 25 birds on 7 May 1990 and 20 from 1 to 5 May 1993. Fifteen was the highest count between 2000 and the end of 2006 and even this lowly threshold was reached just twice: 8 May 2000 and 1 & 2 May 2004. This decline coincides with significant decreases noted on the nearby Somerset and Gwent Levels – formerly major spring staging areas for Whimbrel, now partly abandoned, perhaps as a result of agricultural change (Wernham *et al.* 2002; White 2005).

Whimbrels have always been less frequent and less numerous on Lundy in autumn, reflecting the species' more easterly migration route at this time of year (Wernham *et al.* 2002). The majority pass through in August and September and maximum numbers have reached 20 or more on 12 occasions, 50 on 22 August 1974 being the highest count. There are late autumn records of birds in November (twice) and on two occasions in December: one on 9 December 1958 (on the West Side) and another on 16 December 1990 (on Rat Island).

Chanter (1871) and Parfitt (1876) listed Whimbrel as a "summer visitant", with Parfitt adding "occasional breeder" though he provided no supporting details. Given that Whimbrels nest only in the extreme north of Scotland and are not known to have bred much further south in the 19th century, this claim has to be regarded as highly improbable.

Most of the Whimbrels passing through western Britain in spring probably belong to the population *N. p. islandica* that breeds in Iceland, the Faeroes and Scotland, numbering an estimated 600,000 to 750,000 individuals (Wetlands International 2006). Twenty-one Whimbrels had been ringed on Lundy by the end of 2006, but there are no controls or recoveries involving the island.

Curlew *Numenius arquata* [Eurasian Curlew]

Common spring and autumn migrant in declining numbers; occasional winter visitor; formerly bred.

Though seen less frequently now than at any time since the 1940s, Curlews can crop up almost anywhere, on moorland, rough grassland and fields on the island plateau, occasionally on the lower sidelands and sometimes on rocky outcrops. The tide-washed platform off North West Point below the North Light is a favoured roosting site.

As for Whimbrel, there has been a major decline in numbers since the 1970s, when Curlews averaged about 30 birds per day at their peak in July. The fall in numbers has been most evident since the early 1990s, when the highest count was 28 birds on 22 July. From 1997 onwards, the peak number in all but one year has been eight birds; and in both 2003 and 2005 there were just nine records for the entire year, involving totals of 20 and 17 birds respectively.

Even with the smaller numbers of birds today, spring migration is much less marked than autumn, with scattered records, mostly ones and twos, through April, May and June. The highest spring number is 24 on 11 March 1962. From the 1940s to

Curlew

the end of the 1970s there was a regular and extended autumn passage which started at the end of June, peaked in mid-July and continued to October. Maximum numbers were over 100 on eight days in July and August 1959, 120 on 11 & 12 July 1962 and 200 on 29 August 1974.

Counts of winter visitors are usually in single figures, although there are occasional bigger flocks, the largest of these being 47 on 21 January 1985 and 70 on 7 February 1986. A flock of up to 20 birds on the West Side in January and February 1992 was the last record of wintering Curlews in any number.

Chanter (1871) listed Curlew as an "occasional visitant" but promoted it to "autumn and winter visitant" in his 1877 revision, matching Parfitt's 1876 listing. Crespi (1888) reported breeding in 1888 or shortly before. Loyd (1922) recorded four pairs during May and June 1922, but without conclusive evidence of breeding. Probable breeding occurred in 1929 (Gade, reported by Davis 1954a) and single pairs bred successfully in 1927 and from 1941 to 1944 (Alexander *et al.* 1945; Davis 1954a), while T. Fulford reported finding a nest and four eggs at the end of May 1945 (1945 *Devon Bird Report*).

From the start of LFS recording in 1947, one pair bred or was present during the breeding season in almost every year through to 1973 when at least one young bird fledged successfully. Two pairs may have been present in 1959 and 1973, and possibly three pairs in 1971. While Curlews have been on the island in May and June in some subsequent years, there has been no evidence of any breeding attempt since 1973; indeed LFS records for these months are fewer now than at any time previously. As with Lapwings, agricultural intensification (mainly increases in stocking rates of sheep and more extensive use of fertilisers) and greater disturbance from growing numbers of visitors are likely causes of the demise of the species as a breeding bird on Lundy. However, the species' wider fortunes, involving a 39% decline in breeding numbers in the wet meadows of England and Wales between 1982 and 2002 (Baillie *et al.* 2007), are also bound to be important.

Thirty-two Curlews had been ringed on Lundy by the end of 2006, with three subsequent recoveries. An adult ringed at Pondsbury on 14 September 1958 was recovered 44 days later on 28 October near Brest, France. A nestling ringed on 27 May 1967 was recovered at Noya, La Coruña, Spain, on 16 November 1967. And a juvenile ringed on 6 September 1967 was found near Padstow, Cornwall, on 23 April 1968; perhaps this bird had wintered in the UK or was returning from European or African wintering grounds. Curlews moving through Lundy are likely to include birds from British and Irish, as well as continental, breeding populations (Wernham *et al.* 2002).

Spotted Redshank

Spotted Redshank *Tringa erythropus*

Rare passage migrant, mainly in autumn.

There have been 26 records involving 34 individuals since the first known Lundy occurrence of a single bird on 27 & 28 March 1954. All but five have been in autumn, between 11 July (2007) and 1 October (1996) – coincidentally, the earliest and latest dates are also the two most recent records. Most sightings are of single birds but three occurred on 21 August 1967, 4 to 6 September 1973 and 15 August 1981. One bird stayed from 1 to 11 September 1978. Since 1984 there have been only five records, all of single birds. Since relatively few Spotted Redshanks pass through western Britain and Lundy offers very restricted suitable habitat, this is likely to remain a very rare bird on the island.

Redshank *Tringa totanus*   [Common Redshank]

Uncommon spring and autumn migrant.

The entry for Redshank in the very first *LFS Annual Report* in 1947 – "single birds about the shore, April, July, August, September" – set the pattern for the following 60 years. These four months, in the order August, April, July, September, are the peak periods for Redshank on Lundy, closely followed by May. In all, some 230 birds have been recorded on about 300 days following the first dated LFS sighting by Hugh Boyd on 24 March 1948. Since then, Redshanks have been recorded in all but three years (1950, 1963 and 1970) up to and including 2007, the vast majority of sightings involving single birds.

The earliest documented spring record is 9 March 1937 (Davis 1954a), the earliest LFS record being 11 March 1953. Most spring Redshanks occur in April (31 birds on 56 days) and May (27 birds on 26 days). The two earliest of nine June records are 12th (1992) and 14th (1959); given that British and Irish breeding Redshanks begin to leave their breeding grounds in June (Wernham *et al.* 2002), it is just as likely that these are early-returning birds as they are tail-end northward-bound spring migrants. Hence, the latest reliable spring date is 28 May (1984). More than two Redshanks in a day have been seen on just three occasions, the maximum count being nine on 1 May 1968.

July and August are peak months for autumn migration, with most sightings falling in August (50 birds on 82 days in 32 years since LFS records began). There are three November records, including the latest autumn date – 17 November (1985) – when a peak of eight was counted.

While Redshanks are common winter visitors to the Taw & Torridge Estuary some 35 kilometres to the east, winter occurrences on Lundy are exceptional, with sightings in just four years: February 1961 and 1986 (both possibly very early spring migrants) and December 1954 and 1981. A record 11 birds were seen on 11 & 12 December 1981, with 10 still present on 14 December.

Observations of Redshank have become fewer since the early 1990s, reflecting the general decline in waders recorded on Lundy. In the 15 years 1977–1991 there were precisely 50 records on 100 days, while in the 15 years 1992–2006, Redshanks were recorded 29 times on 41 days. Before very long this species may be classified as rare on Lundy.

Chanter (1871) and Parfitt (1876) listed Redshank as an "occasional visitant". The earliest documented twentieth century records are of a single bird flying over the island on 29 August 1907 (Oldham 1932) and one flying north calling on 27 July 1923 (Loyd 1925). The earliest spring bird (March 1937, mentioned above) was probably recorded by Felix Gade. A party of eight on autumn migration was seen in July or August 1939 (Perry 1940). These are probably four of the seven pre-LFS records mentioned by Dymond (1980), who gave no details.

The Redshanks occurring on Lundy almost certainly include birds from both the British & Irish and Icelandic (*T. t. robusta*) breeding populations, and perhaps also continental breeding birds, though the latter occur mainly on the east coast of England (Wernham *et al.* 2002).

Greenshank *Tringa nebularia*   [Common Greenshank]

Uncommon spring and autumn migrant.

Listed in the nineteenth century by Chanter (1871) and Parfitt (1876) as an "occasional visitant", the first twentieth century record of a Greenshank on Lundy came on 3 September 1947 when the distinctive ringing *tew-tew-tew* call was heard by Robert Moore, author of *The Birds of Devon* (1969). Nowadays, this is a species that occurs infrequently during migration periods, typically being seen at Pondsbury or one of the smaller pools or marshy areas on the island plateau.

The first spring record was as late as 1960 (28 May), since when there have been a further 23 spring occurrences in 21 different years (to the end of 2006). The earliest date is 6 April (1963) and the latest 14 June (1978). Many more sightings have been made in autumn – with records in all but 12 of the 60 LFS years from 1947 to 2006 – extreme dates being 3 July (1950) and 17 October (1988), with a marked peak in the second half of August. Most sightings are of single birds, the maximum being four on 22 August 1966. One seen on 29 December 1987 was exceptional and remains the only winter record.

A lone Greenshank was seen flying north during the boat crossing on 22 October 1988.

Two Greenshanks had been ringed on Lundy by the end of 2006, but there are no controls or recoveries involving the island. Apart from the small population breeding in Scotland, birds passing through southern Britain are thought to breed mainly in north-east Europe, many wintering in sub-Saharan Africa (Wernham *et al.* 2002).

Green Sandpiper *Tringa ochropus*

Rare spring migrant; uncommon autumn migrant.

Listed by Chanter (1871) and Parfitt (1876) as an "occasional visitant", the first twentieth century record of a Green Sandpiper on Lundy was of a single bird on 4 & 5 July 1942 (Alexander & Radford 1942).

There have been spring records in 20 LFS years, but none since May 1995. The earliest spring sighting is a bird that stayed around Millcombe pond from 16 to 19 March 1990, but most occurrences have been in late April and the first half of May. This species is one of the first migrant waders to return from northern breeding grounds, so that single birds seen on 23 June 1953 and 27 & 28 June 1973 were almost certainly already heading south.

Once occurring regularly on Lundy during autumn passage, Green Sandpipers are now uncommon at this time of year. Most have turned up between late July and early September, with October records in five years and one exceptionally late record on 4 November 1980. Sightings are mainly of single birds around ponds and pools on the island plateau – especially Quarter Wall Pond and Pondsbury – and the highest daily count is four on both 30 August 1994 (at Pondsbury) and 1 September 1997.[63]

A Green Sandpiper trapped on Lundy in 1951 was only the third to be ringed in Britain, but there are no controls or recoveries involving the island. The Green Sandpipers passing through Britain breed in the boreal forest zone from Norway and Germany eastwards, wintering in north-west Europe, the Mediterranean and parts of Africa (Wernham *et al.* 2002).

Wood Sandpiper *Tringa glareola*

Rare passage migrant, mainly in autumn.

Lundy's first Wood Sandpiper was observed "haunting two small ponds" in the field behind the Church on 8 June 1930 (Harrisson & Wynne-Edwards 1930). This was followed by two further spring records – a single bird on 2 May 1931 (F.W. Gade, reported by Davis 1954a) and two on 2 May 1938 (F.W. Gade, reported by Palmer 1946) – plus an undated autumn record in 1932. There have since been 34 records involving at least 40 individuals between 1950 (one on 16 September, described as "probably of this species") and the most recent sighting in 2000 (two on 25 July, one remaining to 28 July). Most of these have been in autumn. There are just eight spring records involving nine birds, falling between 25 April (1954) and 19 June (1978), though the latter could already have been an early south-bound migrant, perhaps a failed breeder. Otherwise, the earliest date for returning migrants is 23 July (1990) and the latest autumn record is 16 September (1950). The highest daily count is two, recorded on six occasions. Autumn birds sometimes stay for several days; in 1977 one was seen regularly from 14 to 25 August.

The only Wood Sandpiper to be ringed on Lundy was caught at Pondsbury on 7 September 1951, and there are no recoveries or controls involving the island. Migrants passing through Britain are thought to nest mainly in Fennoscandia, wintering in West Africa (Wernham *et al.* 2002).

Common Sandpiper *Actitis hypoleucos*

Regular spring and autumn migrant; three winter records.

Most Common Sandpipers are seen on Lundy's rocky shoreline – particularly around the Landing Bay, Lametry Bay and Rat Island – though some also occur along the margins of ponds and pools on the plateau. Surprisingly, neither Chanter (1871) nor Parfitt (1876) made any mention of this species and the first documented Lundy record – of two birds – occurred on 1 September 1907 (Oldham 1932). Loyd (1922) recorded two on 12 May 1922, two were shot on 13 February 1929 (Davis 1954a) and two were present on 22 January 1940 (F.W. Gade, reported by Davis 1954a).

Common Sandpiper

In spite of its historical scarcity, Common Sandpipers have been recorded in all but three years (1969, 1971 and 1983) since LFS recording began, occurring in small numbers during both spring and autumn migrations. Spring movements peak in April and early May, although the earliest date is 29 March (1977). There are several midsummer records between mid-June and mid-July which are perhaps most likely to be early-returning migrants, including failed breeders. Most autumn migrants pass through in late July and August, maximum daily counts reaching 10 or more on three occasions: 10 on 17 August 1975, 11 on 12 August 1957 and a peak of 30 on 6 August 1959 near Miller's Cake on the East Side. There continue to be scattered records in September and October and the latest autumn sighting is 7 November (2004, the only November occurrence). There are only three winter records, two of these in 1929 and 1940 (see above) and one on 23 February 1955.

One Common Sandpiper had been ringed on Lundy by the end of 2006, but there are no recoveries or controls involving the island. Birds passing through Lundy are likely to be mainly from the large breeding population in northern and western Britain, perhaps with some migrants originating from Scandinavia (Wernham *et al.* 2002).

Turnstone *Arenaria interpres* [Ruddy Turnstone]

Uncommon spring and autumn migrant and winter visitor; signs of a decline in recent years.

As for Purple Sandpiper, the Turnstone's preference for rocky shorelines in the spray zone – a habitat that on Lundy is largely either inaccessible to birdwatchers, or out of sight from the cliff-tops – probably means that this species is greatly under-recorded. Even so, Turnstones have been seen in all months of the year, mostly in ones and twos, but sometimes in small flocks.

Turnstone was listed by Chanter (1871) and Parfitt (1876) as an "occasional visitant", while Loyd (1925) referred to a sighting of two on 28 May 1861. Oldham (1932) recorded one on 1 September 1907. Davis (1954a) considered Turnstone to be a "scarce and rather irregular spring and autumn passage migrant…occasionally seen in winter", a status that was applied by Dymond (1980), who also noted that in very severe weather this species will sometimes take shelter on the island plateau.

Between 1952 and the early 1980s there were sporadic winter records, but from the mid-1980s to the mid-1990s winter occurrences became more regular, with maximum counts including seven on 11 December 1986, 11 on 29 January 1990 and 14 on 19 February 1990. This trend was not maintained, however, and there have been only two December sightings since 1996 (both in 2000) and none at all in either January or February. In fact, there has been a general decline in numbers and frequency of

Turnstones on Lundy at all times of year over the last decade, with barely 20 records for the period 1997 to 2006, mainly of lone individuals, and none of more than three in a day. No Turnstones were seen at all in 2005.

Until the recent decrease, small numbers occurred in March and April, with a modest peak in spring passage usually occurring in late April or early May, the highest daily count in spring being 18 on 26 April 1965. The latest spring date is 3 June (1971). By the end of June, early-returning adults are already heading south; for example, four birds from 21 to 23 June 1986 and singles on 1 July 1991 and 12 July 1957. Most autumn migrants are seen in August and September, the highest daily count relating to a flock of about 20 on 27 August 1972 – birds that only revealed themselves when flushed from the seaward side of Black Rock, off Shutter Point, by an exceptionally high wave. Other high counts are 10 on 13 September 1949, 11 on 31 August 1957, 12 on 24 August 1959 and 13 on 25 August 1961. Late autumn sightings, in October and November, have been irregular, generally involving from one to six birds, though 12 were present from 3 to 6 November 1967.

Three Turnstones had been ringed on Lundy by the end of 2006, but there are no controls or recoveries involving the island. Ringing and migration studies in western Britain suggest that most of the Turnstones migrating through Lundy are likely to be from the population that breeds in arctic Canada and Greenland, stages in Iceland, and winters on the Atlantic coasts of Europe and north-west Africa (Wernham *et al.* 2002). Wetland Bird Survey (WeBS) data have shown a general decrease in the number of Turnstones wintering in Britain (Collier *et al.* 2005), perhaps as a consequence of milder winters that enable birds to stay further north and east than normal. This could explain why numbers on Lundy have shown such a marked recent decline.

Wilson's Phalarope *Phalaropus tricolor*

British vagrant.

Breeds in western North America, migrating to winter in South America, south of the equator. 214 records for Britain 1950–2005.

There is one Lundy record of a single bird in autumn:

1992 27 Aug to 1 Sep – a juvenile on Pondsbury.

Red-necked Phalarope *Phalaropus lobatus*

Lundy vagrant.

In the Western Palearctic breeds mainly in Iceland, northern Scandinavia, Finland and Russia, migrating to wintering grounds at sea. Fennoscandian birds winter in the Red Sea. 584 records for Britain 1986–2003, with an average of 25 per year 2000–2003, excluding the very small breeding population in the Scottish islands.

There have been two Lundy records, both in autumn. Unfortunately no details of the two occurrences are given in the relevant *LFS Annual Reports* and the original LFS data for these years no longer exist.

1955 11 Nov – one.
1960 18 Oct – one.

In addition, a phalarope, either Red-necked or Grey (*P. fulicarius*), was seen in the Landing Bay on 17 November 1978.

Grey Phalarope *Phalaropus fulicarius*   [Red Phalarope]

Lundy vagrant.

Breeds along arctic coasts with a small Icelandic population at the southern edge of its range. Winters in waters off western and south-western Africa, western South America and the southern United States. 4,417 records for Britain 1986–2003, with an average of 403 per year 2000–2003.

Grey Phalarope

Listed by Chanter (1871) and Parfitt (1876) under "occasional visitants", there is also a record in the Heaven Diaries of a Grey Phalarope shot on 9 December 1881 (Boyd 1950). The only dated pre-LFS twentieth century occurrences are of single birds on 13 September 1941 and 23 October 1943 (F.W. Gade, reported by Palmer 1946).

There have since been eleven further records:

1951 17 Sep – one in the Landing Bay.
1959 12 to 20 Sep – one in the Landing Bay.
1960 16 to 21 Sep – one, with two present on 20 Sep.
1968 25 Sep – one.
1981 22 to 25 Sep – one.
1982 8 & 9 Feb – one.
1992 21 Sep – a juvenile feeding in pools along the main track close to Quarter Wall.
1998 30 Oct – one off Rat Island.
2000 13 Oct – one offshore.[64]
2002 29 Sep – one found dead next to Pondsbury was lightly oiled and probably a victim of pollution.
2005 27 Oct – one on the sea close to Rat Island.

In addition, the 1965-66 *LFS Annual Report* states that "a phalarope seen in the Landing Bay by John Ogilvie is believed to have been of this species" but gives no date, while a phalarope also seen in the Landing Bay on 17 November 1978 was either Grey or Red-necked (*P. lobatus*).

Grey Phalaropes have also been seen in autumn on a handful of occasions during the boat crossing: one or two on 7 September 1948, two on 2 September 1973, one on 24 September 1973 and one on 22 October 1994.[65]

Arctic Skua *Stercorarius parasiticus*   [Parasitic Jaeger]

Rare passage migrant, mainly in autumn.

This is one of several migrant seabirds that occurs commonly in British waters, sometimes in large numbers, but which has been recorded on Lundy far less frequently than might be expected. In fact, records are less than annual, though there may be several occurrences in the same year. Sightings mostly involve birds passing well offshore and Arctic Skuas are only very rarely seen on or over the island itself.

The earliest documented occurrence is of a single bird seen by Norman Joy during the boat crossing on 22 August 1905 (Joy 1922). However, there is no indication of whether the sighting of an individual by Dr T.G. Longstaff on 8 September 1926 (Harrisson 1932) was made on the crossing or actually from the island. The 1942 *Devon Bird Report* notes that one was "seen sometime after July" on Lundy, a record also referred to by Palmer (1946).

Of 33 LFS records of Arctic Skuas seen on or from the island, all have been of single birds except for two on four occasions: 15 September 1953, 20 April 1963 (the only April sighting), 9 July 1991 and 5 October 1999. There are just five spring records, all falling between the early and late dates of 20 April (1963) and 11 June (1981), followed by three occurrences in July – presumed early-returning migrants. A light passage continues during August (three records), while September is by far the peak month with 14 sightings up to and including 2006, followed by October (nine records). There have been no occurrences between 25 October and 20 April.

There are just three instances of birds seen actually 'on' the island: one at Pondsbury on 8 September 1978, one close to Needle Rock on 25 August 1980, and one which turned up on the old Manor Farm Hotel (now Old House) lawn during a south-westerly gale on 26 September 1982.

The following is a complete listing of entries made in the LFS logbook for the 10 years 1997–2006, excluding one annotated as "from boat" on 10 September 1997:

1999   5 May – a dark-morph Arctic Skua chased a Herring Gull across South West Field.
      13 Sep – one.
      5 Oct – two.
      7 Oct – one.
      23 Oct – one.
2003   27 Sep – one.
2005   11 May – one, dark morph, seen flying over Millcombe.
      15 Oct – one.
      25 Oct – one; the latest date yet recorded for this species.
2006   7 Oct – one.
      10 Oct – one.

In LFS years there have been at least 17 sightings of Arctic Skuas during the boat crossing, involving about 27 individuals, the highest counts being four on 23 August 1970[66] and five on 31 August 1980.

Long-tailed Skua *Stercorarius longicaudus*   [Long-tailed Jaeger]

Lundy vagrant.

There is one Lundy record:

1974   20 Jun – a single adult bird at rest in fields close to the Old Light was later seen flying west out to sea before turning south about a mile offshore.

In addition, Alexander & Radford (1942) stated: "On our return voyage to the mainland on the afternoon of September 11th [1942] an adult Long-tailed Skua flew past the boat, travelling south, a mile or two east of the island."

Great Skua *Stercorarius skua*

Rare spring and autumn migrant; has occurred in winter.

All except one of the Lundy 'Bonxie' records involve migrants passing offshore, typically flying by either the North or South End. There has been a significant increase in recent decades, though this remains a scarce species and one which, like Arctic Skua, is seen less often than many birdwatchers would anticipate for an island so far from the mainland.

During the first 30 years of LFS recording covered by Dymond (1980) there were just three sightings from the island, the first of these being a bird that flew past Shutter Point on 14 October 1972. Since then there have been a further 30 observations, mostly of isolated individuals but three were seen on 5 October 1999. The trend towards more frequent records began in the 1980s and continues today, with sightings in 19 years from 1980 up to and including 2007.

Great Skua

Taking all LFS records into account, there have been just four spring occurrences, all between 16 May (1989) and 23 June (1978), while four records in July and two in August mark the start of an extended autumn passage. The vast majority of Lundy's Great Skuas have been seen in September (12 sightings) and October (11), with the latest autumn date being 9 November (2002). However, there are also two midwinter records: a single bird flying north past the island on 11 February 1990 and one sitting in heather by a footpath at the North End on 20 January 2007.

Since 1947 (up to August 2007) there have been at least 25 documented sightings of Great Skuas on the boat crossing[67] to or from the North Devon mainland, involving a total of more than 35 birds, the first being a single bird on 28 August 1948 and the highest count being six on 8 October 1988. There are three winter records for the crossing (17 January 1975 and 19 & 29 December 1978) but only one in spring (28 May 1972).

Mediterranean Gull *Larus melanocephalus*

Lundy vagrant.

The only Lundy record involves three birds:

1978 11 Aug – a second-year bird[68] settled on the water close to the shore in the Landing Bay where it was joined by two juveniles; the three birds flew around for several minutes before departing.

While the 1978 *Devon Bird Report* mentions an increase in Mediterranean Gull records in the county for that year, the species was nevertheless still rare at the time. Nowadays, over 100 birds occur each year in Devon, either as post-breeding visitors in late summer or during the winter. Given that in 2004 the annual total on the Taw & Torridge Estuary, some 35 kilometres from Lundy, was 32, it is surprising that Mediterranean Gulls have not been recorded on or around the island for almost 30 years.

Laughing Gull *Larus atricilla*

British vagrant.

Breeds on the western Atlantic coast from the north-eastern United States south to the Caribbean, moving south to winter from the southern United States to Brazil. 151 records for Britain 1950–2005, with 53 of these, including the Lundy sightings, occurring in 2005.

Laughing Gull was listed by Parfitt (1876) and Chanter (1877) as "reported but not accurately identified". In the late autumn of 2005 two birds reached Lundy, part of an unprecedented influx to western Britain following a period of Atlantic storms. These therefore constitute the first and only occurrences for Lundy:

2005 9 to 17 Nov – one, a first-winter bird, near the Church.
11 Nov – a second bird, an adult, was found dead near St John's Valley having reportedly been seen together with the first-winter individual on 9th.[69]

Little Gull *Larus minutus*

Lundy vagrant.

There have been just five LFS records, all in autumn between August and October and all of single birds:

1973 17 Aug – a juvenile in the Landing Bay.
  25 Sep – an adult in the Landing Bay.
1987 5 Oct – an adult flying south along the East Side.
1989 28 Aug – a juvenile at Pondsbury.
1990 22 Oct – one off North End.

Listed by Chanter (1871) and Parfitt (1876) as an "occasional visitant". One was recorded in October 1891 (H.G. Heaven, reported by Davis 1954a). In addition, singles were seen on the crossing not far off the East Side on 7 September 1948 and on 30 April 1966.

Sabine's Gulls

Sabine's Gull *Larus sabini*

Lundy vagrant.

Breeds in arctic North America, Greenland and Russia, wintering in the South Atlantic and South Pacific. More than 4,651 records for Britain 1968–2003, with an average of 151 per year 2000–2003; considered by the BOU as a passage migrant rather than a nationally scarce migrant.

Four Lundy records have all been in the period July to October:

1958 28 Sep – an immature in the Landing Bay.
1980 18 Oct – one.
1992 13 Jul – an adult in breeding plumage flew south across the Landing Bay. Though earlier in the year than normal, others were seen in south-west Britain and Ireland around the same time.
1997 10 Sep – an adult over the Stanley Bank (off Lundy's east coast), feeding close to a fishing boat and being chased by an Arctic Skua (*Stercorarius parasiticus*).

In addition, one was seen during the boat crossing on 24 August 2002.[70]

Black-headed Gull *Larus ridibundus*   [Common Black-headed Gull]

Uncommon visitor throughout the year, mainly July to September; occasional cold-weather influxes.

Given that this highly mobile species is widespread and often abundant on the nearby mainland (for example, over 4,000 were counted on the Taw & Torridge Estuary, North Devon, in July 2005) it may come as a surprise to learn that Black-headed Gull is quite an unusual bird on Lundy. There are LFS records in all but four years (1960, 1970, 1974 and 1976), but most of these occurrences have involved single birds, with occasional twos and threes, rarely more. This species has been seen in all months of the year, most often between July and September as both adults and young disperse from breeding areas and migrate towards their wintering grounds. Maximum counts include 23 off the North End on 5 September 1999, 28 on 19 August 1987, at least 30 on 1 March 2007 and 43 on 28 August 1979.

There have been winter influxes associated with unusually cold weather; for example, 30 were seen on 15 January 1987, a day after reports of drifting snow on the island. "Considerable numbers" were noted by Gade (1978) during cold winters, especially the exceptionally severe winter of 1962/63. Black-headed Gulls were also among several species that arrived on Lundy during a cold snap in late January/early February 1954 (Davis 1954b).

Parfitt (1876) and Chanter (1877) included "Masked or Bonaparte's Gull *Larus capistratus*" in their lists of species "reported, but not accurately identified" and which Chanter therefore regarded as doubtful. *Larus capistratus* was formerly a scientific name used for the species now named *Larus ridibundus* – i.e. Black-headed Gull – and we have assumed that this is the species to which Parfitt and Chanter were referring. There is one record in the Heaven Diaries of a single bird on 8 April 1881 (Boyd 1950), suggesting that Black-headed Gull was much scarcer in the nineteenth century than nowadays. The only dated record during the first half of the twentieth century is of three adults flying over the island in late June of 1934 (Lack 1934).

Common Gull *Larus canus* [Mew Gull]

Uncommon passage migrant and winter visitor, mainly September to April.

Chanter (1871) and Parfitt (1876) listed Common Gull as an "occasional visitant". Oldham (1932) noted that "several Common Gulls were daily about the cultivated ground near the village" between 28 August and 4 September 1907. Loyd (1925) pointed out that Rousham (1908) and Ross & Rousham (1909) had been mistaken in stating that Common Gulls bred in good numbers on Lundy.

The first LFS record was of a first-summer bird seen on 30 March 1951 and there have been occurrences in 37 subsequent years (to the end of 2006) with sightings in all months. Records are most frequent in September and, especially, October, indicative of post-breeding dispersal and autumn movements to the wintering grounds, while there are fewest sightings in May and June, with just three apiece. The great majority of counts are in low single figures, but the highest daily totals include about 30 on 15 January 1987 (coinciding with a cold snap), 30 on 3 February 1991, 50 on 28 November 1952 and 50 or more on 27 February 1986. It is noticeable that these peak counts have occurred in late autumn and winter, rather than during the early autumn period of greatest frequency. The 1952 *LFS Annual Report* notes that all seven records for that year (involving some 70 individuals) occurred in strong easterly winds and it is likely that many of the Common Gulls that turn up on Lundy are weather-driven birds from the Taw & Torridge Estuary on the North Devon mainland or further up the Bristol Channel – the Upper Severn Estuary, in particular, being a major wintering area supporting tens of thousands of this species.

Lesser Black-backed Gull *Larus fuscus*

Common breeding species and passage migrant; uncommon in winter.

Lesser Black-backed Gulls nest mainly in colonies on the steep grass and thrift slopes of the west sidelands. The largest colonies are situated either side of Dead Cow Point, above Pyramid Rock on the north side of Jenny's Cove, on the sidings above St Mark's Stone, and between North East Point and the northern side of Gannets' Bay, though there are small groups and odd pairs scattered all around the coast, often within Herring Gull colonies.

Small numbers of Lesser Black-backed Gulls begin to arrive in February and through March, with the majority of the breeding birds returning in late March and April. By September most of the breeding pairs and their young have departed, with only small numbers recorded later in the autumn, although there were unusually high counts of 200 birds off the East Side on 15 November 1994 and 450

119

Lesser Black-backed Gull

in the same area on 25 October 1996. In most years few Lesser Black-backs are seen from November to January.

Chanter (1871) and Parfitt (1876) listed this species as "resident all the year", Parfitt adding "and breed there", while D'Urban & Mathew (1895) stated "breeding in small numbers on Lundy island". Blathwayt (1900) referred to Lesser Black-backed Gulls nesting in colonies "in suitable places all round the island" but gave no indication of numbers. In fact, there are no documented details about the size of the breeding population during the early decades of the twentieth century prior to Perry's estimate of 350 pairs in 1939 (Perry 1940). Numbers fell sharply thereafter, to just 36 pairs in 1956, but rose again to 177 pairs in 1972 and the population was apparently stable over the next 20 years. Since the early 1990s, however, there has been a rapid and substantial population increase to an estimated 444 pairs in 2004 – see figure opposite – representing 95% or more of Devon's breeding Lesser Black-backs.

Between 1948 and 1999, 429 Lesser-backed Gulls were ringed on Lundy, 338 of these in just four years: 1995, 1996, 1998 and 1999. Indeed, the 84 birds ringed in 1995 more than doubled the grand total of Lesser Black-backs ringed on the island over the previous 47 years. This impressive achievement is partly explained by the species' rapid population growth, but was largely due to an intensive, targeted ringing effort. Many of the individuals ringed during the 1990s were also fitted with colour-rings that could be read easily in the field. Altogether there have been five recoveries and 22 field sightings away from the island of nestlings ringed on Lundy – see table opposite. These movements have involved: elsewhere in Britain (6), Ireland (2), France (4), Spain (2), Portugal (12) and Morocco (1), indicating that most Lundy Lesser Black-backed Gulls move south-west in autumn to winter mainly on the Atlantic coasts of France, Spain, Portugal and North Africa, though some birds appear to remain in Britain and Ireland.

The Lesser Black-backed Gulls breeding in Britain are of the race *L. f. graellsii* and the pattern of movements described for Lundy nestlings is typical of the national picture for this population, involving southward migration in autumn along the western seaboard of continental Europe. Most birds winter in Iberia, with lower numbers in western North Africa and a few travelling as far as the Gulf of Guinea. Immatures tend to wander further than adults and many remain in southern areas until they are of breeding age. However, not all British Lesser Black-backs migrate and "birds of all ages are to be found in all parts of their range at all times of the year" (Wernham *et al.* 2002).

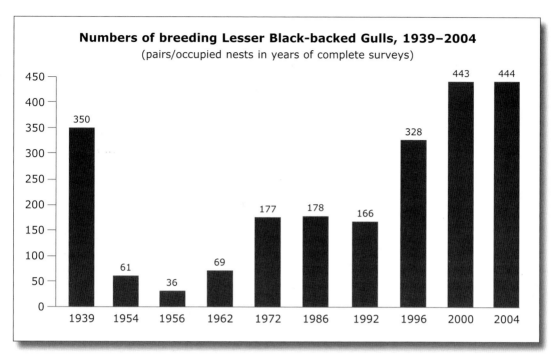

Numbers of breeding Lesser Black-backed Gulls, 1939–2004
(pairs/occupied nests in years of complete surveys)

Two nestlings ringed on the Pembrokeshire island of Skomer, on 7 July 1986 and 7 July 1987 respectively, were both seen alive on Lundy (rings read in the field) on 15 June 1990. By this time both individuals could have reached sexual maturity (three to five years of age is normal), while the date, right in the middle of the nesting season, strongly suggests that they had indeed settled to breed on Lundy. This suggests that the growth of the Lundy colony has been supported – at least in part – by immigration from nearby colonies. In addition, an adult bird ringed on Skomer on 24 May 1994 was found dead on Lundy on 30 July 1997.

It is likely that birds from other British colonies as well as those from populations nesting in other countries (including *L. f. graellsii* from Iceland and western continental Europe and *L. f. intermedius* from Scandinavia) occur around Lundy on migration and/or as winter visitors, but there is no proof of this to date.

Movements of Lesser Black-backed Gulls ringed as nestlings on Lundy
(all are field sightings of colour-ringed birds unless otherwise stated in final column)

Date ringed on Lundy	Place found	Date controlled or recovered	Speculation about date/place of finding
25 Jun 1931	Douro Litoral, **Portugal**	27 Aug 1931	Killed; on migration or in wintering area
14 Jul 1951	Polzeath, Cornwall	07 Oct 1951	Metal ring read in field; on migration or in wintering area
25–29 Jun 1995	Figueira da Foz, Centro, **Portugal**	23 Oct 1995	On migration or in wintering area
25–29 Jun 1995	Figueira da Foz, Centro, **Portugal**	24 Oct 1995	On migration or in wintering area
25–29 Jun 1995	Matosinhos, Porto, Norte, **Portugal**	26 & 27 Oct 1995	On migration or in wintering area
25–29 Jun 1995	Barra, Aveiro, Centro, **Portugal**	29 Mar 1996	On migration or in wintering area
25–29 Jun 1995	Matosinhos, Porto, Norte, **Portugal**	31 Mar 1996	On migration or in wintering area
25–29 Jun 1995	Agadir, **Morocco**	10 Mar 1997	In wintering area
25–29 Jun 1995	Badajoz, Extremadura, **Spain**	02 Dec 1997	In wintering area

continued overleaf...

Date ringed on Lundy	Place found	Date controlled or recovered	Speculation about date/place of finding
25–29 Jun 1995	Hayle Estuary, Cornwall	12 Aug 1998	On autumn migration
25–29 Jun 1995	Mimizan, Landes, **France**	12 Aug 1998	On autumn migration
25–29 Jun 1995	Sesimbra, Lisboa, **Portugal**	28 Oct & 29 Nov 1998	In wintering area
25–29 Jun 1995	Matosinhos, Porto, Norte, **Portugal**	28 Oct 1999	On migration or in wintering area
25–29 Jun 1995	Mimizan, Landes, **France**	30 Nov & 21 Dec 1999	In wintering area
25–29 Jun 1995	Matosinhos, Porto, Norte, **Portugal**	10 Nov 2000	In wintering area
25–29 Jun 1995	Río Eo, Asturias, **Spain**	09 Dec 2000	In wintering area
25–29 Jun 1995	Hossegor, Landes, **France**	23 Dec 2000	In wintering area
25–29 Jun 1995	Hayle Estuary, Cornwall	19 Feb 2001	In wintering area
25–29 Jun 1995	Portimao, Algarve, **Portugal**	12 Nov 2001	In wintering area
23–27 Jun 1996	Radipole, Weymouth, Dorset	23 Feb 1997	In wintering area or on spring migration
23–27 Jun 1996	Les Grissotières, Dolus d'Oleron, Charente-Maritime, **France**	20 Feb 1998	In wintering area or on spring migration
23–27 Jun 1996	Praia da Saude, Lisboa, **Portugal**	28 Aug 1998	On autumn migration
23–27 Jun 1996	Great Saltee, Co. Wexford, **Ireland**	22 Jun 1999	Found dead; in summering area?
23–27 Jun 1996	Aberdovey, Gwynedd	02 Apr 2000	Found dead; in summering area?
23–27 Jun 1996	Ballycotton Lighthouse, Co. Cork, **Ireland**	24 Jan 2002	Found dead; in wintering area?
23–27 Jun 1996	Matosinhos, Porto, Norte, **Portugal**	11 & 15 Nov 2003	In wintering area
27 Jun 1996	Broadwoodwidger, Ashwater, Devon	11 Sep 1996	Found dead; on migration?

Yellow-legged Gull *Larus michahellis*

Lundy vagrant.

The BOU accorded Yellow-legged Gull *Larus michahellis* full species status and added it to category A of *The British List* in 2005, having previously treated it as a race of Herring Gull under the scientific name *Larus argentatus michahellis*. The breeding range includes the Azores, Madeira and Canaries, the Atlantic seaboard of north-west Africa and Iberia, and extends through the Mediterranean as far as the Black Sea. Some authors separate the Atlantic and Mediterranean/Black Sea populations into two subspecies *L. m. atlantis* and *L. m. michahellis*. Yellow-legged Gull is a regular visitor to Britain, mainly outside the breeding season. The taxonomy of Lesser Black-backed, Yellow-legged and Herring Gulls remains complex and controversial and further changes can be anticipated in the years ahead.

There is just one satisfactory record of Yellow-legged Gull on Lundy:

1999 15 May – one at Pondsbury; detailed notes and a sketch were included in the LFS logbook.

The 1989 *LFS Annual Report* states that "a yellow-legged bird was reported on 9 May", but the information entered in the original logbook is much too brief to regard this as a confirmed record.

Herring Gull *Larus argentatus*

Common breeding species; present all year but fewer in winter.

During the breeding season, Herring Gulls – and their evocative calls – are virtually ubiquitous on Lundy. They nest in loose colonies or small groups, and sometimes as lone pairs, around the entire coastline, mainly towards the top of short broken cliffs and on steep boulder slopes. By far the larger part (about 80%) of the population is found on the West Side. One of the largest colonies is situated on the steep slope above Pilot's Quay, interspersed with occasional Lesser Black-backed Gull nests.

Listed by Chanter (1871) and Parfitt (1876) as "resident all the year", the latter adding "and breed there", early observers referred to the Herring Gull as occurring in "prodigious quantities" (Cummings

1909) and "very numerous" (Loyd 1922), or to Lundy as a "great-breeding station" (D'Urban & Mathew 1895). The first estimate of numbers was 3,000 pairs in 1939 (Perry 1940). Since then numbers have fluctuated considerably, from a high of more than 3,500 pairs in 1966 to a low of 497 pairs in 1992 – see figure. There must be some doubt about the 1966 count given the estimates of breeding pairs for the years either side. Human disturbance, mainly egg collecting – over 10,000 eggs were taken between 1939 and 1949 (Boyd 1956) – is suggested as the principal reason for numbers remaining low at a time of large increases nationally. Control measures, too, undertaken at all the island's largest colonies in efforts to slow the decline in auk numbers, kept the population in check: between 1976 and 1983 over 6,500 eggs were pricked. Despite this, Willcox (1986) counted 1,117 breeding pairs. More recent surveys show a stable population of between 700 and 800 pairs, about 20% of the total nesting in Devon.

Most of the breeding birds leave the island in September and return in late winter, with only small numbers present during late autumn and winter. High 'out-of season' counts include 500 on 10 February 1997, 1 & 31 December 2004 and 21 January 2007, and 700 on 15 January 2007. Several hundred birds may come ashore during severe winter storms.

By the end of 2006, 2,930 Herring Gulls had been ringed on Lundy – all as nestlings and mostly prior to 1970 – of which 66 have subsequently been recovered or controlled, 60 of these being away from the island. The average distance moved was just over 110 kilometres, while the longest movements were 514 kilometres (to Lothian Region, Scotland) and 634 kilometres (to Charente Maritime *département*, north-west France). The vast majority of Lundy-ringed Herring Gulls have been found elsewhere in south-west England and South Wales: mainland Devon (20), Glamorgan (15), Cornwall (7), Dyfed (7) and the Isles of Scilly (2). Other reports have come from Hampshire (2), Kent (1), Cheshire (1) and Clwyd (1). In addition, a bird colour-ringed as a chick on Lundy in 1996 was seen on the Taw Estuary, North Devon, on 1 March 1997. The only movements outside the UK are the French recovery mentioned above, a second bird from north-west France (Finistère *département*) and one in Co. Galway, western Ireland. By far the oldest bird was over 15 years old when it was found freshly dead in Kent. These movements are broadly in line with the overall pattern observed for Herring Gulls from breeding colonies in south-west Britain (Wernham *et al.* 2002), though the average distance moved by Lundy birds is somewhat higher, perhaps reflecting the island's offshore location.

There have been three recoveries on the island of Herring Gulls ringed elsewhere: a chick ringed on the Pembrokeshire island of Skokholm in June 1964 was found dead on Lundy in May 1966; a second-year bird ringed in September 1978 on Skomer was found dead on Lundy in May 1985; and a chick ringed in June 1981 in Ille-et-Vilaine *département*, north-west France, was found dead on Lundy in September 1988.

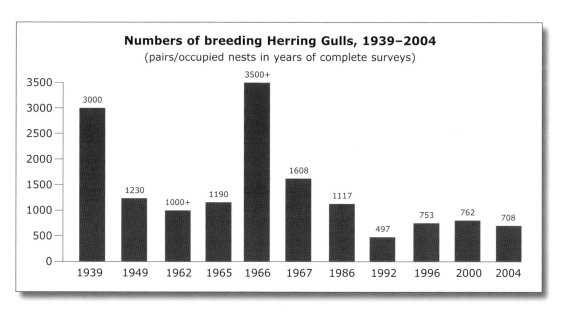

Numbers of breeding Herring Gulls, 1939–2004
(pairs/occupied nests in years of complete surveys)

Iceland Gull *Larus glaucoides*

Lundy vagrant.

Following one seen on 11 April 1939 (Perry 1940), Iceland Gulls have occurred five times since LFS records began in 1947:

1950 5 Apr – one with Herring and Great Black-backed Gulls.
1952 28 Nov – an adult with Herring and Common Gulls.
1954 27 & 28 Nov – a second-year bird.
1976 12 May – one in third-summer plumage.
2004 25 Apr to 20 May – a first-summer bird in Middle Park, occasionally visiting Pondsbury.[71]

The *LFS Annual Report* for 1949 states that on 11 April an Iceland Gull or a Glaucous Gull (*L. hyperboreus*) was seen flying past Puffin Slope "but from the view obtained it was impossible to determine which". An immature Iceland or Glaucous Gull was seen on 1 March 1952.

Glaucous Gull *Larus hyperboreus*

Lundy vagrant.

There are only four, perhaps five, records, all during the 1970s and 1980s, all involving immature birds, and all in April or May:

1974 2 Apr – a first-year bird flew north along the East Side.
1983 12 Apr – one flying north, reported in the LFS log as a second-year bird; another, possibly the same bird, seen on 16 Apr.
1984 26 Apr – one, reported in the LFS log as a third-year bird.
1986 20 May – one, reported in the LFS log as a second-year bird, flew north across Jenny's Cove.

The 1949 *LFS Annual Report* states that on 11 April that year a Glaucous Gull or an Iceland Gull (*L. glaucoides*) was seen flying past Puffin Slope "but from the view obtained it was impossible to determine which". An immature Glaucous or Iceland Gull was seen on 1 March 1952.

Great Black-backed Gull *Larus marinus*

Breeds; present in all months, but few in winter.

Great Black-backed Gulls nest singly or in small groups around more or less the entire coastline of Lundy, favouring open nesting sites on top of stacks, small headlands and prominent ridges.

Listed by Chanter (1871) and Parfitt (1876) as "resident all the year", Parfitt adding "and breed there". The breeding population numbered from two to an estimated 50 pairs between 1900 and 1932 (Blathwayt 1900, Cummings 1909, Hendy 1922, Loyd 1923, Harrisson 1932) before reaching 57 pairs in 1939 (Perry 1940). Numbers have fluctuated since, from a peak of 72 pairs in 1972 to a low of 23 pairs in 1996 – see table. The population has increased steadily since then, reaching 58 pairs in 2004, about 35% of those nesting in Devon. As for Herring Gull, control measures (egg-pricking) were used on Lundy between 1976 and 1983 in an attempt to reduce predation of breeding auks. While the available counts do not indicate any clear impact on breeding numbers, this could be one cause of the significant decrease between 1986 and 1992, given that Great Black-backs are long-lived birds and do not reach maturity for four to five years.

A count of 123 birds (121 adults and two immatures) was made during a survey of the island's perimeter on 3 May 2007.

Most of the breeding birds leave the island during winter, but large influxes can occur during severe storms: at least 600, mostly adults, were present on 1 December 1972.

Ringing studies show that Great Black-backed Gulls tend to stay close to their breeding areas. Adults especially move on average little more than 50 kilometres, while first-year birds and immatures range twice as far – some from south-west England have been recovered on the Atlantic coasts of France and Iberia, mainly in autumn and winter (Wernham *et al.* 2002). Of 131 Great Black-backed

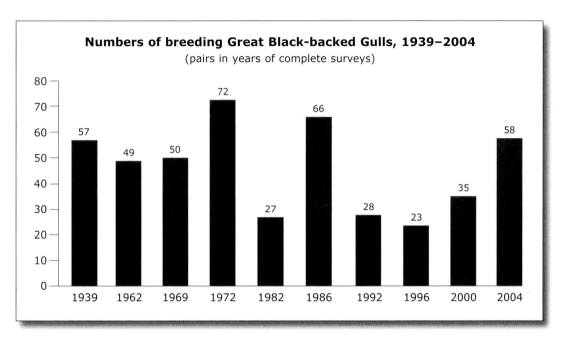

Numbers of breeding Great Black-backed Gulls, 1939–2004
(pairs in years of complete surveys)

Gulls ringed on Lundy between 1947 and 2006, three have been recovered subsequently: one in Cornwall and two on the Devon mainland. Of these, the ring fitted to a nestling on 10 July 1967 was found 121 kilometres away near Kingswear, Devon, almost 26 years later on 23 May 1993, the fate of the bird unknown. There is one recovery on the island of a Great Black-back ringed elsewhere: a bird ringed as a nestling on the Pembrokeshire island of Skokholm in July 1937 was found dead on Lundy on 15 April 1938.

Great Black-backed Gull

Kittiwake *Rissa tridactyla*   [Black-legged Kittiwake]

Common but declining breeding species; uncommon from September to January,

Kittiwakes nest on the sheer cliffs of the West Side, from Jenny's Cove north to Long Roost, though former breeding sites also included major colonies in Kittiwake Gully and Puffin Gully at the North End, and smaller colonies on Gannets' Rock and the seaward side of Shutter Rock in the south-westernmost corner of the island. After breeding is completed in August, birds are usually absent from the cliffs, not returning until the following February or March, although some will occasionally appear on the breeding ledges in good weather in midwinter. Small numbers pass offshore during spring and autumn migration and there are occasional large influxes of storm-driven birds in winter (see below).

Chanter (1871) and Parfitt (1876) listed "Kittiwake Gull" as a "summer visitant", the latter adding "occasional breeder". D'Urban & Mathew (1895) described 700 Kittiwakes being killed and shipped to Clovelly on a single August day, their wings being taken for the millinery trade. During a fortnight of such activity they estimated that 9,000 birds were destroyed, including nestlings that starved as a result of the loss of one or both parent birds (see 'The slaughter of Lundy's seabirds', page 36). Blathwayt (1900) stated that "the Kittiwake is by far the most numerous of the Gulls on the island". Loyd (1922) estimated "about 20 colonies, varying in strength from 30 to 300 pairs". A year later Loyd (1923) reported that numbers had increased considerably, with "several new colonies formed and others much enlarged". Counts in 1939 by Perry (1940) placed the population at a maximum of 3,000 pairs (Perry 1940). Although numbers fluctuated in the years up to the early 1970s, the general trend has been downward. Monitoring of a breeding colony at Long Roost between 1980 and 1988 indicated a

Kittiwakes

126

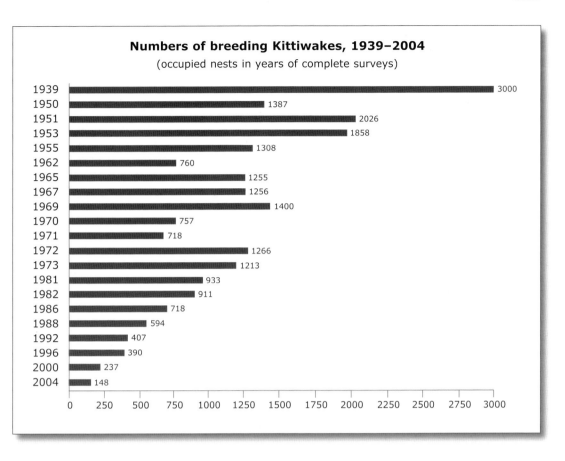

Numbers of breeding Kittiwakes, 1939–2004

(occupied nests in years of complete surveys)

Year	Value
1939	3000
1950	1387
1951	2026
1953	1858
1955	1308
1962	760
1965	1255
1967	1256
1969	1400
1970	757
1971	718
1972	1266
1973	1213
1981	933
1982	911
1986	718
1988	594
1992	407
1996	390
2000	237
2004	148

substantial decline (Davies 1981; Willcox 1987, 1988), while the now abandoned colony at Puffin Gully declined from 422 nests in 1982 to just six nests in 2000. The last eight full-island counts, between 1981 and 2004, show numbers of breeding Kittiwakes to have fallen from 933 pairs in 1981 to an all-time low of 148 pairs (about 15% of the Devon breeding population) in 2004 – see figure. This sharp decline reflects the national picture and sadly it is conceivable that Kittiwakes could soon disappear as a breeding species on Lundy.

During the 1980s and 1990s, Kittiwakes nesting on Lundy were the subject of detailed behavioural studies by the Department of Psychology of Exeter University, and several papers have appeared in *LFS Annual Reports* (e.g. Daniels *et al.* 1995, Beer & Daniels 1996).

Outside the breeding season Kittiwakes are mainly oceanic, with occasional large movements along coastlines or inland associated with atmospheric depressions and strong onshore winds (Wernham *et al.* 2002). Larger counts off Lundy early or late in the year include 400 on 10 February 1997, 500 on 13 December of the same year, and 1,500 on Christmas Day 2002, with 1,000 still present on 28 December. More recently still, 500 were offshore on 25 October 2004 and there was a series of very high counts during the winter of 2006/07, which was characterised by frequent Atlantic depressions; 500 were seen on 18 November, over 750 on 28 December, and 500 or more on three dates in January (including 800 on 20 January) and again on 22 February 2007.

By the end of 2006, 2,535 Kittiwakes had been ringed on Lundy, more than 1,500 of these during the 10 years 1948–1957, with a further 274 in 1966 & 1967 and 714 in 1972 & 1973. Just 21 have been ringed subsequently (to the end of 2006) and although Kittiwakes are long-lived birds, few if any Lundy-ringed birds are likely to be alive today.

There have been 35 recoveries and controls of Lundy-ringed Kittiwakes away from the island, involving: elsewhere in Britain (22), Ireland (2), The Netherlands (1), France (4), Spain (3), Portugal (1),

Morocco (1) and Canada (1). The last of these – a nestling ringed on 10 July 1950 – was shot the following May on Change Island, Notre Dame Bay on the north-east coast of Newfoundland, a distance of 3,525 kilometres from Lundy, giving an indication of just how far this species ranges.

The movements of Lundy-ringed birds fit well within the national pattern described by Wernham *et al.* (2002), fledged young initially moving north-west towards rich feeding grounds off Greenland, then south in late summer or early autumn towards Newfoundland. In late spring Kittiwakes of all ages vacate the deep oceanic areas and concentrate near coasts, although some young birds are thought to remain on the other side of the Atlantic for two years or more before returning to Britain. Birds first breed at three to six years of age. A nestling ringed on Lundy on 28 June 1972 was found on 15 November the same year at Safi on the Atlantic coast of Morocco – at the time, only the second British-ringed Kittiwake to be found in that country. A Kittiwake ringed as a nestling on Lundy on 7 July 1973 was observed breeding on the Atlantic coast at Goulien, Finistère, France – 350 kilometres from Lundy – on 17 April 1982, raising two young. This record proves that Kittiwakes do not necessarily return to breed in the area where they were hatched, though this only applies to a small minority (Wernham *et al.* 2002). A bird ringed on Lundy as a nestling at Virgin's Spring on 7 July 1973 and seen nesting in nearby Kittiwake Gully 19 years later, on 22 July 1992, is probably more typical. There have been no controls or recoveries on Lundy of Kittiwakes ringed elsewhere, so the origins of the birds seen in the waters around Lundy outside the breeding season are unknown.

Bridled Tern *Onychoprion anaethetus*

British vagrant.

The nearest breeding colonies to Britain are in north-west Africa and the Red Sea. Disperses widely in tropical and sub-tropical waters outside the nesting season. 20 records for Britain 1950–2005.

One Lundy record involves the remains of a single bird – the fourth record for Britain:

1977   22 Apr – a wing found some way below the top of the cliffs at Long Roost was provisionally identified as that of a Bridled Tern. This was independently verified by Peter Grant, then Chairman of the *British Birds* Rarities Committee, who checked the "fairly fresh" wing against skins at the Natural History Museum. Close examination indicated that the bird was in first-year plumage and was 8–12 months old when it died.

Little Tern *Sternula albifrons*

Lundy vagrant.

There have been three LFS records and only one previous dated record, a single bird on 18 May 1939 (Perry 1940):

1950   22 Sep – one with seven Common (*S. hirundo*) or Arctic (*S. paradisaea*) Terns.
1955   21 & 24 Sep – one.
1992   21 & 22 Apr – one was watched feeding in the Landing Bay, twice settling on the beach.

Two or three birds were seen in company with Common Terns during the boat crossing on 22 August 1955 (1955 *Devon Bird Report*).

Black Tern *Chlidonias niger*

Lundy vagrant.

Very occasionally seen on the crossing during spring and autumn migration periods (e.g. one on 26 May 1973, 11 on 23 August 1970,[72] three on 2 September 1956 about nine miles out from the island, one on 2 September 1973,[72] two on 23 September 1980, five on 7 May 2000[72] and six on 13 May 2001[72]) but there is only one record for the island itself:

1967   9 Aug – one in the Landing Bay.

Sandwich Terns

Sandwich Tern *Sterna sandvicensis*

Uncommon migrant, late March to early October.

First added to the Lundy list in 1950 – when one was seen in the Landing Bay on 10 April and two the following day – Sandwich Terns were observed from the island itself in only three of the next 20 years: one on 7 September 1953, one in the Landing Bay on 7 September and seven feeding off Rat Island on 30 September 1959, and one on 21 April 1965. Since 1971, however, Sandwich Tern has been recorded almost annually from the island, with sightings in all but seven years to 2007. Seen mostly in ones and twos, usually in the Landing Bay or over the tide races off North and South Ends, there have been slightly more occurrences in spring than autumn, with April and September being the peak months. The highest count is of eight birds on 12 September 2006. Extreme dates are 25 March (2006 – three birds) and 9 October (2006 – a single bird). There are about five records in each of June, July and August, including three birds fishing off North End on 16 July 1987.

There are occasional sightings during the boat crossing, including one at rest on a floating plank on 8 September 1930, three on 27 June 1981 (1981 *Devon Bird Report*) and eight on 4 September 1997.

Common Tern *Sterna hirundo*

Uncommon migrant, April to October.

Listed by Chanter (1871) and Parfitt (1876) as an "occasional visitant". LFS records between 1947 and 1980 show just five spring occurrences and six in autumn, plus a very unusual sighting of three birds on 5 December 1978. However, during this same period there were many records of either Common or Arctic Terns where specific identification was not made. Since 1980 there have been records of between one and three Common Terns in 13 years, split more or less equally between spring and autumn, with most occurrences falling in the months of April and September.

Taking all records into account, early and late dates in spring are 1 April (1996) and 18 May (1988) – though one was seen on the crossing on 26 May 1975 – while extremes in autumn are 27 July (1977, the only July record) and 9 October (2006). In addition, there is a single midsummer record of one on 30 June 1996. Highest counts are of five birds on both 11 April 1969 and 22 August 1973 (but see the paragraph on unidentified Common/Arctic Terns after the Arctic Tern account).

Arctic Tern *Sterna paradisaea*

Rare autumn migrant; only one definite spring record.

Although listed by Chanter (1871) and Parfitt (1876) as an "occasional visitant", there are no satisfactory records until the 1960s.

From the commencement of LFS recording in 1947 until 1978 (the period covered by Dymond, 1980) only one Common or Arctic Tern was definitively identified as an Arctic Tern – a bird seen in the Landing Bay from 7 to 12 September 1967. Omitting terns seen during the boat crossing, there have been a further 13 sightings of Arctic Tern, involving 18 individuals, between 1979 and 2006. The highest count is just five, off the East Side on 2 October 1999, though six Common or Arctic Terns on 25 September 1984 were thought to be Arctic Terns. Taking all confirmed sightings into account, only one has occurred in spring – a single bird on 5 May 1996. Apart from one midsummer record of a bird on 30 June 1996, all occurrences later in the year have been between 30 August (1979) and 3 November (1980), with most in October (seven records).

Occasional sightings on the boat crossing include seven on 25 April 1976 and two on 8 August 1981.[73]

Common/Arctic Terns: Modern field guides and optical equipment have enabled birdwatchers to differentiate between these two species far more readily in recent decades; hence the greater number of firm identifications of both species since the 1980s. The most notable records of unidentified birds are of 12 on 20 April 1987, about 15 on 8 September 1953 and 12 October 1958, and some 140 – the largest number ever seen from Lundy – feeding in the tide race off Rat Island during bad weather on 5 October 1958. More recently, eight were seen migrating south on 1 September 2005. Twenty were seen during the boat crossing on 2 September 1956, about nine miles out from Lundy.

Guillemot *Uria aalge*   [Common Murre]

Common breeder, but in smaller numbers than formerly; uncommon from August to October, then occasional sightings until January.

Sitting and watching the often-frenzied comings and goings of Guillemots and Razorbills around their breeding colonies is one of the immense pleasures of birdwatching on Lundy in spring and early summer. While numbers are lower than they once were, it is still possible to see serried ranks of Guillemots packed tightly onto unfeasibly narrow-looking ledges, primarily from Jenny's Cove northward along the West Side, but with smaller colonies scattered elsewhere around the island's coastline.

Guillemots

130

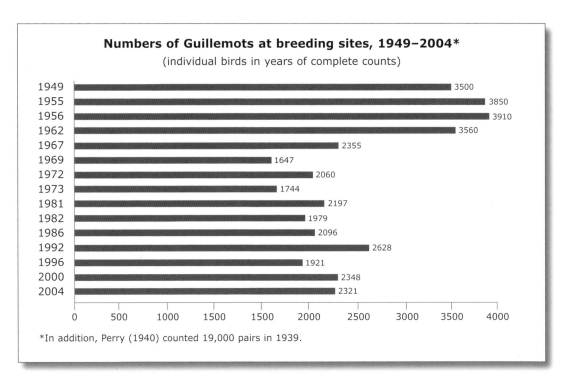

Numbers of Guillemots at breeding sites, 1949–2004*

(individual birds in years of complete counts)

Year	Value
1949	3500
1955	3850
1956	3910
1962	3560
1967	2355
1969	1647
1972	2060
1973	1744
1981	2197
1982	1979
1986	2096
1992	2628
1996	1921
2000	2348
2004	2321

*In addition, Perry (1940) counted 19,000 pairs in 1939.

Guillemots start to visit the breeding ledges in January and February, although birds may come ashore temporarily during fine weather earlier in the winter; for example, 40 on 7 November 1994 (the earliest such record), 400 Guillemots and Razorbills on ledges in Jenny's Cove on 28 December 1980, and 350 Guillemots in the same area on 24 December 1985. Regular attendance at the colonies begins from early March onwards, and the last of the breeding birds have usually left the island by the end of July. Sightings are scarce from August to October, with small numbers seen irregularly thereafter until January. Occasional ones and twos seen inshore during this period may often be oiled or sick individuals.

Young Guillemots leave the colony when only partly grown and still unable to fly. They are accompanied by the male parent which continues to feed the youngster for several more weeks, at the same time undergoing its main moult and therefore becoming flightless itself (Wernham *et al.* 2002).

As is the case for Razorbills and Puffins, Guillemots have declined considerably on Lundy since Perry (1940) estimated 19,000 breeding pairs in 1939. By 1949 the population had crashed to some 3,500 individuals but numbers remained stable at around this level until the early 1960s. After 1962, numbers fell to a new low of 1,647 birds in 1969, ironically the year of 'Operation Seafarer', the first national census of breeding seabirds. The population appears to have more or less stabilised again since then, fluctuating between 1,744 birds (1973) and 2,628 birds (1992) – see figure. The seabird census in 1996 recorded 1,921 birds, a reduction of 700 compared with 1992. Guillemots were present in the waters around Lundy in the last week of February and early March 1996 when pollution from the *Sea Empress* tanker disaster on the nearby coast of south-west Wales was at its height. Some 220 birds, mainly Guillemots, were washed ashore on Lundy, and it is likely that many more perished at sea, causing the island's breeding population to fall significantly that year. However, numbers had apparently recovered by the 2000 census and remained more or less unchanged four years later.

Chanter (1871) and Parfitt (1876) listed Guillemot as a "summer visitant", Parfitt adding "constant breeder". D'Urban & Mathew (1895) referred to "immense numbers" breeding on the island and wrote of the Guillemot's eggs from Lundy as "ranking high for the boldness and variety of their markings". Loyd (1922) stated: "Lays in enormous numbers from the north end to three-quarters of the way down on both sides of the Island, and said to be extending southward each year." Sample counts by Perry

(1940) and Southern & Reeve (1941) showed that about 1% of Lundy's Guillemots are 'bridled' (i.e. they have a white eye-ring joined to a white line that curves back towards the upper neck, looking rather like half-spectacles).

A total of 2,701 Guillemots had been ringed on Lundy by the end of 2006, mainly during a period of intensive seabird ringing between the late 1940s and mid-1950s, though smaller numbers were ringed in the mid-1960s and early 1970s. There have been 102 recoveries, but it is unlikely that any Lundy-ringed birds are still alive. This is a dispersive rather than truly migratory species (Wernham *et al.* 2002) and the movements shown by Lundy birds reflect the national pattern, with reports from the Irish Sea and English Channel coasts, the North Sea as far afield as southern Norway, and the Atlantic seaboard of France and Spain, south to Portugal. About two-thirds of the Lundy recoveries are from elsewhere in Britain, but those found farther afield involve: France (23), the Channel Islands (6), Ireland (2), Portugal (2), Spain (1), The Netherlands (1) and Norway (1). The longest movements were by two birds ringed as chicks on 8 July 1948 and 29 June 1973 and both found in Almada, on the Tagus Estuary, Portugal, on 14 February 1949 and 22 February 1990, respectively, having travelled some 1,430 kilometres from Lundy. At well over 17 years, the second bird was also the longest lived among the 102 recoveries, but though still alive at the time of finding, it was reportedly in poor condition. Most of the recoveries involve birds found dead, with oil the primary factor in about a quarter of cases.

A study of Lundy's Guillemots

Tony Taylor carried out MSc research on Lundy's Guillemots throughout the breeding seasons of 1973–1975 and in 1978. A group of about 60 pairs was observed daily from a hide in Jenny's Cove, and their behaviour and breeding success were recorded. The main findings were that:

(a) Breeding success was strongly influenced by group size and ledge width. Almost 90% of pairs that were surrounded by other birds on broad ledges, or which had neighbours on both sides on narrow ledges, raised chicks to fledging. At the other extreme, the egg of a pair that was completely isolated on a broad ledge lasted for less than two days on average. This means that Guillemots benefit from synchronised, colonial breeding and that much of their breeding behaviour is geared to maximising group protection of eggs/chicks from predation.

(b) While gulls were major egg/chick predators of Guillemots, this seemed to involve a few 'specialist' individual gulls. In addition, gulls defending an area round their nest chased off other gulls and crows, meaning that Guillemots breeding within such an area benefited. Even if the local breeding gulls did take some eggs/chicks, the Guillemots still bred more successfully than if they had no defending gulls and a predation 'free-for-all'.

(c) Disturbance, by gulls and indirectly by humans, reduces breeding success. For an incubating or brooding Guillemot, the presence of its mate greatly helps in defending their egg/chick from predators. In undisturbed conditions, 'off-duty' birds spent much of their time with their mates on the ledges. One factor which tended to make these 'off-duty' birds leave their ledges was gull alarm calls. The gulls called in response to raptors and humans, and the adult Guillemots appeared to be using the gull alarms as a warning that they themselves could be in danger. Hence, any disturbance of gulls that causes 'off-duty' Guillemots to leave their ledges reduces breeding success by increasing exposure of eggs/chicks to predation.

Razorbills and (left) Puffin

Razorbill *Alca torda*

Common breeder, though in smaller numbers than formerly; uncommon between August and February.

During the breeding season (April to July), Razorbills are to be found in scattered cliff-side colonies from the South End, around Shutter Point, along the West Side north to Long Roost (particularly from Jenny's Cove northward) and down the East Side as far south as Gannets' Rock, then more thinly to the Quarry Beach area. They frequently nest higher up the cliffs than Guillemots and more often use the crevices between granite blocks and boulders rather than open ledges. Razorbills occasionally come ashore to visit their nesting areas during fine weather in February, but the colonies do not become established until late March to mid-April. From then on the breeding season is in full swing, though as with other auks, first thing in the morning is the best time for seeing the greatest numbers – the uncomfortably early start being more than made up for by the experience of a busy colony (and the promise of a second breakfast in the Tavern afterwards!). Both adults and young leave the cliffs by the end of July and Razorbills are rarely seen ashore in August. Between September and November, individuals and small parties are regularly seen passing offshore, and occasionally feeding or resting inshore.

Midwinter records are unusual, though 50 were present on 24 December 1979, and some 400 Razorbills and Guillemots were seen on ledges in Jenny's Cove on 28 December 1980.

Like Puffins, Guillemots and Kittiwakes, Razorbills have declined greatly since an estimated 10,500 pairs in 1939 (Perry 1940) – though the reliability of Perry's figures was questioned by Alexander *et al.* (1945). By the early 1950s the population was put at around 2,500 pairs (Davis 1954a) and by the early 1960s had declined to just over 2,000 individuals. Further losses up to the beginning of the 1980s suggested a long period of decline, though the population appears to have stabilised since then at between 800 and 1,000 birds – see figure overleaf.

Prior to Perry's 1939 population estimate, many authors referred to the Razorbill's abundance on Lundy but did not give any real indication of numbers. Chanter (1871) and Parfitt (1876) listed "Razor-billed Auk" as a "summer visitant", Parfitt adding "constant breeder"; Blathwayt (1900) stated that "Razorbills…still breed on the island in enormous numbers"; Cummings (1909) wrote of Razorbills continuing to breed "in their accustomed legions"; while Hendy (1922) reported them "nesting in immense numbers" in 1914. Loyd (1923) compared his observations in 1922 and 1923, reporting that in 1923, Razorbills had "increased in a remarkable manner. Their numbers must be nearly doubled since last season".

As regular visits to the nesting colonies do not usually occur until late March, the Lundy population may have been relatively unaffected by the 1996 *Sea Empress* oil spill – unlike Guillemots which arrive much earlier – although several oiled Razorbills were washed ashore on the Landing Beach.

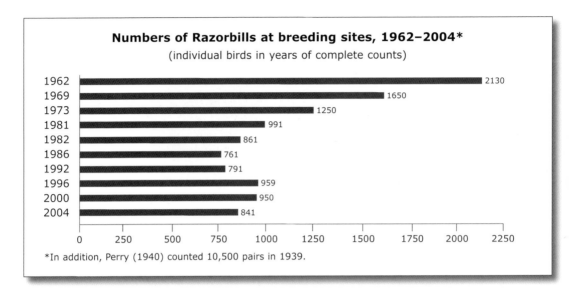

Numbers of Razorbills at breeding sites, 1962–2004*

(individual birds in years of complete counts)

Year	Count
1962	2130
1969	1650
1973	1250
1981	991
1982	861
1986	761
1992	791
1996	959
2000	950
2004	841

*In addition, Perry (1940) counted 10,500 pairs in 1939.

A total of 1,237 Razorbills had been ringed on Lundy by the end of 2006, with 62 recoveries notified away from the island. As most auk ringing was carried out between the late 1940s and the early 1970s, the number of recoveries has dwindled over the years and there are probably no Lundy-ringed Razorbills left alive; only three have been ringed since 1980.

On leaving the breeding ledges in midsummer, most birds remain in the vicinity of the colony either to complete their growth (young of the year) or to moult (adults) before dispersing further afield by October. On average, immature Razorbills move greater distances than adults (Wernham *et al.* 2002). There are recoveries of Lundy birds from a wide area of the Atlantic and North Sea coasts of Britain and continental Europe, including the west of Ireland, the Firth of Clyde, the English Channel and Bay of Biscay, south-west Norway and the Danish coast, the western seaboard of the Iberian Peninsula, and along the southern shore of Spain into the Mediterranean as far east as Algeria and north-west Italy. Just over half of the recoveries (35) are from elsewhere in Britain, the others involving: France (11), Spain (8), Portugal (2), Italy (2), Algeria (1), Morocco (1), Norway (1) and Denmark (1). These movements are consistent with the national pattern described by Wernham *et al.* (2002), Razorbills occurring further south and east than Guillemots, especially in the western Mediterranean and off north-west Africa. The longest-elapsed period between ringing and recovery of a Lundy-ringed Razorbill is seven years (July 1954 to July 1961) but as this bird was an adult when ringed, it could have been several years older. There has been one recovery on Lundy of a bird ringed elsewhere: a Razorbill found dead (oiled) in late October 1978 had been ringed as a chick on Great Saltee Island, Co. Wexford, Ireland just three months earlier on 1 July 1978.

Ancient Murrelet *Synthliboramphus antiquus*

British vagrant.

Breeds in coastal colonies around the northern Pacific, dispersing south in winter. Regularly recorded inland in North America, generally after storms.

A single bird occurred on Lundy in 1990, 1991 and 1992. It remains the only individual recorded in Britain and the entire Western Palearctic, and is perhaps the most extraordinary of the many rarities to have occurred on Lundy over the years.

1990 27 May – one in breeding plumage found at Jenny's Cove remained until at least 23 Jun, with three further reports to 6 Jul.[74]

1991 14 Apr to 20 Jun – one returned to the Jenny's Cove area and was seen almost every day, most often early in the morning; from early May onwards it spent the day hidden among rocks.[75]

134

Ancient Murrelet

1992 30 Mar to 29 Apr – one, again in Jenny's Cove, tending to be visible only in the early morning, later entering a hole among rocks close to the Devil's Chimney.

The murrelet was first seen flying into Jenny's Cove by, among others, the late Gordon Vaughan – dedicated Devon ornithologist and stalwart of Devon Bird Watching & Preservation Society – during an RSPB excursion to the island. It was later identified by Richard Campey, Keith Mortimer and John Waldon, whose descriptions of the bird were accepted by the BOURC and BBRC. On the day of its discovery the murrelet stayed in Jenny's Cove for about an hour, spending its time swimming with Razorbills, Guillemots and Puffins. When coming close to Razorbills, the bird would crash-dive, resurface several metres away and then return to swim close to the other auks. Over the course of an hour it made short, sporadic flights before slowly drifting out to sea with the accompanying auks. In all during its stay in 1990, it was observed by some 4,000 visiting birdwatchers (Campey 1990).

Writing in *British Birds* a few years later John Waldon recalled:

"The lack of a good reference guide made positive identification difficult at the time: no-one had expected to find a murrelet on a summer visit to Lundy. It was only on the boat on the way home, when we were feeling somewhat mixed emotions of elation and confusion, that we looked at Tuck & Heinzel's *A Field Guide to the Seabirds of Britain and the World* (1978) and found, somewhat to our surprise, that the illustration of Ancient Murrelet *S. antiquus* clearly matched the bird we had seen. We were, then, confident that what we had seen was, incredibly, an Ancient Murrelet." On returning to the mainland "most people's reaction was one of incredulity: even a suspicion that the whole thing was a hoax" (Waldon 1994).

Little Auk *Alle alle*

Lundy vagrant.

There have been nine records since the start of LFS recording in 1947:

1950 30 Jun – the remains of one found near Pilot's Quay.
1958 5 Nov – two off the North End.
1978 18 Dec – one found dead in the Landing Bay.
1979 21 Dec – one.
1990 30 Oct to 3 Nov – one close inshore in the Landing Bay and Lametry Bay.
  26 Nov – one found dead on the Divers' Beach, probably the same as the above.
2000 12 Nov – one in a weak state at the South End, being harassed by Ravens, died later that day.
2006 29 Jan – two in Hell's Kitchen, seen from the Battlements and the Divers' Beach, flew off west towards Benjamin's Chair.
2007 16 Jan – one in the Landing Bay off Miller's Cake. (Record subject to acceptance by the Devon Birds Records Committee).

Chanter (1871) and Parfitt (1876) listed Little Auk as an "occasional visitant", but there is only one dated pre-1950 record, a single bird on 7 September 1926 (T.G. Longstaff and Sir S. Renishaw, reported by Harrisson 1932).

Puffin *Fratercula arctica* [Atlantic Puffin]

Uncommon breeding species; formerly bred in large numbers; very rare between mid-August and early April.

Lundy and Puffins are so inextricably linked – in Old Norse 'lundi' means Puffin and 'ey' stands for island; thus 'Lundy' literally means Puffin Island – that the idea of the island without its trademark seabird is unthinkable. Yet Puffin numbers have dropped to such a low level that the species seems on the verge of disappearing from the island altogether.

This alarming prospect stands in stark contrast to F.L. Blathwayt's vivid account of his visit to the island in May 1900:

> "The chief colony of the Puffins is at the northern end, where the birds burrow in the soft soil among a *débris* of huge granite boulders scattered about in wild confusion. The number of the birds must be enormous, as, when one approaches the colony, all the rocks and the sea beneath appear to be covered with Puffins and Razorbills; while hundreds more are swinging round and round in a large circle, which extends some distance over the water. I was much struck by the remarkable tameness of the birds. As long as I kept fairly still they appeared to have no fear at all, and in a few minutes I had Puffins and Razorbills all round me, and some almost within arm's length" (Blathwayt 1900).

Chanter (1871) and Parfitt (1876) listed Puffin as a "summer visitant", Parfitt adding "constant breeder". Hendy (1914) recorded them "nesting in countless thousands, particularly at the N.W. end". Loyd (1922) reported the species as breeding "in great numbers at the north end, but said by men who have spent many years on the Island to be decreasing season by season". A year later, in 1923, he thought their numbers were probably double those in 1922 (Loyd 1923). Harrisson (1932) reported Puffins in 1930 as being "limited to two large colonies at the north end" and quoted Gade as saying there had been a considerable decrease in 1931.

Puffins are among the most difficult seabirds to census meaningfully but it is clear that there has been a dramatic decline in the Lundy population since it was estimated at 3,500 pairs in 1939 (Perry 1940). At this time the majority of the island's birds nested on Puffin Slope and adjacent areas of cliff and sideland at the North End. In questioning Perry's figures following a visit to the island in July 1942, Alexander *et al.* (1945) noted that "Mr. Harman and Mr. Gade were of the opinion in 1942 that, owing to mortality from floating oil at sea resulting from enemy action, the number of auks *had* decreased considerably".

In 1962 it was estimated that 93 pairs nested, since when surveys between 1981 and 2004 have documented the steady decline in numbers. The last count in three figures came in 1981 when 129 birds were present at nesting sites from Battery Point on the West Side to North West Point and as far south as Gannets' Rock on the East Side. Maximum numbers since have fluctuated between 87 (1982) and nine individuals (2003) with an annual average maximum of 32 birds from 1982 up to and including 2005. The remaining population is now centred around St Philip's Stone on the West Side just south of Threequarter Wall.

A detailed study in 1999 showed that, with a maximum of 49 birds, numbers were slightly up on the previous count in 1997 (30 birds). Mating was observed in 1999, burrows were excavated, nesting material taken in, and nine burrows were occupied throughout the season, indicating up to nine successful breeding attempts, though proof was only obtained in one case (Cole & Reach 1999). During the same study, non-breeding birds were seen investigating burrows later on in the season (non-breeding immature birds arrive at colonies from June onwards, and most maximum counts on Lundy have occurred in late June and early July). Hence, early-season counts are more likely to give an accurate estimate of the breeding population. The presence of immature non-breeders also suggested that there was a pool of birds from which natural recolonisation might occur, if the factors causing the decline in Lundy's population could be identified and overcome.

During the five nesting seasons 2000 to 2004 there was no evidence of successful breeding by Puffins, even though three pairs were seen entering burrows in May and June 2001 at St Philip's Stone, birds were observed mating and carrying nest material, and one was seen entering a burrow with nesting material on 25 July 2004. However, better news came in 2005 when four of six burrows at St

Philip's Stone appeared to be active in mid-July, and a chick, probably close to fledging, was seen on 13 July. Observations during 2006 suggested six active burrows, again all in the vicinity of St Philip's Stone, but no chicks were evident. The first Puffins of 2007 were seen on 5 April – two birds emerging from burrows at St Philip's Stone – with up to four, including a mating pair, seen during the first week of May. At least one chick was observed and photographed in mid-July (see www.lundybirds.org.uk), while adults were feeding young at three other burrows (Nicola Saunders, personal communication).

On 26 June 2001, assistant warden Ian Reach saw Puffins flying around Gannets' Rock, with groups of up to five birds together on the water and sightings of three Puffins ashore on the base of Gannets' Rock itself. These birds were wandering around ledges, possibly indicating the presence of crevice nesting sites. However, there were no further reports from this area until sightings of birds on the water in June and July 2007 (Stuart Leavy, personal communication).

Puffins are rarely seen from the island after mid-August, and there have been just four September and two October records since 1947, each of single birds, the latest date being 23 October (1988). There are also occasional sightings during the boat crossing (e.g. one on 20 September 2003). The earliest spring record is 6 March (1983) but more often the first birds are seen in early April.

Various factors have been put forward as to the causes of the decline in Lundy's Puffin population. These include changing sea temperatures, affecting the availability of the Puffin's food supply (sand-eels and Sprats), pollution in the Bristol Channel emanating from upstream industry, and pollution in the species' North Atlantic wintering grounds arising from the destruction of shipping convoys during the Second World War. The latter is certainly an intriguing possibility given the apparent collapse of the population following the high counts in 1939. Rats are also thought to have been partially responsible for the decline of Puffins on Lundy. By the early 1990s most of the remaining breeding birds were occupying crevice sites in cliffs rather than burrow sites in the sidelands, perhaps an indication of rat predation.

With Puffins teetering on the verge of extinction on the island, it remains to be seen, from the monitoring of seabird populations following the rat eradication programme initiated in 2001 (see Manx Shearwater, page 64), whether Lundy will continue to be known as the 'Isle of Puffins'.

Puffin

Ten Puffins had been ringed on Lundy up to the end of 2006 (the last one in 1980), but there have been no subsequent controls or recoveries, and no controls on the island of Puffins ringed elsewhere. Puffins ringed at other colonies in south-west Britain (notably the Pembrokeshire islands of Skokholm and Skomer) have been recovered outside the breeding season around the Atlantic and Irish Sea coasts of Britain and Ireland, western Norway, the Atlantic seaboard of France, Spain, Portugal and north-west Africa, and the western Mediterranean, showing a similar overall distribution to Razorbill (Wernham *et al.* 2002).

Of birds and burrows – Puffins in the breeding season

"Birds come to the colonies in the early spring immediately after their flightless period. It is not known when they arrive offshore, but they may come directly to the nesting area from their winter quarters as the first records of the spring are of birds on the water close inshore under the colonies. Birds then come and go with an irregular cycle of presence and absence but numbers gradually increase. During the first visits the birds do little but float around in small groups...After a couple of days they swim about in pairs...and courtship starts. On Skokholm the average first [arrival] date in spring was 4th April.

As days pass, the birds spend more and more time both on the water below the colonies and on land. During the first landings they tend to stay on the exposed rocks but gradually they gain confidence and scatter over the colonies to the holes where they bred in the previous years. A Puffin usually remains faithful both to its mate and its burrow from one season to the next, if each survives the winter.

The behaviour of the birds gradually changes until, when disturbed, they dive down their burrows rather than flee to the sea." Some matings are apparently attempted on land but "the bulk of these copulations appear to be unsuccessful and most matings presumably occur on the water well away from human eyes.

Puffins are among the earliest seabirds to lay, virtually throughout their range. In Britain, only Shags lay earlier. The early laying is probably because the Puffin's incubation and chick period are so long that early laying is essential if the young are to be fed when food is abundant. At Welsh colonies, egg laying starts in the last week of April and lasts about a month. The peak is usually at the start of May but, rarely, as late as the third week.

Puffins sometimes breed in their third year of life, but most seem not to breed until about the fifth year. The mean expectation of further life for a Puffin once it reaches breeding age is about 20 years, giving a total age of 25 years."

Extracts from *The Puffin* by Mike Harris (1984)

Pallas's Sandgrouse *Syrrhaptes paradoxus*

British vagrant.

This species breeds on dry steppe in Central Asia. During the late nineteenth and early twentieth centuries there were major 'irruptions' when huge flocks moved west into Europe, perhaps in response to food shortages, with significant numbers reaching the UK and even nesting here. Particularly large invasions occurred in 1863, 1888 and 1908. It was during the 1888 irruption – when around 5,000 Pallas's Sandgrouse were seen in Britain and Ireland – that a flock of seven stayed on Lundy for about three weeks (D'Urban & Mathew 1895). There have been only four accepted UK records since 1950, involving just seven birds. It is thought that habitat destruction (conversion of steppe to farmland) has caused a major population decline, making it unlikely that the invasions of bygone times will be repeated.

Rock Dove / Feral Pigeon *Columba livia*   [Common Pigeon]

Rock Doves probably bred historically, but no definite records for the twentieth (or twenty-first) century. Feral Pigeon is a common visitor in small numbers.

Although listed by Chanter (1871) and Parfitt (1876) as an "occasional visitant", there is no conclusive proof that Rock Doves have occurred on Lundy, though the strong probability is that historical records of pigeons relate to this species. Davis (1954a) wrote: "The 'pigeons' mentioned in an Inventory of 1325 or 1326 were probably of this species. They were also stated by Polwhele (Hist. of Devon 1797) to exist on Lundy. Dr E. Moore (1837) said that the island was the "chief Devonshire resort" of Rock Doves in the breeding season." The 1946 *Devon Bird Report* gives two present on 15 & 18 October that year, with one on 20 October, but, as concluded by Davis (1954a), these seem likely to have been domestic Feral Pigeons rather than wild Rock Doves.

Feral Pigeons (including lost, tired or sick racing pigeons) occur in small numbers throughout the year, usually along the more sheltered East Side and typically around habitation where they are often fed by well-meaning visitors. Such birds quickly become reliant on artificial feeding and may try to enter the Tavern or shop – especially when their friendly visitor has left the island – whereupon they have to be destroyed for reasons of food hygiene. There has been no systematic recording of Feral Pigeons over the years and they have not been included in the register of 'bread and butter' species that has formed the core of the LFS logbook since 1988. However, our own observations suggest that most sightings are of one to three birds.

Stock Dove *Columba oenas*

Uncommon but regular spring and autumn migrant.

Prior to the first LFS record of a single bird on 27 March 1949 only two sightings of Stock Dove had been made: another single bird on 4 September 1926 (Harrisson 1932) and one or more on 3 May 1939 (Perry 1940). There were records in a further 14 years up to and including 1973, while from 1975 onwards Stock Doves have occurred annually on Lundy (to 2006), and there are records for every month. The vast majority of occurrences (over 100) are of single birds, with 29 records of two or three birds, and nine instances of small parties of four or more together. Nine were seen on 28 February 1976 and 1 March 1976, and 12 were present on 25 November 1972. April is the peak passage period in spring (more than 30 records up to 2006), while autumn passage is mainly in October (more than 40 records) and into November (18 instances). There are just three winter sightings: two in December and one in January, the latter as recently as 20 January 2004. The village area and the wooded combes of the East Side are the favoured locations.

Only one Stock Dove has been ringed on Lundy (to the end of 2006), having been trapped in autumn 1961 by Dudley Iles, the sole visiting bird ringer that year. There are no recoveries or controls involving the island.

Woodpigeon

Woodpigeon *Columba palumbus* [Common Wood Pigeon]

Probably breeds in most years; spring and autumn migrant in small numbers; sporadic in winter.

Woodpigeons on Lundy are rarely seen away from the wooded combes of the east sidelands. They are usually present in small numbers at all times of year, with occasional large influxes of passage birds, especially in autumn. Chanter (1871) and Parfitt (1876) listed the species as an "occasional visitant". Between one and four pairs have bred almost annually since Loyd (1922) first recorded a few pairs nesting in 1922; Perry (1940) reported two nesting pairs in 1939. Exceptionally, five or six pairs were present in 1977. Breeding birds usually arrive in March and depart in October.

Small numbers occur on spring passage in April and May, with the highest count being 36 on 2 May 1973. Autumn passage extends from August to October, with some notable late movements in November, including 66 on 4 November 2001, an influx of 75 birds on 21 November 1991[76] and about 400 on 1 November 1975. Between 25 October and 16 November 2003 several flocks of between 40 and 60 birds passed through the island, coinciding with much larger movements on the south coast of Devon (2003 *Devon Bird Report*). In 1959 a late autumn movement of Woodpigeons noted by Irish Sea bird observatories as far west as Cape Clear, Co. Cork, Ireland (Sharrock 1973) was reflected on Lundy. The biggest movements were of 150 birds heading north on 26 October, flocks of 60 and 150 moving north on 3 November, well over 100 on the island on 4 November and 52 on 5 November, followed by small numbers until about 100 flew south on 18 November. A late flock of 20 on 12 December 1959 remains the highest number for that month. Winter sightings are few and normally involve only one or two birds.

British Woodpigeons are highly sedentary in nature (Wernham *et al.* 2002) and large-scale movements through Lundy such as that observed in 1959 are most likely in response to locally high populations and/or depleted food sources in the birds' area of origin. Of 14 Woodpigeons ringed on Lundy (to the end of 2006), two have been recovered: a nestling ringed on 29 July 1952 was found dead in Torquay, South Devon, on 12 January 1954; and a full-grown bird ringed on 21 May 1978 was shot on 11 January the following year, 31 kilometres away at Woolfardisworthy (Woolsery), North Devon.

Collared Dove *Streptopelia decaocto*   [Eurasian Collared Dove]

Regular migrant, usually in small numbers, especially in spring; summer resident in some years; has bred; has overwintered.

Collared Doves were first observed on Lundy on 28 May 1961, when one was seen by W.L. Roseveare and F.W. Gade.[77] This was also the first record for Devon of a species that only began nesting in Britain in 1955 following a dramatic westward spread across continental Europe. Since 1963 they have been seen on Lundy in every year, initially as passage migrants only, but from 1966 as a non-breeding summer visitor. The first instance of overwintering occurred in 1991/92, with birds present in winter in seven of the following eight years up to 1999/2000. However, none has been recorded in winter since (up to 2006/07). The first year in which the species was recorded in every month was 1995 and breeding was first confirmed in 1998. The village and farm buildings are predictably the areas most favoured by Collared Doves, though they often fly to roost in the mature trees at the top of Millcombe.

The typical annual pattern of Collared Dove sightings involves the arrival of ones and twos in late March or early April, with numbers building through April and May before declining during June. Small numbers may be present in July and August, with ones and twos through September and October. High numbers were noted during the mid-1970s when peak counts in the three principal months of spring migration were 35 on 2 June 1974, 50 on 25 May 1977 and 60 on 30 April 1976; 60 were also seen on 10 May 1981. To date these movements have only been rivalled in 1991 when a remarkable influx occurred in the spring: after the first arrival on 14 April, birds were seen on most days to the end of the year, with numbers increasing to 60 in late May and early June, peaking at 80 on 8 June but dropping to about 15 during July. The highest autumn count is also from 1991 when 15 were seen on 22 October. Since 2000, numbers have reached double figures on only three occasions at any time of year, the maximum count being just 15 on 14 May 2001.

A juvenile was seen in late June 1985, but there was no concrete proof of breeding on the island until a pair nested in the Black Shed in 1998. Single pairs also bred in 2000 and 2001 (two clutches of eggs laid), but there have been no breeding records since, up to and including 2007.

In late April 2007 we twice witnessed Peregrines attacking apparently migrant Collared Doves, one off North West Point on 29 April, the other off Pilot's Quay the following day. In both cases the doves were brought down but not killed by the falcons, only to be taken and eaten by Great Black-backed Gulls. In the first case the Collared Dove was forced onto the sea, where it was set upon by a pair of gulls. On the second occasion a harrying Black-back caused the Peregrine to drop its still live prey onto the water.

Collared Dove was added to the island ringing list in 1973 and by the end of 2006 a total of 21 had been ringed. There has been one subsequent control and one recovery. A full-grown bird ringed on Lundy on 3 May 1991 was found alive – feeding with racing pigeons – and subsequently released at Malahide, Dublin, Ireland, on 4 August 1992. Another full-grown bird, ringed on 29 April 1990, was found dead at Tregaron, Dyfed, mid-Wales, on 11 July 1993. Both of these movements are consistent with the general north-westerly or westerly direction shown by Collared Doves ringed in the UK and recovered away from the immediate area of ringing (Wernham *et al.* 2002).

Turtle Dove *Streptopelia turtur*   [European Turtle Dove]

Increasingly scarce migrant, still regular in spring but rare in autumn.

Most Turtle Doves on Lundy are encountered on the East Side, south of Quarter Wall – especially in Millcombe, St John's Valley and St Helen's Combe, but also on the plateau, often feeding along tracks and paths and flying into cover or perching on walls when disturbed. Spring records of Turtle Doves passing through the island show this species to be a regular migrant. However, the number of days on which Turtle Doves are now seen – averaging just over 10 days per year for the period 1997 to 2006 – falls far below the 20, sometimes 30 or more days shown by LFS records from 1950 into the mid-1990s: observations were made on 46 days in spring 1951, and on 28 days in both 1993 and 1994, but just 10 and nine days in 2004 and 2005 respectively. The rapid decline in recent years reflects national surveys

Turtle Doves

conducted by the British Trust for Ornithology (BTO) which show that Turtle Dove numbers are down to about a fifth of those in 1970, with a 45% decline between 1994 and 2005 (Baillie *et al.* 2006). The species is now 'red-listed' as being of high conservation concern nationally. The causes may include a combination of hunting pressure during migration, drought in the species' African wintering quarters, and reduced nesting habitat and food availability due to the intensification of farming practices in Britain.

Spring passage is protracted, usually from early May (although the first date has been noted in April on 22 occasions) through to July, with peak migration from mid-May to mid-June. The earliest spring record is 16 April (1951 and 1955).[78] Most observations are of single birds. Maximum numbers are 30 on 29 May 1960 and in late May 1964, 32 on 20 May 1965 and an astonishing series of counts – not reflected in the *LFS Annual Report* – for May 1979. There were daily sightings of up to 17 birds between 7 & 14 May, followed by a huge influx of 97 on 15th, with about 50 present on both 16th & 18th, and 30 on 21st. Turtle Doves were seen every day thereafter to the end of June, one remaining until 10 July. Since 15 were seen on 4 May 1994, peak spring counts have been in single figures.

By comparison, autumn passage is slight, with mostly single birds passing through the island in August or September, occasionally into mid-October. One "tried to land on the [paddle-steamer] *Waverley* between Ilfracombe and Lundy" on 16 October 1988 (1988 *Devon Bird Report*). There is just one November record, of a bird seen on 7 & 11 November 1978. The peak autumn count is of eight birds on 10 September 1951. In the years since 1995 there have been just five autumn sightings, all of single birds, and only two records since the turn of the century (singles on 4 October 2003 and 23 September 2004).

Chanter (1871) and Parfitt (1876) listed Turtle Dove as a "summer visitant", Parfitt adding "frequent breeder", while D'Urban & Mathew (1895) were "assured by the Rev. H.G. Heaven that this Dove has occasionally nested in a small patch of stunted cover". Loyd (1922) described the species as "very numerous up to the end of May, flocks of as many as thirty being met with". Harrisson (1932) listed Turtle Dove as an "erratic breeder" but without giving substantiating detail. T. Fulford, writing in the 1941 *Devon Bird Report* about a visit to Lundy from 1 to 10 June 1941, noted "a flock of about a score could be seen any day on the Island".

Twelve Turtle Doves had been ringed on Lundy by the end of 2006, but there are no controls or recoveries involving the island. Spring and autumn migrants pass through south-west France, Iberia and Morocco, heading to or from wintering grounds in the Sahel zone of Africa. Large numbers have traditionally been hunted in south-west Europe (Wernham *et al.* 2002).

Great Spotted Cuckoo *Clamator glandarius*

British vagrant.

Breeds in Portugal, Spain, southernmost France, western Italy and parts of the eastern Mediterranean. Most winter in sub-Saharan Africa. 38 records for Britain 1950–2005.

Great Spotted Cuckoos return to their breeding grounds relatively early in the spring, 'overshooting' birds occasionally reaching Britain in March. There is one Lundy record:

1990 23 Feb – one of indeterminate age and in poor condition found trapped in the Black Shed (adjoining the Tent Field near the helipad) was caught and released near the Tavern.[79]

Cuckoo *Cuculus canorus*   [Common Cuckoo]

Uncommon and declining spring and autumn migrant; probably bred regularly in the past; breeding not confirmed since 1999.

Cuckoos can be encountered virtually anywhere on the island, but especially in Millcombe and the other East Side combes or perched on the drystone walls of the plateau. Their instantly recognisable call is deeply embedded in British folklore as the harbinger of spring. While you may still be lucky enough to hear Cuckoos on the island between April and June, the species' story on Lundy reflects the declining English population, which BTO data show fell by nearly 60% between 1979 and 2004 (Baillie *et al.* 2007). The precise reasons for the decline are unknown but may include intensification of agriculture (leading to decreased food and habitat availability), declining numbers of some host species, and adverse factors on the sub-Saharan wintering grounds or along the migration route. Cuckoo is currently 'amber-listed' (of medium conservation concern) in the UK as a whole.

F.W. Gade (reported by Davis 1954a) noted an increase in the late 1930s, followed by a sharp fall in Meadow Pipit numbers, with both species less numerous after the Second World War. From the 1950s to the early 1980s LFS records tend to show a pattern of arrival from mid-April, with adult Cuckoos recorded frequently until midsummer, then mainly juveniles seen from late July through to early or mid-September. It seems that breeding was presumed to have occurred regularly during this period, but hard evidence of successful breeding is patchy: one egg was found in 1952; "one or two young were reared on the island" in 1973; one newly fledged juvenile was seen in June 1976, with another being fed by a Meadow Pipit in August of the same year; up to three juveniles were seen in July 1977; and one juvenile was seen on 26 June 1981. Records have declined substantially since the mid to late 1980s, with a particularly noticeable decrease in late-summer and autumn sightings. For the 10 years 1997–2006 the species is best described as an uncommon spring migrant and rare autumn migrant, with a single confirmed breeding record – a recently fledged juvenile being fed by a Meadow Pipit on 31 July 1999.

Cuckoo

Cuckoo was listed by Chanter (1871) and Parfitt (1876) as a "summer visitant", the latter adding "constant breeder". There have been five occurrences in March, including the earliest spring record to date on 4 March 1940 (F.W. Gade, reported by Davis 1954a[80]). While the earliest LFS record is of one heard on 13 March 1996, the vast majority of LFS first dates for the year have been in April, with over half during the period 14 to 24 April. Formerly, when the species was more regular in autumn, last dates were typically in late August or early September, but autumn Cuckoos are now rare. There are four records for the first week of October, with one of these birds remaining until 12 October (1994), the latest sighting for the island. The highest daily counts are up to seven in late July 1952 and seven on 19 May 1962, presumably juveniles.

Forty-two Cuckoos had been ringed on Lundy by the end of 2006, with just one recovery: a juvenile ringed on 29 July 1952 was found in the Lot-et-Garonne *département* of south-west France on 25 August 1956. The species' decline is reflected in ringing totals: during the 20-year period 1950–1969, 28 individuals were ringed, falling to 12 in the period 1970–1989 and just three birds between 1990 and 2006.

Black-billed Cuckoo *Coccyzus erythrophthalmus*

British vagrant.

Breeds widely in northern and eastern states of the USA and in southern Canada. Winters in north-west South America. 12 records for Britain 1950–2005, many of dead or dying birds.

There is one Lundy record of a single bird:

1967 19 & 20 Oct – one seen briefly near the Old Light on 19th was found dead nearby the following day. The 1967 *LFS Annual Report* and the BBRC report stated the bird to be a first-winter female; however examination of the corpse by Leicester Museum (where the specimen presumably still resides) identified the bird as a first-winter male (Waller 1967a).[81]

Yellow-billed Cuckoo *Coccyzus americanus*

British vagrant.

Breeds widely in North America, from southern Canada to central Mexico, migrating to wintering grounds in South America. 43 records for Britain 1950–2005, many of dead or dying birds.

One was found dead beneath the Old Light in October 1874 (D'Urban & Mathew 1895). The fact that Chanter (1871) and Parfitt (1876) listed Yellow-billed Cuckoo as an "occasional visitant" implies that there had been at least one previous occurrence, though none is documented. There have since been three LFS records, all of single birds and all in October:

1986 31 Oct – a first-winter bird seen briefly in St Helen's Copse and lower Millcombe.[82]
1987 16 Oct – a first-winter bird in Millcombe.
1989 25 Oct – one on the Terrace near the Heligoland trap.

Barn Owl *Tyto alba*

Lundy vagrant.

There are three LFS records:

1957 10 Oct – one in VC Quarry.
1978 12 Nov – one in St John's Valley and around the village.
1981 14 & 15 Nov – one.

Barn Owls apparently occurred more regularly in the past, with Chanter (1871) and Parfitt (1876) listing the "White Owl" as an "occasional visitant". There are six dated pre-LFS records: one shot about 25 January 1881 (Heaven Diaries 1870–1905, reported by Boyd 1950); a pair present for over a year from July 1922 (Loyd 1923); one for a few days from 3 November 1928; one seen on several occasions between 15 November and 10 December 1932; one for some weeks in September and October 1936; and one for a few days in January 1939 (all F.W. Gade, reported by Davis 1954a). The scarcity of subsequent records is likely to reflect the national population decline during the second half of the twentieth century.

Little Owl *Athene noctua*

Lundy vagrant.

Given that this is a largely sedentary species which has shown a significant contraction of its breeding range in the UK since the 1970s, it is unsurprising that there have been only two records on Lundy since the start of LFS recording in 1947, remarkably both on 1 June:

1955 1 Jun – one.
1984 1 Jun – one calling outside the Tavern and later in Millcombe. Sadly, history does not relate whether those listening to the owl were inside the pub at the time!

There are also two dated records for the first half of the twentieth century: one on 15 June 1933 which had probably been present for some time (Davis 1954a) and one on 7 November 1944 (F.W. Gade, 1944 *Devon Bird Report*).

Tawny Owl *Strix aluco*

Lundy vagrant.

Though a common breeding species on the neighbouring mainland of England and Wales, Tawny Owls are extremely rare visitors to Lundy, with 10 records occurring in seven years between 1957 and 1978. Most have been in autumn and all have been single birds:[83]

1957 14 Oct – one.
1958 8 Apr – one.
1972 24 to 30 May – one heard in Millcombe and near the (then) Manor Farm Hotel on most nights.
    27 to 29 Oct – one seen in Millcombe.
1974 20 Mar – one in Millcombe.
1975 26 & 28 October – one.
1976 3, 5 & 6 Sep – one.
1978 31 Aug & 1 Sep – one.
    2 Nov – one.
    22 Nov – one.
    These three sightings were in Millcombe and St John's Valley, as well as in a small garden (now gone) close to the Tavern; perhaps one long-staying individual?

Long-eared Owl *Asio otus*

Lundy vagrant.

There have been 18 records, all of single birds, since 1947. This species occurred regularly (almost annually) between 1989 and 2002, but the spring 2007 record was the first for nearly five years. The vast majority of sightings have been in autumn, with a clear peak in October (10 records), and mostly in Millcombe or along the Terrace.

1954 15 Oct – one caught and ringed.
1962 25 to 27 May – one in Millcombe.
1966 28 Jul – one trapped and ringed.
1967 20 Mar – one on the Terrace.
1975 16 Oct – one on the Terrace.[84]
1989 6 Oct – one in Millcombe and on the Terrace was seen daily until 10 Oct, then again on 15 & 18 Oct.
1990 30 Sep – a first-year bird caught and ringed on the Terrace and seen on seven occasions until 19 Nov.
1991 28 Oct – one being mobbed by small birds in Millcombe.
1993 21 Oct – one among the rhododendrons near St Helen's Copse.

145

1994   14 Oct – one in Millcombe.
      15 Nov – one in Millcombe.
1995   11 Oct – one on the Terrace.
1996   18 Oct – one in Millcombe.
1998   5 Aug – one in Millcombe.
2000   12 Oct – one at dusk on the Terrace.[85]
2002   27 Oct – one roosting on the Terrace.
      27 Nov – one.[86]
2007   5 May – one very pale individual, presumed a male, roosting in sycamores between the Battlements and Millcombe House gates (see photo on page 14).

A report of two Long-eared Owls shot by a shepherd was considered by Hendy (1922) more probably to refer to Short-eared Owl. This makes the only definite pre-LFS record one that stayed for several weeks after being released from a rabbit trap in January 1930 (F.W. Gade, reported by Davis 1954a).

Of the three birds ringed by the end of 2006, an individual ringed on 30 September 1990 was found dead (road casualty) near Stonehenge, Wiltshire, on 26 March 1994. There are no other recoveries or controls involving the island.

Short-eared Owl *Asio flammeus*

Uncommon spring and autumn migrant and rare winter visitor.

Moorland areas on the island plateau, especially near Pondsbury, are favoured by hunting Short-eared Owls, though they can be put up from roost wherever there is good ground cover, including the east sidelands. Recorded in all but two years (1968 and 1970 – possibly owing to lower observer coverage) since 1950, Short-eared Owls are predominantly migrants, but there are mid-December to February records in nine years between 1978 and 2003 indicating that the species may overwinter on occasion.

Spring records fall between mid-March and 30 May (2006), with the bulk of observations during April. Single birds have also been recorded on four days in each of June and July; in 1981 one was seen

Short-eared Owl

146

on eight dates between 29 June and 9 August, possibly indicating a summering individual or a very early-returning migrant. Autumn records are far more numerous, the main passage starting in mid-September, peaking in October and continuing to the end of November. Other than for 1981 (see above), there are just six August records, most falling between 21 August and the end of the month. On 18 October 2006 one was found by torchlight sitting next to the track from the top of St John's Valley to the Castle.

The vast majority of sightings are of single birds, high counts being four on 16 November 1958, 14 March 1959, 18 November 1989 and 6 November 1993, and five around Pondsbury on 28 October 1991. The maximum, however, is a remarkable six in the north of the island – Gannets' Combe and Brazen Ward – on 13 February 1989, a year that produced an exceptional series of sightings on 24 days.

This species is listed by Chanter (1871) and Parfitt (1876) as an "autumn and winter visitant". Hendy (1922) wrote of his visit to Lundy in 1914: "A shepherd told me had shot two *long*-eared Owls. Date not given. As he added that they came with the Woodcock, they were probably Short-eared."

Two Short-eared Owls have been ringed on Lundy (to the end of 2006). One ringed on 18 September 1964 was found dead on the island a few days later. The other was caught and ringed by LFS warden Cliff Waller while out rabbiting on the night of 2 November 1966.

Nightjar

Nightjar *Caprimulgus europaeus*   [European Nightjar]

Lundy vagrant; formerly more frequent and may have bred.

Nightjars were once more common on Lundy than they are today: both Chanter (1871) and Parfitt (1876) listed the species as a "summer visitant", the latter adding "constant breeder". However, there are no confirmed breeding records, and the Heaven Diaries contain only one reference, to a single bird on 29 May 1885 (Boyd 1950). Nevertheless, Gosse (1865) wrote that he was "somewhat surprised to learn [from the Rev. H.G. Heaven, then owner of Lundy] that the goatsucker is a regular summer visitor" (goatsucker being an old country name for Nightjar). F.W. Gade suspected nesting in 1942 when one or two birds were present in June and July (Davis 1954a) and again in 1943 when "two very young birds were seen on Lundy in September" (Palmer 1946).

From the commencement of LFS recording in 1947, Nightjars were seen almost every year on either spring or autumn passage – and sometimes both – until 1962. There were several instances of churring males and seven different birds were reported in 1951. The number of Nightjar records fell from at least 24 in the 1950s, to six in the 1960s and just six since 1970 (to the end of 2006):

1972 20 Sep – a male watched by torchlight near Stoneycroft.
1978 22 May – one.
1980 18 Aug – one.
1992 10 Oct – one flushed from rhododendrons north of St Helen's Copse.
2000 11 May – one flushed from bracken at the top of the west sidelands between Old Light and The Battery.

2001 13 May – one in rhododendrons beside the Lower East Side Path.

Taking all records into account, the earliest documented date in spring is 5 May 1927 (Davis 1954a), while the latest confirmed date in autumn is 10 October 1992, though one was reported by inexperienced birdwatchers on 22 October 1954. Most have occurred in May/June and August/September and there is only one July record, entered in the oldest surviving LFS logbook as "a Nightjar in Quarries 'churring' for a long time at approx 1600 BST" on 2 July 1948.

Although the Nightjar population increased nationally from an estimated 3,400 churring males in 1992 to 4,200 in 2004, marking a reversal of the declines noted in earlier decades, there have been contractions of both range and population in north-west England, north Wales and Scotland (Baillie *et al.* 2007), perhaps explaining why there has been no sign of a recovery in numbers moving through Lundy.

Two Nightjars had been ringed on Lundy by the end of 2006, but there are no recoveries or controls involving the island.

Swift *Apus apus*   [Common Swift]

Common spring and autumn migrant and non-breeding summer visitor.

Seeing the first Swift of the year is always an exciting moment for birdwatchers, as keenly anticipated as hearing the first Chiffchaff or seeing the first Wheatear. In most years the vanguard reaches Lundy in the second half of April, typically during the last week. While the earliest April date is 8th (2000), there are also at least five March records: two birds on 30 March 1978; two on 25 March 1995; one on 17 March 1998, followed by 10 the next day; and one that was watched for five minutes over Quarter Wall on 9 March 1977, with a further sighting – perhaps of the same bird – on 12 March. Anxious to press north, spring migrants can be seen flying low and purposefully, either singly or in loose groups, sometimes battling into quite strong headwinds. They may occur anywhere over the plateau, the sidelands or even out to sea, perhaps using the shelter afforded by the island's cliffs. Small feeding flocks gather occasionally, but most birds seem to pass straight through, trawling for insects as they go.

Spring migration peaks in early to mid-May, but maximum counts vary considerably from year to year, presumably depending in large part on prevailing weather conditions. By far the highest number recorded on any one day (to the end of 2006) was an estimated 2,000 Swifts on 16 May 1978. Unfortunately, the entry in the LFS logbook contains no further information about this extraordinary event, but only 15 were seen the following day. The next two highest spring counts are of 400 on 19 May 1951 and 500 on 9 May 2005.

Although they do not breed on Lundy, Swifts are seen regularly throughout the late spring and early summer; being supreme flyers they can cover long distances very rapidly and are known to range widely in response to weather patterns and consequent availability of aerial insects (Wernham *et al.* 2002). Return migration, which begins in mid-July and peaks in August, has been poorly recorded in recent years, given that there have generally been few birdwatchers on the island at this time. The three highest post-breeding counts were all made more than 25 years ago: 300 on 13 July 1972, 350 on 6 July 1980 and 400 on 17 August 1958.

Small numbers of late-moving Swifts have been seen in September in the majority of LFS years, but there have been October sightings in just eight years, the latest of these being one on 11 October (1951). During the last 20 years (up to and including 2006) there have been only two October records: a single bird on 7 October 1998 and six on 6 October 2000.

Chanter (1871) and Parfitt (1876) listed Swift as a "summer visitant" and though Parfitt and Harrisson (1932) suggested that the species might have bred, this seems unlikely.

Six Swifts had been ringed on Lundy by the end of 2006. While none of these has been controlled or recovered, an adult ringed at Sinterland Sewage Farm, Altrincham, Greater Manchester, on 30 June 1978, possibly close to its breeding area, was controlled on Lundy on 8 May 1984. Presumably on its way north to breed once again, this bird had already successfully completed at least 14 intercontinental, trans-Saharan flights during its lifetime.

Alpine Swift *Apus melba*

Nationally scarce migrant.

Breeds in southern Europe, wintering in sub-Saharan Africa. 482 records for Britain 1950–2005. Considered by the BBRC until the end of 2005.

There are five accepted Lundy records, all of single birds, but none since 1976:

Alpine Swift

1959 9 to 11 May – one first seen around the Church and Castle.

1965 28 Sep – one north of High Street gate.

1969 15 & 16 May – one at Puffin Slope on 15th, seen the next day at Brazen Ward.

1973 22 & 25 to 28 May & 1 Jun – one seen over the south-east part of the island feeding with hirundines and later with two Swifts (*A. apus*); also seen around Tibbett's Hill.

1976 23 Aug – one.

A record in the 1962 *LFS Annual Report* of an Alpine Swift over the Lighthouse Field on 25 April 1962 (also included in the 1962 *Devon Bird Report*) appears not to have been submitted to the BBRC (there is no trace of its acceptance or rejection) and was excluded by Dymond (1980).

Kingfisher *Alcedo atthis*   [Common Kingfisher]

Lundy vagrant.

Listed by Chanter (1871) and Parfitt (1876) as an "occasional visitant". Davis (1954a) referred to "five dated records (one March, four August) and several undated ones in the past thirty years". There have been 13 LFS records (listed below), the first three of which were undoubtedly included among the five dated sightings mentioned by Davis. All are of single birds, and all except one between late June and the end of September, probably dispersing youngsters. The locations, where known, are well scattered around the coastline, no doubt reflecting the abundance of rock pools suitable for fishing. A remarkable occurrence, not included in the list below, concerns one seen flying south-east during the boat crossing on 13 November 1989.

1949 20 Aug – one flying east past Seal's Hole at the South End.

1952 29 Aug – one.

1953 21 Mar – one (the only spring record).

1957 2 Sep – one.

1960 18 Aug – one.

1961 Jul – one at North End late in the month.

1972 20 Sep – one at Kittiwake Gully.

1973 7 Sep – one in the Landing Bay.

1975 19 Aug – one flying south at Gannets' Combe.

1976 19 Aug – one.

1980 8 Jul – one at Quarter Wall Pond flew off northwards along the main track.

1989 6 Sep – one flew south past the Devil's Limekiln.

1999 22 Jun – one in Lametry Bay.

Bee-eater *Merops apiaster*   [European Bee-eater]

Nationally scarce migrant.

Breeds widely in southern and eastern Europe, migrating to wintering grounds in sub-Saharan Africa. 871 records for Britain 1958–2003, with an average of 45 per year 2000–2003. The breeding range has expanded northwards in recent years, with a corresponding increase in British records. Considered by the BBRC until the end of 1990.

There are four LFS records, three since 2002, involving a total of six individuals:

1985   12 May – one feeding from a fence in the Tent Field and seen shortly afterwards near Pondsbury.
2002   16 May – two flew east over the village, then south over the Castle and on out to sea.
2005   17 Aug – one near Threequarter Wall on the West Side (constituting the first August record for Devon).
2007   25 May – two on a fence at the southern end of St Helen's Field, observable from the Tavern.

The only previous record of Bee-eaters on Lundy concerns a flock of six seen by F.W. Gade on 19 May 1940 (Palmer 1946). They departed on 26 or 27 May but reappeared from the north-east and passed straight through to the south-west on about 2 June (F.W. Gade, reported by Dymond 1980).

Roller   *Coracias garrulus*   [European Roller]

British vagrant.

Breeds in southern and eastern Europe, migrating to wintering grounds in sub-Saharan Africa. 106 records for Britain 1950–2005.

There is one Lundy record of a single bird:

1949   25 Aug – one, probably a female, first seen by LFS warden Hugh Boyd on telegraph wires on Castle Hill in the morning, later on a field-boundary post, and in the afternoon on telegraph wires by the Tent Field. The bird was watched from a distance of 20 yards gliding to the ground and picking up insects.

In an article in *Devon Birds*, the magazine of the Devon Bird Watching & Preservation Society in April 1950, Hugh Boyd wrote of the Roller: "Though its plumage lacked a little of the brilliance of the male in breeding plumage, the beauty of the bird in flight was unforgettable – a combination of kingfisher-blue, chestnut, and black."

Hoopoe   *Upupa epops*   [Eurasian Hoopoe]

Nationally scarce migrant.

Breeds commonly in southern Europe, with a more scattered breeding distribution further north. Migrates to Mediterranean and sub-Saharan wintering grounds. Prone to arrival in Britain when overshooting its breeding grounds on spring migration. 4,262 records for Britain 1968–2003, with an average of 81 per year 2000–2003.

Dymond (1980) reported Hoopoe as a rare spring and autumn migrant, recorded in all except nine years between 1947 and 1978. Since then there have been records for a further 16 years (up to 2006) involving at least 22 individuals; all except three of these have been in spring, mainly in April/May. Taking all dated records into consideration, the earliest and latest dates are 17 March (1990) and 30 June (1951) in spring, and 10 August (1967) and 25 October (1981) in autumn. Nearly all occurrences have been of single birds, but two were present from 25 to 30 August 1967[87] and 21 April 1992.

The following is a complete list of occurrences for the 20-year period 1987 to 2006:

1988   8 May – one seen on the Devon Bird Watching & Preservation Society day-trip.
         15 May – one near Pilot's Quay, then seen flying south; probably still present on 16 May.
1989   26 Mar – one in Millcombe.
1990   17 to 22 Mar – one on the East Side and the Terrace.
         30 Apr – one near the Castle.
1991   3 & 4 May – one in Millcombe.
1992   21 Apr – two, with one still present on 22, 26 & 30 Apr.
1993   30 May – one.

1994 2 to 9 Apr – one.
       1 & 6 May – one.
1995 9 & 10 Apr – one.
1997 31 Mar to 2 Apr – one in Millcombe and St John's Valley.[88]
1999 28 Aug – one at Quarter Wall.
2000 8 to 10 Apr – one.
       30 Apr – one in Millcombe.
2004 30 Aug – one near St John's Stone.[89]

While there has been only one record since 2000, it is too early to tell if this is representative of a longer-term downward trend. More northerly breeding populations in continental Europe have been declining for some years and *The Migration Atlas* (Wernham *et al.* 2002) reports an apparent "shallow decrease" in British sightings in recent decades. Fraser & Rogers (2006) reported annual mean numbers in Britain for the decades since the late 1960s as:

1968–1979	1980–1989	1990–1999	2000–2003
118	133	119	81

Lundy records have been fairly consistent over the same period:

1968–1979	1980–1989	1990–1999	2000–2003
8	7	8	3

Listed by Chanter (1871) and Parfitt (1876) as an "occasional visitant". D'Urban & Mathew (1895) stated that "some years ago [Hoopoe] was seen almost every year on Lundy" – a situation that persisted from the onset of LFS recording in 1947 until recent years. Prior to LFS recording there were dated records in just six years: 1886 – one on 7 May; 1888 – one on 2 May (both Heaven Diaries, reported by Boyd 1950); 1906 – one in April (Joy 1922); 1923 – ones and twos present from mid-March to May with "five together in the quarries" on 10 May during a large influx to southern Britain that spring (Loyd 1923, 1925); 1941 – one on 2 May (F.W. Gade, reported by Palmer 1946); and 1943 – one on 6 April (F.W. Gade, reported by Palmer 1946) and one from 16 to 20 April (Rogers 1943).

Wryneck

Wryneck *Jynx torquilla*   [Eurasian Wryneck]

Nationally scarce migrant.

Historically a widespread breeding species in England, including Devon, but rapid decline and extinction during the nineteenth and twentieth centuries. Continues to breed widely in continental Europe, wintering in sub-Saharan Africa. 5,037 records for Britain 1986–2003, with an average of 302 per year 2000–2003.

The first documented record of a Wryneck on Lundy was not until 1949 (11 May), but there have been sightings in 37 subsequent years, up to and including 2006. The sheltered combes of the East Side and the Terrace are the species' preferred areas. Most occur in autumn, particularly in September and the first ten days of October, with the earliest and latest dates being 28 August (1981) and 30 October (1987). Given that Wrynecks are discreet, well-camouflaged and solitary birds on migration, they may be quite elusive, even when they remain in the same general area for several days. This sometimes makes it very difficult to assess how many birds are involved in a series of sightings spread over a period of days or weeks. Ringing has demonstrated that more than one bird has sometimes been present, even though no more than one has been seen at a time. At least three different birds were seen in the autumns of 1967, 1976, 1987, 1988 and 1992. Taking such difficulties into account, the minimum total of autumn individuals is estimated to be about 60 (to the end of 2006). There have been 12 records in spring: one in March, six in April and five in May, with extreme dates of 29 March (1965) and 19 May (1984). All these have been of single birds and there has never been more than one spring sighting in any given year.

The following is a complete list of occurrences for the 10 years 1997–2006 (only 2002 was blank):

1997 11 & 12 Apr – one in Millcombe.
20 to 22, 25, 26 & 28 Sep – one.
1998 15 & 16 Sep – one in Millcombe; possibly the same bird seen on 16th near the quarries.
11 Oct – one on the Terrace.
1999 2 May – one in Millcombe.
5 Sep – one in Millcombe.
2000 17 Sep – one in Millcombe.
6 Oct – one.
9 to 13 Oct – one above the Sugarloaf.
2001 13 Oct – one, first seen in a birch tree along the Upper East Side Path just north of the Ugly, flew into a sycamore in Millcombe where it was mobbed by two Yellow-browed Warblers (*Phylloscopus inornatus*).
2003 9 to 12 Sep – one in Millcombe, with a second bird present on 10th.
21 Sep – one in Millcombe.
28 Sep & 1 to 7 Oct – one in Millcombe.
2004 31 Aug – one, trapped and ringed in St John's Valley.
8 Sep – one in the south-west corner of the island.
17, 19, 21 to 23, 25 & 26 Sep – one, possibly two, between the Sugarloaf and the Terrace.
2005 18 & 20 Sep – one in St Helen's Combe.
2006 11 Oct – one on the Upper East Side Path flew to St Helen's Combe where it was trapped and ringed.

Nineteen Wrynecks had been ringed on Lundy by the end of 2006, but there are no controls or recoveries involving the island.

Great Spotted Woodpecker *Dendrocopos major*

Lundy vagrant.

Given the scarcity of mature trees on Lundy, the island's remote location and the rather sedentary habits of the three British woodpecker species, it is hardly surprising that woodpeckers are exceptionally rare on the island. Indeed, there have been no accepted records of either Green or Lesser Spotted Woodpecker (see page 284), while the first sighting of Great Spotted Woodpecker was not until 1949.

There have now been 14 Lundy 'Great Spot' records (to the end of 2006). Eleven of these were autumn arrivals: two in August, four in September and five in October. Apart from one case of overwintering (see below), the latest date in autumn is 24 November (1962). The three spring arrivals have all been in April. A female first seen in October 2005 overwintered on the island, remaining throughout the early spring of 2006. Both this bird and the male present in October 2004 were examined in the hand and showed wing-length, plumage and moult characteristics attributed to the continental race *D. m. major*[90] (breeding in Scandinavia and northern Eurasia). Wernham *et al.* (2002) stated that there is "considerable evidence from the biometrics of birds caught at east coast and Scottish bird observatories that *major* occurs in small numbers in Britain in most autumns". In contrast, Great Spotted Woodpeckers of the British race *D. m. anglicus* "show remarkably little tendancy to undertake long-distance movements…95% of all recoveries are within 40 km of the ringing site".

1949   2, 4 & 5 Oct – one, first seen by LFS warden Hugh Boyd in South Quarry (i.e. Quarry Pond) and subsequently on the Terrace.

1957   18 to 26 Sep – one.

1959   31 Aug to 1 Sep – one at Quarry Pond.

1962   24 Sep – a first-year bird "that stayed and was seen or heard almost every day in any part of the island where there was a tree or fence post for it to work on". It was joined by a second (also first-winter) bird on 21 Oct and both stayed to 6 Nov, whereupon one departed, the other remaining until 24 Nov; both were caught and ringed.

1964   13 to 17 Sep – one in Millcombe.

1965   13 Sep – one.

1967   21 Aug – one.

1969   26 Apr – one.

1975   23 to 29 Apr – one in Millcombe.[91]

1997   9 Apr – a female in Millcombe.

2004   8 to 11 Apr – a female in Millcombe.

10 to 30 Oct – a first-year male seen in Millcombe, St Helen's Copse and the Terrace area; caught and ringed on 25 Oct, it showed characteristics of the continental race *D. m. major*.[92]

2005   6 Oct to 11 Dec – a female seen on 25 days in Millcombe, St John's Valley, flying over the Brick Field and, on the last two occasions, in Quarter Wall Copse. It was caught in Millcombe and ringed on 17 Oct, when it was confirmed as showing characteristics of the continental race *D. m. major*.[93]

2006   The 2005 bird stayed on through the winter, was heard calling in Quarter Wall Copse on 21 Jan and was seen in Millcombe on many days between 14 Mar & 24 Apr (heard drumming on 17 Apr) and may still have been present on 15 May when drumming was reported again from Millcombe.

Eastern Phoebe *Sayornis phoebe*

British vagrant.

Breeds in eastern United States and much of Canada, occurring in woodland and farmland, often close to habitation. Winters in south-eastern USA and Mexico.

The one Lundy record was – and remains – the first for Britain and the Western Palearctic:

1987   24 & 25 Apr – one, first seen in Millcombe on 24th and later in willows near Brambles Villa in St John's Valley.

The phoebe was first seen in the early morning of 24 April and tentatively identified by visitors as an Orphean Warbler (*Sylvia hortensis*), the dusky 'hood' of this species being the closest thing they could find in a field guide. In fact, the bird's identity remained a mystery throughout its two-day stay,

Eastern Phoebe

but three separate descriptions entered in the LFS logbook all remarked that its behaviour – flying from a perch to take insects – recalled a flycatcher. However, this bird showed none of the features of a European flycatcher and, having taken detailed descriptions, it was only once back on the mainland that the fortunate observers were able to consult North American field guides and discovered they had witnessed a 'first' for Britain, as excerpts from the subsequent write-up in *British Birds* make clear:

> On 25 April 1987 C. McShane, K. Mitchell and A. Wood arrived on the island for a week's bird ringing to be told by the warden that several visitors had reported a possible Orphean Warbler. At 16.00 that day, Colin McShane walked into St John's Valley and "immediately saw a bird fitting the warden's description, but, even after just a few seconds, it was obviously not an Orphean Warbler; indeed, it was not a warbler at all. It behaved in typical 'flycatcher' fashion, with an upright stance, 'sitting on its feet', and making fluttering sallies to catch insects on the wing and on the ground, each followed by a short flight to another exposed perch. It had a slow deliberate tail-wagging…[and] plunged into a small stream on a couple of occasions. We watched the bird for about an hour in superb light, making notes and drawings. After we had reset the mist-nets the bird perched on the poles, on the guys and even, once, on the top shelf string, but refused to get caught and, at 18.00, flew off into the next valley; it was never seen again" (McShane 1996).

Intriguingly, an Eastern Phoebe was reported at Slapton Ley, on the South Devon coast, on 22 April 1987 (just two days before the Lundy occurrence) and listed in the *Devon Bird Report* for that year. However, the record was not accepted by the Records Committee of the British Ornithologists' Union (BOURC 1999).

Bimaculated Lark *Melanocorypha bimaculata*

British vagrant.

Breeds in arid regions in the extreme south-east of Europe and western/central Asia. Mainly migratory, wintering in the Middle East, north-east Africa and south-west Asia. 3 records for Britain 1950–2005.

The sole Lundy record, of a single bird, was also the first for Britain:

1962 7 to 11 May – one in the Tent Field near Benjamin's Chair, first seen feeding with a flock of Linnets.

The following is a condensed extract of some of the many fascinating observations related in Michael Jones's paper for *British Birds*:

> "For the first day or two the bird was always feeding voraciously on short pasture cropped by sheep, often with Turtle Doves, and when disturbed would fly fairly low in a circle and quickly return to the same spot. It was frequently chased by Skylarks and was easily distinguishable from them both on the ground and in flight and even at a distance with the naked eye, by its larger size, plumper build, much stouter bill and lighter colour. It walked with a rather bold and rolling swagger which was reminiscent of a Starling, but was never observed to hop. By the third day it had begun to sing regularly, particularly when it was startled, and it then did so both from the ground and in flight. The song was a rather chirpy trill with more of a rattle than a Skylark's and rising and falling very little. It seemed abrupt, monotonous and subdued, each phrase disjointed and as though squeezed out with an effort, which may have meant that it was still not the full song. Although the bird was on the island for a total of five days, it was seen only by Richard Carden and myself because no other ornithologists were present. Neither of us had any experience of the Calandra Lark and so, in spite of discrepancies in the description, we concluded that this is what it must be. However, when the details were submitted to the Rarities Committee, they had no hesitation in identifying it as a Bimaculated Lark" (Jones 1965).

Short-toed Lark *Calandrella brachydactyla* [Greater Short-toed Lark]

Nationally scarce migrant.

Breeds in southern Europe, north-west Africa and western/central Asia, migrating to winter in the arid Sahel zone of Africa. 636 records for Britain 1958–2003, with an average of 18 per year 2000–2003. Considered by the BBRC until the end of 1993.

Since the first occurrence in 1972 there have been a further 15 Lundy records of Short-toed Larks (to the end of 2006),[94] divided more or less evenly between late spring (May/June) and autumn (late September to late October):

1972 16 to 20 Oct – one on the Airfield, trapped and ringed on 17th.
1979 28 Sep – one just north of High Street gate.
1981 28 May – one given as 'possible' in both the LFS logbook and the 1981 *LFS Annual Report* but submitted to and accepted by the BBRC.[95]
1983 29 Sep to 2 Oct – one.[96]
1984 31 May to 3 Jun – one.[97]
1986 13 to 16 Oct – one, mainly in the Castle Hill area, but seen at North Light and the head of Gannets' Combe on 16th.[98]
1987 23 & 25 to 27 Oct – one in the Airfield area.
1988 25 to 27 May – one, first seen in flight at Quarter Wall and later in the area of Quarter Wall Cottages.[99]
1993 2 & 4 May – one at the Rocket Pole and in South West Field.[100]
       12 to 14 May – one (considered different to the bird seen earlier in the month) at Quarter Wall Cottages.
1994 12 & 14 to 16 Oct – one feeding on Castle Hill on several occasions; two birds probably present on the last day.
1996 17 May – one at Quarter Wall.
       3 to 5 Jun – one near Threequarter Wall.
1999 30 Sep – one by Rocket Pole Pond.
2003 12 to 15 May – one near Halfway Wall.
2005 27 & 28 May – one seen near the stonecrusher in the Tent Field.

Just one Short-toed Lark had been ringed on Lundy by the end of 2006 (in 1972) and there are no controls or recoveries involving the island.

Woodlark *Lullula arborea*   [Wood Lark]

Lundy vagrant.

The British breeding population of Woodlarks has undergone considerable fluctuation, with a rapid decline between the 1950s and 1980s, followed by significant recovery from 241 pairs in 1986 to 1,633 pairs in 1997 and 3,084 pairs in 2006. The 2006 survey (organised by the BTO, Forestry Commission, Natural England and RSPB) found the first nesting pair in Wales for more than 25 years; all other pairs were in England. The British population is considered to be partially migratory (Wernham *et al.* 2002).

The first reported Woodlark on Lundy was a single bird seen in St Helen's Field (not the Tillage Field as reported in that year's *LFS Annual Report*) on 18 October 1950, after which records were annual until 1960. This involved six Woodlarks in spring and 12 in autumn, as well as at least two birds in January/February 1952. Thereafter occurrences became more sporadic and all post-1960 records, to the end of 2006, are given below. There have been no spring records since 1977 and five of the last six occurrences have been in October. Given the species' improving fortunes in England and Wales, it is perhaps surprising that there have not been more frequent sightings in recent years.

1966 14 Oct – one in the Brick Field.
1973 14 Oct – one.
       24 Oct – one.
1976 28 Apr – one.

155

1977 18 Apr – one.
1978 3 Jun – one.[101]
1979 10 Oct – one.
1980 22 & 23 Aug – one.[102]
1985 28 Oct – one, first heard calling in company with four Skylarks and subsequently seen in flight.
1988 26 Oct – one heard and seen flying down the East Side.
1992 29 Oct – one flying south, calling, along the East Side had earlier been seen at Pondsbury.
1998 8 Oct – one by Millcombe pond flew off north.

Skylark *Alauda arvensis* [Sky Lark]

Common breeder; common spring and autumn migrant; sporadic in winter with influxes during exceptionally cold weather.

One of the most evocative sounds of Lundy is the song of Skylarks, starting in early February and continuing into July. Their preferred habitats are rough grassland (e.g. in Middle Park) and moorland (e.g. around Pondsbury) on the island plateau. Skylarks breed every year but their population has, until recently, been poorly recorded, with estimates given in only ten *LFS Annual Reports*. These vary from lows of 15 pairs in the late 1940s and 1950s to between 40 and 50 pairs in three years during the 1960s; 57 pairs in 1984; 27 pairs in 1985; 18 occupied territories in 1996; between 44 and 72 pairs in 2000 (see below); and 67 territories in 2004. Although continuing to breed in good numbers on Lundy, Skylark is 'red-listed' in the UK as a whole, meaning that it is a species of high conservation concern owing to a fall of more than 50% in the breeding population since 1970 (Baillie *et al.* 2007).

Skylark

Breeding birds usually arrive on the island in late February or March and generally small spring movements occur in most years during March and April, the highest count being an exceptional 330 or more on 18 April 1971.[103] Many of the breeding birds leave the island by late summer, but ringing has shown that at least some are still present in autumn. Autumn passage – more substantial than spring – builds from around mid-September and continues to the end of November, with peak numbers usually during October; a record 500 were counted on 10 October 1986. Thereafter, numbers dwindle to a handful, with Skylark disappearing from the island altogether in some winters. High counts in December are of 40 birds on 14th 1981 and 6th 1986; January highs are 150 during a cold spell late in the month in 1952 and over 200 on 24 January 1988, but such numbers are exceptional.

Assessing breeding Skylark numbers with any degree of accuracy can be extremely difficult within short windows of time, as evidenced by four separate and unrelated surveys carried out in 2000. RSPB and English Nature staff and volunteers found 44 pairs during the period 19 to 26 May (Lock 2001), while a survey by Tony Parsons (2002) between 10 and 17 June produced an estimate of 72 territories. Parsons' report states that "virtually all territories were in, or immediately adjacent to, unimproved grassland, sometimes with scattered low bracken, heather, rushes or other plants but with grasses dominant". John Hutchinson (see below) found 47 territories south of Halfway Wall, with an estimated 20 territories further north, while in our own survey (unpublished) carried out between 29 April and 13 May, we mapped 56 territories. Thus it can said that in 2000, the Skylark population on Lundy was somewhere between 44 and 72 territories!

From 1994 to 2000, Dr John Hutchinson, then based at the University of Bristol's School of Biological Sciences, undertook detailed studies of the breeding population based on unique marking of individuals. Over the seven field seasons a total of 415 birds (both nestlings and fully grown birds) were marked with combinations of colour-rings, in addition to standard BTO metal rings. Research originally focused on the extent to which the song output of one Skylark depended on how much neighbouring larks sang, but then moved on to collaboration with Dr Simon Griffith, then at the University of Leicester, looking at extra-pair paternity (i.e. the incidence of females being inseminated by males other than their mates). A significant quantity of information on morphology (i.e. physical measurements) was also gathered. The table below shows the number of summer territories, as recorded by detailed mapping, backed up by colour-ring observations.

Skylark summer territories, 1995–2000

	South of Old Light	From Old Light to Quarter Wall	From Quarter Wall to Pondsbury	From Pondsbury to Halfway Wall
1995	nc	19	nc	nc
1996	11	12	nc	nc
1997	9	14–15	nc	nc
1998	13	10	nc	nc
1999	11	11	16	8
2000	6	13	11	7

nc = area not counted

Some observations were made of densities north of Halfway Wall, but almost none of the population in this area was ringed. The impression was of rather lower densities, with perhaps another 20 territories to add. The species tended to avoid the improved pasture south of Quarter Wall and the few birds occasionally using these fields had huge territories, suggesting it was poor habitat. Elsewhere, mowing/rolling of bracken in summer could have had an adverse impact on Skylarks, as many nests were in such habitat, but no specific investigation of this issue has been made (Dr J. Hutchinson, personal communication).

Chanter (1871) and Parfitt (1876) listed Skylark as "resident all the year", the latter adding "and breed there". By way of an historical footnote, an entry in the Heaven Diaries for 8 April 1886 stated: "Fred Ward caught Lark damaged by wind against barn revived and imprisoned it for captive melody" (Boyd 1950). Thankfully, such practices belong in the past and are nowadays illegal.

By the end of 2006, 608 Skylarks had been ringed, generating just one recovery: a Skylark ringed on Lundy as a fully grown bird on 6 September 1956 was found dead on the island almost six years later on 27 July 1962. There have been no controls or recoveries to indicate where Lundy's breeding Skylarks go outside the nesting season, or to shed light on the movements of passage birds. However, the findings of Wernham *et al.* (2002) suggest that, in addition to Skylarks breeding elsewhere in Britain, some continental migrants are likely to pass through Lundy in autumn, perhaps en route to wintering grounds in Ireland or Iberia.

Shore Lark *Eremophila alpestris*   [Horned Lark]

Lundy vagrant.

Shore Lark is included in a list of birds about which Parfitt (1876) stated: "Mr H.G. Heaven very kindly writes me: 'The following have been observed by myself or reported to me by trustworthy persons, but not accurately identified'..." Chanter (1877) therefore regarded these records as doubtful. The first dated record is of a single bird present for several days from 24 March 1944[104] (F.W. Gade, reported by Moore 1969). There have been five further occurrences, involving a total of seven individuals. Though Shore Lark is generally thought of as a winter visitor to the UK, three of the LFS records have been in May, the other two in November. It is striking that all of the sightings for which locations are known have been in the vicinity of the Rocket Pole.

1978 7 & 8 May – one in the flat area of short heather between the Rocket Pole and the Devil's Limekiln.
1980 1 to 5 & 7 Nov – one, with two seen on 3rd & 5th (there are no details of location).
1983 19 & 20 May – one by the Rocket Pole.
      22 & 23 Nov – two (no further information is available).
1992 22 May – one, thought to be a first-year male, in the Rocket Pole area.

Sand Martin *Riparia riparia*

Common spring and autumn migrant; occasional in summer; said to have bred.

Some of Lundy's most magical birdwatching moments come on benign spring and autumn days when hundreds, sometimes thousands, of migrating Swallows and martins swarm through the island, over the plateau and sidelands, and low over inshore waters. Sand Martins, usually in the minority, can often be seen lining up side-by-side with Swallows and House Martins on the fences at Quarter Wall or in St Helens Field, enabling the subtleties of their brown and white plumage to be appreciated. Pondsbury is another favoured stopping-off site, small flocks of Sand Martins sometimes gathering, repeatedly swooping back and forth across the water to drink and feed on insects.

The first Sand Martins of spring have appeared in March in all but 14 years since LFS records started in 1947, the earliest arrival date being 7 March (1983).[105] Peak spring passage occurs from mid-April to mid-May, maximum daily counts varying between years from tens to several hundreds. The highest spring counts to date (up to and including 2006) are 800 on 12 April 1982 and 20 April 1992.[106] Odd ones and twos – probably failed breeders and the first dispersing juveniles – can occur in late June and early July before the main southward passage gets under way in the second half of July, when peak counts have included 350 on 27 July 1977 and 400 on 19 July 1951, but numbers are typically much lower (e.g. 40 on 18 July 2004). Autumn passage continues through August and most of September, with small numbers occurring into October in all but two years (1988 and 2004) since 1975. The highest daily estimate during autumn migration (up to and including 2006) is an astonishing 2,000 on 18 September 1978. The two next highest counts are 500 on both 18 September 1960 and 28 August 1982.[107] The latest autumn date is also the only November record: two on 2 November 1978.

Listed by Chanter (1871) and Parfitt (1876) as a "summer visitant", the latter somewhat improbably added "constant breeder". Nevertheless, Sand Martins are said to have bred in the nineteenth century (D'Urban & Mathew 1895). Several pairs reportedly appeared to be nesting in rock crevices above Constable Rock in the north of the island in 1924 (Lewis 1924) and in 1930 (three or four pairs, Harrisson 1932). However, the habitat seems unsuitable and the evidence is slim. More recently, at least eight birds were seen fighting over drainage holes in the retaining wall of the road between the Landing Beach and the Divers' Beach in April 2001, but with no later evidence of breeding.

Since the first Sand Martin was caught and ringed in Millcombe on 30 September 1958, a further 140 birds had been ringed on Lundy by the end of 2006. Two of these individuals have been controlled. A first-year bird ringed on Lundy on 30 August 1961 was caught at Slapton, South Devon, three days later, clearly on its way south, though like most Sand Martins from British and Irish colonies it would probably have moved east along the south coast of England to cross the channel from Hampshire, Sussex or Kent, before moving down the west coast of France, crossing Spain and skirting the western edge of the Sahara to winter in the Sahel zone of Africa (Wernham *et al.* 2002). An adult Sand Martin ringed on the island on 29 April 2000 was caught at Buckden Gravel Pits, Cambridgeshire, 84 days later on 22 July, perhaps still at its breeding colony.

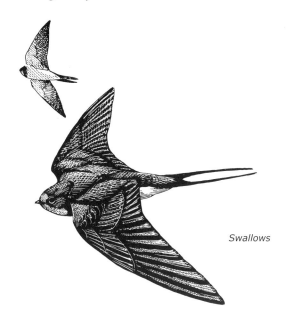

Swallows

Swallow *Hirundo rustica*   [Barn Swallow]

Common and at times abundant spring and autumn migrant; breeds in very small numbers from time to time.

To be on Lundy during a time of peak Swallow migration in either spring or autumn is to witness one of the most impressive and inspiring sights that British birdwatching has to offer. When conditions are favourable, wave after wave of birds pass through, sometimes in a broad front, at other times bunched into flocks of varying sizes; perhaps flying low over the surface of the island, or maybe taking shelter in the lee of the cliffs if there is an adverse wind. In settled weather, Swallows and martins can be seen lining up on barbed wire fences, particularly around Quarter Wall and St Helen's Field. Occasionally, migrants get caught out by bad weather on the island and are unable to feed for several days, rapidly losing condition, as was the case in the last week of September 2005 when exhausted birds were seen sitting on the ground, barely able to fly after a period of low cloud, rain and high winds. When conditions improved, the Swallows that had been 'trapped' on the island were too weak to feed, while new arrivals from further north were flying strongly, passing quickly south along the East Side.

The first spring migrants regularly reach Lundy in the last few days of March (the earliest on record being 20 on 11 March 2000 and three on 11 March 2007) but peak passage gets under way in mid-April, continuing through May before tailing off in early June. Day totals of 1,000 are not exceptional, with the highest estimates (up to and including 2006) being 2,000 on 16 May 1978, 3 to 5 May 1992 and 19 April 2002, 5,000 on 26 April and 13 & 14 May 2004, and 6,000 on 26 April 2005.

Chanter (1871) and Parfitt (1876) listed Swallow as a "summer visitant", Parfitt adding "constant breeder". Loyd (1925) stated that one pair bred annually in the porch of the Church from 1896, and that two pairs nested in 1923. F.W. Gade (reported by Davis 1954a) recorded one pair in most years from 1926 to 1942. Perry (1940) noted a single nesting pair in 1939. Breeding has continued to occur sporadically in LFS years, with one, occasionally two pairs rearing one or two broods. Nests have been built in various buildings, including the Church porch, Old Light, Stoneycroft and farm buildings, while a pair bred at Quarry Pond in 2004. A late brood in 1971 didn't leave the nest until 26 September. Apart from any breeding pairs, numbers of Swallows are generally low in midsummer, with those seen presumably being non/failed breeders and dispersing young.

In autumn, significant movements south may already be taking place by late August and these typically peak in September and continue well into October. There are frequent records of up to 2,000 in a day, with the maximum autumn counts (to the end of 2006) being 7,000 on 24 September 1985, 7,500 on 12 September 2005, 10,000 on 25 September 1997 and 12,000 on 25 September 2002. There is some indication that the numbers recorded in both spring and autumn have been higher in recent years than during the period covered by Dymond (1980). Whether this reflects a true increase or differences in recording is impossible to say for certain, but the BTO Breeding Bird Survey shows that the UK breeding population increased during the period 1994–2004. Other BTO data show fluctuations in the UK population since the late 1960s, but no long-term trend. These fluctuations are thought to be linked to conditions in the species' African wintering grounds and along the migration route (Baillie *et al.* 2006). The latest sightings are typically of ones and twos in the first week or so of November, but the latest by far was one seen on 3 December 1998. Exceptional November counts have included 50 on 1 November 1978 and 17 on 4 November 2002.

A total of 6,155 Swallows had been ringed on Lundy by the end of 2006, with 11 subsequent controls or recoveries. Swallows are extreme long-distance migrants, wintering in southern Africa. There are no Lundy controls or recoveries showing movements outside Britain and Ireland (including the Channel Islands), but those listed in the table below suggest that many of the birds passing through Lundy may breed in Ireland. There are also records showing rapid movement between Lundy and the south coast of England in autumn.

(a) Swallows ringed on Lundy and controlled or recovered elsewhere

Age/sex	Date ringed on Lundy	Place found	Date controlled or recovered	Speculation about date/place of finding
Juvenile	16 Sep 1984	Co. Tyrone, Northern Ireland	04 Jun 1985	In breeding area
Full-grown	28 Sep 1984	St Alban's Head, Dorset	01 Oct 1984	On autumn migration
Juvenile	28 Sep 1984	Par Beach, Cornwall	16 Sep 1986	On autumn migration
Juvenile	12 Oct 1987	St Alban's Head, Dorset	19 Oct 1987	On autumn migration
Juvenile	20 Oct 1991	Portland Bill, Dorset	22 Oct 1991	On autumn migration
Juvenile	29 Sep 1992	Lisselton, Co. Kerry, **Ireland**	21 May 1994	In breeding area
Juvenile	12 Oct 1993	Ballymacoda, Co. Cork, **Ireland**	09 Aug 1995	In breeding area

(b) Swallows ringed elsewhere and controlled on Lundy

Age/sex	Date ringed	Place ringed	Date controlled on Lundy	Speculation about date/place of ringing
Juvenile F	05 Sep 1989	Penclacwydd, Dyfed	11 May 1990	On autumn migration
1st-year	30 Sep 1991	La Rochelle, Guernsey, Channel Islands	04 May 1992	On autumn migration
Juvenile	30 Aug 1995	Youghall, Co. Cork, **Ireland**	20 Sep 1995	On autumn migration
Juvenile	17 Sep 2002	Arklow Marsh, Co. Wicklow, **Ireland**	02 May 2003 (found dead on Lundy 06 Jun 2003)	On autumn migration

House Martin *Delichon urbicum* [Common House Martin]

Common spring and autumn migrant; occasional during summer and has bred in several recent years.

Chanter (1871) and Parfitt (1876) both listed "Martin" as a "summer visitant", Parfitt adding "constant breeder". Harrisson (1932) thought that cliff-nesting was probably attempted in 1930, but N.V. Allen (in Palmer 1946) described the species as a passage migrant that has "not yet stayed to breed". In 1974 two half-completed nests were built on the Old Light, but it was 1981 before House Martins eventually joined the list of Lundy breeding birds, one pair successfully raising young at Paradise Row (Quarters).

In 1987 a small breeding colony was established on the south face of Rat Island, where one half-built and three complete nests were seen being visited by House Martins on 14 July. Two adults and four juveniles were still there on 29 September. Breeding took place at the same site in 1988 when at least one brood was thought to have fledged successfully, while on 28 August another nest with large young was found about three metres above the high-water mark on the eastern side of Sentinel Rock. In 1989, in addition to the two established sites, three new nests were found above the eastern entrance of the Needle's Eye cave, and an estimated six pairs bred altogether. Three pairs nested in 1990 and two pairs in 1991, but there was no firm evidence of breeding success in the latter year. Apart from one bird prospecting for nest sites on the shop on 24 June 1992, there have been no further reports of breeding behaviour. However, there is an abundance of suitable cliff habitat, much of it rarely visited by birdwatchers, so nesting attempts may have been missed in other years.

The first House Martins of spring typically appear in the first half of April, although there have been March records in 14 LFS years (to the end of 2006). An exceptionally early individual was reported on 27 February 1998. Numbers usually build up from mid-April and peak in the second half of May, occasionally early June. The largest passage on record occurred in mid-May 2004 when consecutive daily estimates from 12 to 17 May were of 1,000, 1,500, 1,000, 1,000, 1,000 and 800 House Martins. An estimated 800 and 1,000 birds respectively moved through the island on 15 & 16 May 2005. Such numbers are, however, quite exceptional, spring maxima having generally varied between 40 and 300 birds (rarely 500) in other years since 1980.

Apart from those years in which breeding has occurred and birds have therefore been present throughout the summer, small numbers of House Martins occur sporadically from late June to early August, probably including a mix of non/failed breeders and the first dispersing juveniles. However, the main autumn passage takes place in September and early October. The highest counts (to the end of 2006) are of 500 on three occasions: 18 September 1978, 25 September 1997 and 12 September 2005, 600 on 4 October 1987 and 1,000 on 3 & 4 October 2005. Numbers usually fall away quickly towards the end of October, with late birds seen in November in 10 LFS years and one exceptionally late individual on 4 December 1979.

By the end of 2006, 309 House Martins had been ringed on Lundy, but there are no controls or recoveries involving the island. House Martins winter in Africa, south of the Sahara, migrating on a broad front through Europe and North Africa (Wernham *et al.* 2002).

Red-rumped Swallow *Cecropis daurica*

Nationally scarce migrant.

Breeds in southern Europe, migrating to sub-Saharan wintering grounds. 508 records for Britain 1950–2005. Considered by the BBRC until the end of 2005.

Of seven Lundy records of single birds, four have been in autumn and three in spring:[108]

1952 27 Mar – one hawking along cliffs between Goat Island and The Battery, in company with a Swallow and two Sand Martins (Davis 1953c).[109]

1980 22 Oct – one. A record of one on 14 & 15 Oct was rejected by the BBRC (*British Birds* 75, p. 533).

1987 24 Oct – one hawking for insects in Millcombe and St John's Valley.

1989 18 May – one at Quarter Wall Pond and later in St John's Valley.

1996 26 Apr – one in the Terrace area.

2001 26 Oct – one flying north along the East Side.

2003 12 Sep – one was seen over the village.

Richard's Pipit

Richard's Pipit *Anthus richardi*

Nationally scarce migrant.

There are both migratory and resident races of this globally widespread species. The migratory races breed across central and eastern Asia, from Kazakhstan, across southern Russia and northern China, to the Sea of Japan. Most winter in south and south-east Asia, but birds of the westernmost migratory race *A. r. richardi* may winter in southern Spain, and North and West Africa (Wernham *et al.* 2002). It seems most likely that it is birds from this population that are seen regularly at coastal migration 'hotspots' in Britain, including Lundy. 3,351 records for Britain 1958–2003, with an average of 120 per year 2000–2003. Considered by the BBRC until the end of 1970 and again from 1976 until the end of 1982.

Puzzling over the archives...

In the course of researching this book, we have discovered that there is less consistency in the records published by the BBRC, DBWPS and LFS for Richard's Pipit than for any other national vagrant or nationally scarce migrant recorded on Lundy. Although this species was not added to the island list until 1957, at least 60 individuals have been reported since, up to and including 2006. Perhaps Richard's Pipit came to be regarded as a regular Lundy bird and thus less of a rarity in need of full description; perhaps there was uncertainty because it moved off, back on, and off again from the list of species considered by the BBRC; and perhaps information exchange between the different organisations was sometimes poorly coordinated in the past. Whatever the explanation, several records of Richard's Pipit that we believe to be reliable have apparently 'fallen through the cracks', never having been formally submitted to, or accepted by, the relevant county and/or national committee. Others, however, have been published that we consider to be unreliable. We have undertaken a comprehensive review of all available information and have made a complete listing for 1957 to 2006, showing our findings and conclusions regarding the validity of each record. A few additional details are given in the endnotes. We hope this will serve to clarify the status of Richard's Pipit on Lundy and help to complete and harmonise the information held by the various bodies involved. We hasten to add that the problematic records are for some years ago and that the situation is now much improved.

Most Richard's Pipits are seen in and around the open fields that characterise the southern part of the island plateau, though it is often the loud, sparrow-like *schreep* flight call that first draws attention. They are typically very 'flighty' birds and – being strong flyers – often move considerable distances when disturbed, making it difficult to get good, prolonged views on the ground, especially given a propensity for feeding in fairly long grass. The first Lundy record was of a single bird on 1 October 1957. At least 60 individuals have been seen (to the end of 2006), all but three in autumn. The exceptions are spring records of single birds on 22 April 1989 (during an unprecedented influx into England at that time), 5 to 8 May 1990 and 21 May 1991; though we regard the latter two as very doubtful (see below). Autumn records have all fallen within an eight-week period from 14 September (1963) to 8 November (1975), although nearly two-thirds of new arrivals have occurred during the last 10 days of September and the first 10 days of October. Most reports are of single birds, but two or three in a day have been recorded on several occasions (e.g. three on each of 23 September 1966,[110] 21 September 1967, 27 September 1970 and 26 October 1973). At least six different birds were seen in the autumns of 1973 and 1994, including four together flushed from the Brick Field on 1 October 1994 – the highest daily count yet recorded. The presence of multiple individuals over several days or weeks makes it impossible to put a very precise figure on how many birds have been involved.

The following is a complete, annotated list of all Richard's Pipit sightings on Lundy that have been published in the *LFS Annual Reports*. The figure following the year is the *minimum* number of individuals recorded that year. Square brackets indicate rejected records, or those that appear not to have been submitted at the time and for which there are insufficient surviving details to sustain a claim now. In principle, the BBRC should have considered all records from 1958 to 1970 and from 1976 to 1982, while records for other years should have been reviewed at county level for inclusion in the *Devon Bird Report* (*DBR*).

1957	1	1 Oct – one, first LFS record. Prior to formation of BBRC; brief but good description given in 1957 *LFS Annual Report*; accepted for the *DBR*.
1958	1	[17 to 21 Sep – one. Rejected by the BBRC.] 4 Oct – one. Accepted by the BBRC.
[1960]	0	[29 Sep – one, probable. Rejected by the BBRC.]
1963	2	14 Sep – one. Accepted by the BBRC. 22 Sep – one. Accepted by the BBRC.
1966	3	18 to 20 Sep – one, with two on 22nd and three on 23rd. All accepted by the BBRC.
1967	3	21 Sep – three, with two on 23rd. All accepted by the BBRC. [19 to 23 Oct – one. No trace of acceptance or rejection by the BBRC; no surviving description.] [3 Nov – one. No trace of acceptance or rejection by the BBRC; no surviving description.]
1968	1	26 Sep – one. Accepted by the BBRC.
1970	3	26 Sep – two, with three on 27th, two on 28th and one on 29th. All accepted by the BBRC.
1972	2	20 to 24 Sep – one. Accepted for the *DBR*. 29 Sep to 1 Oct – one. Accepted for the *DBR*.
1973	6	16 Sep – one. Accepted for the *DBR*. 28 Sep – one. Accepted for the *DBR*. 23 to 25 Oct – one, with at least three on 26th and one on 27th October. Accepted for the *DBR*. 1 Nov – one. Accepted for the *DBR*.
[1974]	0	[23 Sep – one at Quarter Wall Pond, with two reported at Quarter Wall on 24 Sep. Not included in the *DBR*; no description in the LFS logbook.] [20 Oct – one at Quarter Wall. Not included in the *DBR*; no description in the LFS logbook.]

1975	4	20 Sep – one, North East Point. Accepted for the *DBR*.
		27 Sep – one. Accepted for the *DBR*.
		12 & 14 Oct – one, seen in the Lighthouse Field on 14th. Accepted for the *DBR*.
		3, 6 & 8 Nov – one.[111]
1976	1	26 Sep – one. Accepted for the *DBR*.
[1977]	0	[26 Oct – two 'possibles', heard only. Not included in the *DBR*.]
1983	2	27 Sep – one. Not included in the *DBR*, but seen by knowledgeable and experienced observers.
		29 Sep – one (noted in the LFS logbook as a different bird). Not included in the *DBR*, but seen by knowledgeable and experienced observers.
[1987]	0	[8 Nov – one. Not included in the *DBR*; no description; LFS logbook simply states "reported by visiting twitchers".]
1988	4	22 Sep – two in South West Field south of the Old Light. Not included in the *DBR* but good description in LFS logbook.
		26 to 28 Oct – one. Not included in the *DBR* and though there is no description the LFS logbook entry was made by a highly experienced observer.
		5 & 6 Nov – one seen at Halfway Wall, then flying south on 5th; and at Pondsbury and fields in the south-east of the island on 6th. Not included in the *DBR*, though there is a very brief yet good description in the LFS logbook, entered by a highly experienced observer.
1989	4	22 Apr – one seen by the Ugly flew off calling over Millcombe towards the Church – the first spring record. Not included in the *DBR* but seen by a highly experienced observer, though LFS logbook entry very brief.
		24 to 26 Sep – one seen near the Castle and in South West Field. Not included in the *DBR* but the LFS logbook entry was made by a highly experienced observer.
		4 & 5 Oct – one on Ackland's Moor and along the East Side. Not included in the *DBR* but the LFS logbook entry was made by a highly experienced observer.
		9 Oct – one at Pondsbury. Not included in the *DBR*.
1990	2	[5 to 8 May – one in Middle Park and by the Old Hospital. Accepted for the *DBR*, but no description or observer's name given in the LFS logbook.]
		[21 Jul – one reported on the East Side. Accepted for the *DBR*, though the midsummer date is highly unusual for Britain and there is no supporting description or observer's name in the LFS logbook.]
		9 Oct – one in the Tent Field. Accepted for the *DBR*.
		19 Oct – one in the Tent Field. Accepted for the *DBR*.
1991	1	[21 May – one at Tibbett's. Accepted for the *DBR*, but no description or observer's name given in the LFS logbook.]
		8, 9 & 11 Oct – one seen around the village, at the Old Light and on the Airfield. Accepted for the *DBR*.
1993	2	5 & 6 Oct – one around the East Side, Castle Hill, Rocket Pole and South West Field. Accepted for the *DBR*.
		19 & 20 Oct – one between Quarter Wall and Halfway Wall. Accepted for the *DBR*.
1994	6	1 to 29 Oct – birds on most days; four on first day flushed together from the Brick Field; on subsequent days records from the quarries, South West Field, Quarter Wall Cottages, Castle Hill, Rocket Pole Pond, Quarter Wall and Tillage Field; at least six individuals altogether. Accepted for the *DBR*.
1995	2	9 Oct – two in St Helen's Field, one remaining on 10 Oct. Accepted for the *DBR*.
1996	1	23 & 24 Sep – one in flight over Pondsbury on 23rd and in various locations between the Old Light and the Church the following day. Accepted for the *DBR*.
1998	1	28 to 29 Sep – one in the Brick Field. Accepted for the *DBR*.
2001	1	23 to 25 Oct – one in the Tillage Field. Accepted for the *DBR*.
2002	1	22 Sep – one, first seen on Castle Hill, flew off north and was later seen in Middle Park and north of Halfway Wall. The same or a second bird was seen on the Airfield on 24 Sep. Accepted for the *DBR*.[112]

2003	1	29 to 31 Oct – one near the Airfield was trapped and ringed on 31st. Accepted for the *DBR*.
2004	2	12 Oct – one in South West Field. Accepted for the *DBR*.[113] 14 Oct – one flew north over the Terrace. Accepted for the *DBR*.[113] 27 Oct – one flushed near Quarter Wall. Not included in the *DBR*, though the LFS logbook includes a brief but good description.
2005	2	17 to 27 Oct – one, with a second bird on 18 Oct, seen in a variety of areas from the Castle to the Old Hospital, but mainly on the Airfield. Accepted for the *DBR*.
2006	1	21 Oct – one flew south past the village and out over Castle Hill. Accepted for the *DBR*.

Tawny Pipit *Anthus campestris*

Nationally scarce migrant.

Breeds in southern and eastern Europe, North Africa and parts of Asia. Birds breeding in Europe migrate to winter in the Sahel zone of Africa. 1,128 records for Britain 1958–2003, with an average of 15 per year 2000–2003. Considered by the BBRC until the end of 1982.

There are 10 Lundy records,[114] all single birds in autumn, and all except one in the period mid-September to mid-October:

1950	6 & 7 Oct – one near the (then) LFS Observatory at the Old Light.
1951	19 Sep – one. 29 Sep – one. While no details of this sighting are contained in the 1951 *LFS Annual Report*, the original observer has confirmed the location as South West Field (Brian White, personal communication).
1966	2 Nov – one.
1983	7 to 10 Sep – one.
1986	9 Oct – one on the Airfield.
1988	10 & 11 Sep – one seen flying north along the East Side past St Helen's Combe; probably the same bird seen the following day on cliffs between South End and the Old Light.[115] 11 & 12 Oct – one flushed from a field near the Old Light flew across Ackland's Moor, calling; the same or another bird was seen the next day flying past Rocket Pole Pond.[115]
1989	15 Oct – a first-winter bird on Castle Hill.
2003	21 Sep – one in St Helen's Field.

Olive-backed Pipit *Anthus hodgsoni*

British vagrant.

Breeds in Russia, east of the Ural Mountains and in Asia from the Himalayas east to Japan. A long-distance migrant, wintering in the Indian sub-continent and south-east Asia. 282 records for Britain 1950–2005.

There is one Lundy record of a single bird:

| 1989 | 24 to 29 Oct – one seen briefly at Quarry Pond on 24th was relocated in the North Quarry, where it stayed until 29th, with the exception of 27th when it was present in Millcombe and St John's Valley. It was caught and ringed on 26th. |

Tree Pipit *Anthus trivialis*

Uncommon spring and autumn migrant.

Tree Pipits are more often heard than seen on Lundy, with the shrill flight call of day-flying migrants being picked out by experienced ears during spring and early autumn birding trips. It is fairly unusual to get a good view of one perched or on the ground, and they often fly considerable distances if disturbed. Millcombe and St John's Valley and the immediately adjoining grassland are the most favoured areas. While ones and twos are the norm, small groups occur from time to time.

Spring migration typically begins in mid-April and runs to mid or late May, though the earliest and latest dates on record are 29 March (1965) – the only March occurrence to date – and 17 June (1986). Numbers are usually very small, the maximum daily count having reached double figures in only seven LFS years and the all-time record standing at 15 on 2 May 1972 and the same number in Millcombe on 22 April 1975.

Autumn movements have occasionally been noted from early August, with an exceptionally early bird at Pondsbury on 28 July 1997, but the main migration period is from late August to early October, usually peaking in September. Numbers are generally slightly higher than in spring, though this is not always the case. The highest daily count has reached 10 or more in 14 LFS years (to the end of 2006), with 25 the maximum number on 5 September 1958, 16 September 1960, 23 August 1972 and 28 August 1973. Late birds are often seen well into October, the latest date being 31 October (1967).

The first LFS record was of a single bird on 4 September 1948. Pre-LFS mentions of Tree Pipit on Lundy are few. Perhaps the first was by Davenport (1897) who wrote: "As may be imagined, we saw no tree pipits"! Hendy (1922) reported "several" on 11 June and "many" on 12 June 1914. Harrisson (1932) mentioned "probably several" in early September 1926 and 1927.

Tree Pipit is currently 'amber-listed' (of medium conservation concern) in the UK, having undergone a major population decline between the mid-1980s and mid-1990s, followed by stabilisation and a very modest increase (Baillie *et al.* 2006). Although the numbers passing through Lundy seem never to have been particularly great, there does appear to have been a general decline since the early 1980s, particularly in autumn, and it is noticeable that the highest spring and autumn counts given above are all from the 1950s, 1960s and 1970s.

Sixty-five Tree Pipits had been ringed on Lundy by the end of 2006, but while there are no controls or recoveries involving the island, onward autumn migration from Britain is thought to be largely through Portugal to African wintering grounds (Wernham *et al.* 2002). An unusually large Tree Pipit that was trapped and ringed in St John's Valley on 18 September 1986 showed measurements more typical of a Tawny Pipit and was initially identified as such (Duncan 1989).

Meadow Pipit *Anthus pratensis*

Breeds; common passage migrant in spring and autumn; scarce or absent in winter.

In any season, separating Meadow Pipits from Skylarks is one of the first challenges on Lundy for anyone new to birdwatching. 'Mipits', as they are often referred to, are found all over the island, both on the plateau and the grassy sidelands. Lewis Loyd (1925) captured this well in describing the species as "one of the most numerous of the passerine birds which breed on the island, as well as being the most widely and evenly distributed" – a situation that persists today.

Breeding birds arrive in late February and March, and sometimes into April, while the passage of more northerly bound migrants continues through April, with stragglers into May. The peak spring count by some margin was of 1,000 birds on 14 & 15 March 1981, with 600 on 16 March 1986 the next highest.

There is comparatively little information about the size of the breeding population. Wynne-Edwards & Harrisson (1932) estimated about 275 pairs in 1930 and Perry (1940) put the population at about 200 pairs in 1939. Felix Gade, who lived on Lundy throughout most of his life from 1926, stated that the population was markedly smaller following the Second World War (reported by Dymond 1980). This observation was confirmed by surveys that found about 50 pairs in 1962 and at least 48 pairs in 1984. Since then, however, the breeding population has increased. Two surveys in 2000 located 108 territories in May (Davis & Jones unpublished) and 179 in June (Parsons 2002). Censuses in 2001 and 2004 found 131 territories (Lock 2001) and 138 territories (Lock 2004) respectively.

Autumn migration is much more pronounced than spring passage and begins in August when most of the breeding birds leave the island, their movements often obscured by arrivals from further north. The main passage period occurs in the second half of September and early October, with movements continuing into November and, in some years, December (e.g. 150 on 14 December 1981). Day counts of several hundred birds are common, with 1,000 or more recorded at least 18 times. There

Meadow Pipits

are three counts of 2,000 – on 7 October 1954, 25 September 1986 and 28 September 1994 – but the record currently stands at 3,000 birds on 10 October 1986.

Chanter (1871) and Parfitt (1876) listed Meadow Pipit as "resident all the year", Parfitt (1876) adding "and breed there". However, LFS records show that numbers are very low in winter, with barely a handful seen in most years, and sometimes none at all. In fact, the highest recorded January counts are of 10 birds on 27 January 1991 and 11 on 21 January 2007.

Of 3,215 Meadow Pipits ringed on Lundy by the end of 2006, there have been six controls or recoveries, all in coastal areas: in Britain (1), France (1), Spain (2) and Portugal (2) – see table. The wintering range of British breeding birds varies with the severity of the winter and extends from lowland areas of Britain and Ireland south to the Mediterranean and north-west Africa, especially Morocco (Wernham *et al.* 2002). Of the Lundy-ringed recoveries, only one bird appears likely to have been wintering in Britain, having been found freshly dead a short flight away on the North Devon coast in mid-December.

Meadow Pipits ringed on Lundy and controlled or recovered elsewhere

Age/sex	Date ringed on Lundy	Place found	Date controlled or recovered	Speculation about date/place of finding
Full-grown	16 Oct 1949	Buck's Cross, nr Bideford, North Devon	11 Dec 1949	In wintering area
Nestling	03 Jun 1953	Aveiro, **Portugal**	27 Dec 1953	In wintering area
1st-year	26 Aug 1959	Finistère, **France**	19 Jan 1960	In wintering area
1st-year	23 Sep 1959	Santander, **Spain**	07 Dec 1960	In wintering area
Full-grown	21 Sep 1982	Bucelas, Lisboa, **Portugal**	31 Oct 1982	On autumn migration or in wintering area
Adult	29 Jul 1997	La Coruña, Galicia, **Spain**	24 Mar 1998	On spring migration

Red-throated Pipit *Anthus cervinus*

Nationally scarce migrant.

Breeds in northern Scandinavia and northern Russia, wintering in sub-Saharan Africa and south-east Asia. 423 records for Britain 1950–2005. Considered by the BBRC until the end of 2005.

Of six Lundy records – all except one of single birds – four have been in spring and two in autumn:

1959 7 & 8 May – two in the Tillage Field; one caught and ringed on the second day was the first to be ringed in Britain.

1969 17 May – one in Gannets' Combe.

1973 31 Oct to 2 Nov – one in the vicinity of Pondsbury and Halfway Wall.

1976 20 Apr – one on the Airfield.

1984 28 & 29 Sep – one originally seen in the Lighthouse Field and later by the main track near Tibbett's was heard near Tibbett's the following day.

1997 5 May – one on Ackland's Moor.

One Red-throated Pipit had been ringed on Lundy by the end of 2006, and there are no controls or recoveries involving the island.

Rock Pipit *Anthus petrosus*   [Eurasian Rock Pipit]

Common breeding resident; extent of migratory or dispersive movements involving Lundy unknown.

Rock Pipits are confined to the rocky beaches, cliffs and sidelands all round the island, though they do make occasional forays onto the plateau (e.g. one was caught in the long-dismantled Garden Trap at Stoneycroft in June 1952). Since much of the coastline is not easily visible and difficult of access, it is unsurprising that there are few complete surveys of the breeding population. Chanter (1871) and Parfitt (1876) listed the species as "resident all the year", Parfitt adding "and breed there". Wynne-Edwards & Harrisson (1932) found 41 pairs in 1930 and Perry (1940) reported 20 pairs in 1939. Counts in 1949, 1951 and 1953 located between 35 and 40 pairs, and the population was considered stable until just 13 pairs were found in 1965. It is very likely that the population in 1965 was still recovering from the freezing winter weather in 1962/63 because surveys in each of the following two years showed increases to 20 and then 23 pairs.

Information is then virtually non-existent until surveys were carried out in May of 2000 and 2004. The first of these located 29 territories, suggesting that the population had remained stable (Lock 2001). The 2004 survey revealed an astounding 51 territories – 14 between St James's Stone and North West Point, where previously there had been four (Lock 2004). It is tempting to infer that Lundy's Rock Pipits have benefited from the eradication of rats. High autumn counts in 2004 (33 on 22 September) and in 2005 (30 on 16 October[116]) may also be indicative of a larger breeding population. Most of the birds counted in October 2004 were on the island plateau rather than on the cliffs and beaches. Given that a population in the range of 35–40 pairs equates to one territory for every 400 yards of coastline (an assessment made by Peter Davis in the 1953 *LFS Annual Report*), competition may dictate the greater use of other parts of the island, both during and outside the breeding season.

There is little in the way of information on Rock Pipit numbers or distribution in winter, though non-territory holding birds, including first-winter birds, probably gather into flocks and forage in different parts of the island. Nineteen birds were counted on 25 February 2006.

Sixteen Rock Pipits had been ringed on Lundy by the end of 2006. A single recovery – of a bird ringed on the island on 16 September 1960 and found dead on 1 July 1965 near Brittas Bay, Co. Wicklow, Ireland (a distance of some 335 kilometres) – shows that there is at least some autumn movement involving Lundy; perhaps dispersal of young, perhaps more purposeful migration.

Yellow Wagtail Motacilla flava

Uncommon spring migrant; common early autumn migrant in small numbers; occasional in summer. Formerly more numerous, particularly in autumn.

Yellow Wagtails

This delightful bird is most likely to be seen feeding among livestock on improved or semi-improved grassland in the south of the island, particularly Brick, Tillage and St Helen's Fields, but the penetrating flight call is often the only clue to the presence of migrants passing overhead.

Lundy is on the western fringes of the Yellow Wagtail's breeding range and spring migration appears always to have been rather sparse. Passage generally begins in the second half of April, reaching a modest peak at the end of the month or in the first half of May, occasionally later. The earliest records are of singles on 22 & 27 March 2007, 23 March 1956 and 5 April 1985. While the highest count in one day is 10 on 25 April 1952, three to five is more typical of the spring maximum. Late migrants – mostly single birds – may occur well into June, and there are occasional July records, which seem likely to include a mixture of dispersing young (e.g. a juvenile on 17 July 1989) and non/failed breeders returning south.

Autumn migration occurs between mid-August and the end of October, peaking from late August to mid-September and falling off rapidly thereafter. There are two November records: one on 1 November 2003 and an exceptionally late individual on 19 November 1976. The maximum counts recorded are 40 on 7 September 1979, 45 on 4 September 1982, 50 on 8 September 1977 and 60 on 16 September 1951.

Yellow Wagtail is listed as a species of 'amber' (medium) conservation concern in the UK, showing a population decline of 64% from 1970 to 2004 (Eaton *et al.* 2006). Possible causes include loss of nesting habitat due to drainage and intensification of wet grassland, and severe drought in the Sahel zone of Africa where the species winters. The national decline has been reflected on Lundy, with a general trend towards smaller numbers of birds on fewer days, particularly during the once substantial autumn passage. For example, during the autumn migration of 1956, Yellow Wagtail was logged on 38 days between 21 August and 1 October (just four days were blank). In 2005 there were records on only 10 days during the same period. The last autumn records of more than six in a day were 11 on 1 September 1996 and 10 the next day.

The great majority of Yellow Wagtails seen on Lundy are of the subspecies *Motacilla flava flavissima* that breeds in Britain (largely in England and the Welsh Marches) and coastal areas of north-west continental Europe. Birds showing characteristics of the nominate subspecies *M. f. flava*, Blue-headed Wagtail, which breeds across much of continental Europe, have been reported on at least 28 occasions in spring, mostly in May, with the earliest being 18 April 1996 (two birds[117]). Other dates on which two birds (the maximum) were seen are 23 May 1958, 14 & 17 to 20 June 1981 and 10 May 1987. There are also five autumn records of Blue-headed Wagtail, falling between 14 September (1961) and 7 October (2001), plus one July record: 9 July 1972.

Birds showing characteristics of the Fennoscandian subspecies *M. f. thunbergi*, Grey-headed Wagtail, have been recorded four times: 21 September 1970, 2 July to 13 August 1973 (in Middle Park throughout its stay), 2 June 1987 and 17 June 1997. A male showing characteristics of the southern European subspecies *M. f. cinereocapilla*, Ashy-headed Wagtail, was seen in St Helen's Field on 1 May 2007 and a description has been submitted to the BBRC (James Diamond, personal communication). Finally, birds thought to belong to one of the east European or west Asian subspecies have occurred three times: 24 to 28 October 1983,[118] 1 November 2003 and 30 August 2005.[119]

Chanter (1871) and Parfitt (1876) both listed "Ray's Wagtail" – an old name for this species – as a "summer visitant". Parfitt's addition of "occasional breeder" was quoted by D'Urban & Mathew (1895) but no evidence was given to support this claim. Wynne-Edwards & Harrisson (1932) described Yellow Wagtail as an "irregular breeder" and listed one pair breeding in 1930 but without any substantiating detail. Oldham (1932) reported seeing "half a dozen among pasturing cattle" in late August/early September of that year.

Four Yellow Wagtails had been ringed on Lundy by the end of 2006, but there are no controls or recoveries involving the island. Birds of the British breeding race *M. f. flavissima* winter in Senegal and Gambia, migrating through western France, Iberia and North Africa, using a route slightly further to the east in spring than in autumn. There is some evidence that birds breeding in south-west Britain migrate directly to the Portuguese coast in autumn (Wernham *et al.* 2002).

Citrine Wagtail *Motacilla citreola*

British vagrant.

Breeds in eastern Europe and is gradually extending its range westwards. Migrates to wintering grounds in India and south-east Asia. 178 records for Britain 1950–2005.

The sole Lundy record was also the first for Devon:

1998 6 Aug – a first-winter bird caught and ringed in St John's Valley.

Grey Wagtail *Motacilla cinerea*

Uncommon spring migrant; common autumn migrant in small numbers; occasional summer records; rare in winter.

Grey Wagtails are typically seen singly, most often around the walled gardens, stream and marshy pond in lower Millcombe, but daytime migrants can be heard calling in flight anywhere on the island, many passing through without stopping.

There is a small but regular spring passage between late February and the end of May, with a peak in March. This involves mostly single birds, though four is the maximum daily count (on 30 March 1999 and 10 April 2006). There are occasional records of ones and twos passing through during June and July, but there is no indication that nesting has ever been attempted, even though Parfitt (1876) and Chanter (1877) listed Grey Wagtail as a "summer visitant", Parfitt adding "occasional breeder". It seems likely that summer records relate to local dispersal from mainland breeding populations in Wales and south-west England.

The main autumn migration begins in late August, continuing to the end of October and occasionally into November, with a marked peak in September. During detailed recording in the autumn of 1973, 79 Grey Wagtails were logged flying south in September, with 28 in October. While most daily counts are of ones and twos, three to five in a day is not unusual. The maximum counts to date are of 15 on 20 & 24 September 1973.[120]

Records are few and far between from mid-November to late February, with just a handful of sightings of single birds. There are two cases of possible overwintering, with records on scattered dates between December and February in 1982/83 and again in 1989/90, but the evidence is too thin to draw any firm conclusion for either winter. There have been no winter records since 1990.

Sixty-three Grey Wagtails had been ringed on Lundy by the end of 2006, but there are no controls or recoveries involving the island. Birds breeding in northern Britain move south for the winter, mostly to southern parts of Britain or Ireland, but some reach France and possibly Iberia. In addition, Grey Wagtails breeding in Scandinavia and continental Europe migrate south-west in autumn, some passing through Britain to wintering grounds further south (Wernham *et al.* 2002). Migrants occurring on Lundy may therefore include birds of British, continental and Scandinavian origin.

Pied Wagtail

Pied / White Wagtail *Motacilla alba* [White Wagtail]

Pied Wagtails nest most years in small numbers and are common spring and autumn migrants, but rare in midwinter. White Wagtails occur annually during both spring and autumn migrations.

Pied and White Wagtails can be encountered anywhere on the island in spring and autumn, but especially around the village and farm, Old Light, Castle Hill, Brick and Tillage Fields and other areas of close-grazed grassland. Between one and five pairs of Pied Wagtails (*M. a. yarrellii*) have nested in most years since LFS records began, typically in holes in walls close to habitation, but also in natural rocky crevices, such as at Quarry Pond. These birds are generally present from March to October.

Between March and May and particularly from August to October, Pied Wagtails are common migrants, moving between breeding grounds further north in the UK and wintering grounds that are largely in southern England, western France and Iberia (Wernham *et al.* 2002). Many individuals and small groups pass straight through, particularly in fine weather, flight calls from high overhead drawing the attention of alert birdwatchers. Spring passage can begin as early as mid-February, while the last autumn movements often continue into November. There are occasional sightings – mainly of single birds – in December and January, but the island is largely vacated during winter. In spring high counts are often recorded in late March, with the peak for the month being 35 on 27 March 1981.[121] In April and May the picture becomes more difficult to interpret, due to the overlap in migration periods of Pied and White Wagtails (described below), but small movements continue throughout the spring, with passage overall much lighter than in autumn.

171

White Wagtails (*M. a. alba*) breed in Iceland and continental Europe, wintering in the Mediterranean basin south into tropical Africa (Wernham *et al.* 2002). Given Lundy's west-coast location, the majority of White Wagtails passing through the island are likely to be Icelandic breeders en route to or from their southern wintering grounds. In spring most White Wagtails occur between mid-April and mid-May, somewhat later than peak movements of Pieds, with maximum counts being 13 on 20 April 1976 and 26 on 16 May 1978. However, it is likely that some White Wagtails have been overlooked, since reasonably close views and a degree of experience are needed to separate the two races. For this reason it is considered that some spring counts of 'Pied' Wagtails, especially in April/May, are likely to include an unspecified proportion of Whites.

In autumn the two sub-species are even more difficult to distinguish, and many records are simply of 'alba' wagtails, grouping Pied and White together. The main migration period is from late August until mid-October, with peak numbers typically occurring in early to mid-September. Large flocks have built up in some years; for example, in the 1961 *LFS Annual Report* Dudley Iles reported that over 200 'alba' wagtails roosted in the Brick Field on 2 September that year, and that "all of the albas watched and caught were Whites". The highest ever count for the island was of 250 on 3 September 1982, also including "a large proportion" of Whites. These numbers are exceptional, however, and autumn peaks did not exceed 50 during the 10 years 1997–2006.

Chanter (1871) and Parfitt (1876) listed Pied Wagtail as "resident all the year", the latter also adding "summer visitant" and "occasional breeder". Loyd (1922) reported "several pairs found nesting in the gardens, farm buildings, etc." in 1922. Wynne-Edwards & Harrisson (1932) recorded six pairs breeding in 1930. Perry (1940) listed two pairs in 1939. Alexander *et al.* (1945) found one family party in June 1942.

Between 1947 and 2006, 170 Pied/White Wagtails were ringed on Lundy but there has been just one recovery: a nestling Pied Wagtail ringed on the island on 27 June 1958 was found dead near Bude, Cornwall, on 17 December 1960. There are no other indications of where Lundy's breeding wagtails go in winter. In addition, there has been one control on the island of a bird ringed elsewhere: an adult Pied Wagtail ringed at Dungeness, Kent, on 17 August 1952 was caught at the North Light on 11 September 1956 during its southward migration. The skeleton of a White Wagtail ringed as a nestling in northern Iceland on 20 June 1956 was found at the North Light on 24 October 1956, adding weight to the theory that most White Wagtails occurring on Lundy are Icelandic breeders.

Waxwing *Bombycilla garrulus* [Bohemian Waxwing]

Lundy vagrant.

There are just four dated records of this nomadic winter visitor from Scandinavia and Russia, which is particularly scarce in western England. Two of the records are for the 2004/05 winter, which saw an unprecedented influx, both nationally and regionally, with significant numbers reported from mainland Devon. Chanter (1871) and Parfitt (1876) listed Waxwing as an "occasional visitant" but there are no dated records other than those listed below:

1990 1 & 3 Nov – one seen at Quarter Wall and at the top of Millcombe – the first confirmed Lundy record.

1997 6 May – one perched in sycamores next to the blue door at the top of Millcombe on a very cold, unspring-like day.

2004 22 Oct – one in Millcombe, probably part of a national autumn and winter 'invasion' which otherwise did not reach Devon until January 2005.

2005 30 Jan – one seen twice, near the Laundry and in the beer garden, in the village.[122]

Wren *Troglodytes troglodytes* [Winter Wren]

Common breeding resident.

In recent years Lundy has certainly held its fair share of the UK's estimated eight-and-a-half million Wrens – in 2000 the country's most numerous bird (Baillie *et al.* 2006). The highest densities occur in the well-vegetated eastern combes and sidelands but there are territory-holding birds around most of the coastline, including the wild and rocky West Side. Wherever you find yourself on the island's perimeter, you can be sure there will be a Wren not too far away.

Wren was listed by Chanter (1871) and Parfitt (1876) as "resident all the year", the latter adding "and breed there". Wynne-Edwards & Harrisson (1932) reported 11 breeding pairs in 1930, while Perry (1940) recorded 35 territories in 1939. N.V. Allen counted 50–60 birds in October 1944 (1944 *Devon Bird Report*). There have been full or partial censuses in nine years. One of these surveys, along the East Side in 1985, revealed at least 21 territories. In our own intensive (unpublished) survey of the island's landbirds over a two-week period in May 2000 we mapped 43 Wren territories: 30 on the East Side (including Millcombe and the village/farm area), 10 on the West Side and three at South End. A month later, when Wren activity might be expected to be less obvious with birds intent on gathering food for hungry young, Parsons (2002) mapped 32 territories using a hand-held Global Positioning System (GPS) receiver, producing a virtually identical distribution. The next complete survey, in 2004, located 44 territories: 34 on the East Side, 12 on the West Side and four at South End (Lock 2004). The spread of territories in all three surveys matches very closely, giving a good indication that the resident population is both stable and highly sedentary, at least during the breeding season.

As for all insectivorous species that overwinter in the UK, Wrens are vulnerable to the effects of prolonged cold spells and in decades past, numbers on Lundy have fluctuated accordingly. After the exceptionally severe 1962/63 winter, only one pair bred – a family party was seen in Millcombe in mid-June 1963 – and a maximum of seven birds were counted on 22 September. However, as Wrens are double-brooded, raising between five and eight young per brood, the population recovered relatively rapidly, reaching an estimated 28 pairs by 1975.

Wren

A series of apparently all-island counts of between 31 and 43 Wrens in October of every year from 1999 to 2006 – possibly including passage migrants (see below) – has shown the population to be rather stable at present. Winter observations suggest that Wrens concentrate in the more sheltered south-east of the island, including around the village and farm, where they are more likely to find the insects needed to see them through to spring.

There is some evidence of autumn movements of Wrens through Lundy. Studies by the LFS wardens during the 1950s revealed modest increases in their numbers in October; for example, over a third of the 39 Wrens trapped in 1952 were caught in the first week of October, a feature noted in several subsequent years. Most bird observatories around the British and Irish coast detect elevated numbers of Wrens in late autumn, mainly in October. While the majority are dispersing British or Irish birds of the race *T. t. indigenus*, ringing recoveries show that at least some are passage migrants of the nominate race *T. t. troglodytes* that breeds in continental Europe (Wernham *et al.* 2002). Two individuals seen on Lundy on 14 November 1954 were "quite unlike the local birds" and thought at the time to be of continental origin, though field separation of the two races is of dubious reliability.

In spite of the circumstantial evidence that the Wrens occurring on Lundy are not entirely sedentary, there are – as yet – no ringing recoveries or controls to prove this. On the contrary, of 978 Wrens ringed by the end 2006, only one – a second-year bird ringed on 27 April 1996 – has been recovered, on 12 November three years later…on Lundy. There are also numerous examples of Wrens that have been ringed on the island and retrapped there, which only goes to show that Wrens may be extremely perky and active birds, but they go nowhere fast!

Dunnock

Dunnock *Prunella modularis*

Common breeding resident in apparently declining numbers; small influxes of passage migrants detected occasionally in autumn.

Though conspicuous early in the breeding season when their rather plaintive rattling song and 'wing flicking' courtship display draw attention, Dunnocks can also be one of the easiest birds to overlook. Their behaviour later becomes skulking and unobtrusive, presenting challenges when it comes to surveying the population, and breeding census results can be tricky to interpret; for example, a single territory may contain two singing males (Gibbons *et al.* 1993).

Chanter (1871) and Parfitt (1876) listed "Hedge Accentor" as "resident all the year", Parfitt adding "and breed there". Twenty-three pairs were recorded in 1930 by Wynne-Edwards & Harrisson (1932), Gade reported 15 to 20 pairs in 1931 (Davis 1954a), and Perry (1940) reported six nesting pairs in 1939.

Dunnocks are considered to have bred in every year since LFS recording began in 1947, but the population has fluctuated from one or a handful of pairs to as many as 20 pairs (in 1996), though given the complexities of Dunnock family life it would probably be more accurate to substitute "pairs" for "singing males". Breeding has typically occurred in and around Millcombe and northwards along the East Side to the Terrace, with the occasional territory recorded on the lower slopes of the East Side, perhaps as far north as Halfway Wall Bay in years of higher numbers. The variation in numbers of breeding birds from year to year probably depends largely on winter survival – the harder the winter, the greater the mortality among the resident population.

However, there also appears to have been a recent decline in numbers that seems more likely to be linked to a shortage of dense ground-cover shrubs due to overgrazing by goats, deer and rabbits in Millcombe and St John's Valley and the removal of large areas of rhododendron on the East Side. For example, during late April and early May 2007 a maximum of just three singing males was recorded, all of these from rhododendron on the East Side. Only one Dunnock was seen in Millcombe during this period and none was trapped by ringers operating in Millcombe and St John's Valley. During winter 2006/07 the maximum count was just two.

Maximum autumn counts for the 10 years 1997–2006, mostly in October, were of between nine and 25 birds – the resident population perhaps augmented by passage migrants. As Dunnocks are less vocal at this time of year and tend to remain hidden, these numbers may well have been underestimates of the actual numbers present.

British breeding Dunnocks are highly sedentary, with young birds generally moving only very short distances from their place of hatching (Wernham *et al.* 2002). There have been numerous retraps on Lundy within and between years and all six recoveries from among the 868 birds ringed by the end of 2006 were found on the island. Of these, the longest-lived bird was one ringed in its first year on 22 September 1984 and found freshly dead almost five years later on 6 September 1989. In some years there have been suggestions that migrating or dispersing Dunnocks may pass through the island, usually during October; in 1962, for example, an unusual concentration was noticed below Halfway Wall in mid-month. Most of the time, however, detecting even the resident birds – let alone migrants – is hard enough. In 1985 there were about seven Dunnock territories during the breeding season and 32 individuals were counted in early October (the maximum daily count on record), yet 61 birds were ringed that year (the highest annual total to date).

Alpine Accentor *Prunella collaris*

British vagrant.

Breeds in the high mountain ranges of southern, central and eastern Europe. Most descend to lower altitudes in winter, with some moving relatively long distances. 15 records for Britain 1950–2005, mostly in spring, with seven in May.

The sole Lundy record was only the fourth for Devon, following three nineteenth century occurrences along the south coast:

1993 8 May – one was watched at close range feeding actively amongst the rocks and grazed turf at the western end of Halfway Wall above Jenny's Cove.

Robin *Erithracus rubecula*   [European Robin]

Common breeding resident present in small numbers; uncommon spring migrant; common autumn migrant in small numbers.

Robins on Lundy are largely restricted to the East Side, generally between St John's Valley and the Terrace, occasionally as far north as Gannets' Combe. However, migrants also use the stone walls on top of the island and are sometimes seen in the Stoneycroft area in autumn. Their song, along with that of Wren, is a familiar sound on the island as resident birds defend feeding and breeding territories year-round.

Chanter (1871) and Parfitt (1876) listed Robin as "resident all the year", Parfitt adding "and breed there". Loyd (1925) stated that "several pairs nest annually in cultivated and sheltered spots, notably the pleasure grounds and the quarries". Crespi (1888), Davenport (1897), Cummings (1909) and Ross & Rousham (1909) all mentioned Robin but gave no indication of their breeding numbers. Wynne-Edwards & Harrisson (1932) considered that nine pairs bred in 1930. Perry (1940) noted spring passage on 29 March 1939 and recorded six breeding pairs that year. Apart from an absence of breeding birds in 1962 and 1963 after two successive hard winters, Robins would appear to have nested in every year since LFS records began in 1947. However, estimates of the breeding population have been made in only 17 years, varying between one pair in 2000, 10 pairs in 1953, 1958 and 1972, 12 pairs in 1973 and 2004, and an astonishing high of 30 pairs in 1975. The *LFS Annual Report* for that year states "30 pairs on territories in April including

Robin

10 at Millcombe and the remainder down the east side but largely towards the south end". While the figure of 30 pairs seems improbably high, twelve pairs bred two years previously in 1973, leading Dymond (1980) to speculate that a series of mild winters may have contributed towards such a high breeding population. By 1984, two years after a very cold period during the winter of 1981/82, the population had fallen to six pairs. Thereafter numbers fluctuated between one and four pairs until a census in 2004 found 12 territorial pairs (Lock 2004).

Suspected migrants have occasionally been recorded in spring, mostly in March, but the pattern of occurrence is masked by the presence of resident birds. Migration is more obvious in autumn in some years, particularly between late September and early November. Although recording of Robins in autumn has been patchy over the years, there is some evidence to suggest a small increase in numbers passing through the island recently. Between 1947 and the end of the 1970s, daily maxima were generally 20 or below. During the 1980s and 1990s, peak counts of more than 20 were recorded in at least 13 years, with a high of 50 on 10 October 1988. Since 2000, up to and including 2006, there have been 10 further counts of 50 or more – in 2001 (on five days), 2002 (once), 2004 (twice) and 2005 (twice). In 2001, counts of 40 to 65 birds were made on 10 days between 8 October and 5 November, with the peak of 65 reached on 21 October. The highest count to date is 75 on 29 October 2004.

Robins remain on the island throughout the winter, but counts at this time of year are few and far between. The highest count by some margin is 20 on 27 December 2000, with two counts of 10 on 1 January in both 1981 and 1989 being the next highest.

A total of 1,687 Robins had been ringed on Lundy by the end of 2006, two of which were later controlled or recovered away from the island. In addition, many retraps and several recoveries on the island of Lundy-ringed birds – for instance, a Robin ringed as a juvenile on the Terrace in 1951 and subsequently retrapped there in each of the next five years – suggest that the breeding population is largely sedentary. Amazingly, both of the Robins showing movement away from Lundy – see table (a) – were ringed on the same day, one turning up near Swansea less than a month later. The bird recovered in Cornwall in January 1985 was found dead during cold weather. It may have already been on the mainland for several months, or it could have been forced to leave Lundy in search of food because of the severe cold. Another bird, ringed on Lundy in September 1983, was found dead on the island in February 1985 during the same spell of harsh weather.

Wernham *et al.* (2002) indicated that British breeders, of the race *E. r. melophilus*, are largely sedentary, but there is a degree of post-juvenile dispersal and a few individuals move longer distances, exceptionally as far as Spain. Overall though, only 10% of Robins ringed in Britain during the breeding season but recovered outside the breeding season had moved more than 20 kilometres. This is consistent with the low number of movements to/from Lundy. However, the nominate race *E. r. rubecula*, which

(a) Robins ringed on Lundy and controlled or recovered elsewhere

Age/sex	Date ringed on Lundy	Place found	Date controlled or recovered	Speculation about date/place of finding
1st-year	16 Sep 1984	Langland Bay, Swansea, Glamorgan	14 Oct 1984	Autumn dispersal or migration
1st-year	16 Sep 1984	Liskeard, Cornwall	16 Jan 1985	Cold weather movement

(b) Robins ringed elsewhere and controlled or recovered on Lundy

Age/sex	Date ringed	Place ringed	Date controlled or recovered	Speculation about date/place of ringing
1st-year	03 Oct 1987	Bornholm Island, **Denmark**	30 Dec 1987	On autumn migration
2nd-year	10 Apr 1996	Nanjizal, Land's End, Cornwall	27 Apr 1996	On spring migration

breeds in continental Europe, is much more mobile and varies from wholly migratory (Fennoscandia), to partially migratory (most of range), to largely sedentary (southern Europe). Of the migratory / partially migratory populations, females are more likely to migrate than males, and first-years more likely to do so than adults. Migrants move west and south into western Europe and the Mediterranean (including North Africa). Falls of continental birds occur on the east coast of Britain from August to November, peaking in October. Most appear to be from Fennoscandia, heading for wintering grounds further south and west. Others come from the Baltic States, Poland and eastern Germany west to Belgium. It seems likely that small numbers of continental birds pass through Lundy and other west coast passage 'hotspots' in most years, but the 1987 Danish-ringed bird is the only conclusive link to the continent. The movement of this individual, ringed on the Danish island of Bornholm, 40 kilometres south-east of the southern tip of Sweden, and killed by a cat on Lundy in late December the same year, is in line with the finding of Wernham *et al.* (2002) that a few *E. r. rubecula* winter in Britain. Most passage Robins probably move on quickly, though some may establish temporary territories. Northward migration peaks in March, with most continental breeding territories occupied by late April.

Thrush Nightingale *Luscinia luscinia*

British vagrant.

Breeds in northern and eastern Europe, including parts of Scandinavia, extending east across Russia. Migrates to winter in eastern sub-Saharan Africa. 158 records for Britain 1950–2005.

There is one Lundy record, of a single bird in autumn:

1981 24 Sep – a first-winter bird at the top of Millcombe was trapped and ringed.

Nightingale *Luscinia megarhynchos* [Common Nightingale]

Rare spring and autumn migrant.

Glimpses of this habitually skulking bird of dense vegetation are often tantalisingly brief, though on rare occasions Nightingales have been seen out in the open, as in May 2005 when one was watched at length feeding on the ground between clumps of gorse above Brambles (St John's Valley).

In all, there have been 35 Lundy records, the first (trapped and ringed) on 31 August 1957 and the most recent on 7 May 2005. Fourteen have been in spring and 21 in autumn. All occurrences have been of single birds except for three on 27 May 1991, and most have been seen in either Millcombe or St John's Valley.

Spring migrants have been recorded between 12 April (1996) and 5 June (also 1996, seen at Hanmers), with most occurrences between mid-April and mid-May. Felix Gade wrote in *My Life on Lundy* (1978, p. 444): "In April [1963] Diana [Keast] heard a nightingale singing in Millcombe; this was the first Lundy record of a singing nightingale, and it was confirmed by both Albion [Harman] and Michael Jones [LFS warden]". Song has been noted on just one other occasion and so appears to be very much the exception, though non-birdwatching visitors often assume that any bird heard singing in the dark in spring or early summer must have been a Nightingale, rather than the much more likely Blackbird, Song Thrush, Robin or Sedge Warbler.

Autumn birds have occurred from 30 July (1989, a juvenile in Millcombe) to 18 October (1984[123]), with the majority of sightings falling between late August and mid-October.

Following a run of almost annual occurrences between 1970 and 1991 there has been a dearth of Nightingales in recent years, with two in 1996 (April and June) and one in 2005 (May) being the only records during the 15 years up to and including 2006. While no firm conclusions can be drawn from such a small sample, BTO surveys show that the UK breeding range has contracted markedly and that the population size has also fallen. Given Lundy's location on the westernmost fringes of the Nightingale's range, it seems likely that this iconic species will remain an irregular and elusive visitor.

Eight Nightingales had been ringed on Lundy by the end of 2006, but there are no controls or recoveries involving the island.

Bluethroat *Luscinia svecica*

Lundy vagrant.

The red-spotted nominate race *L. s. svecica* breeds mainly north of the Baltic, from Scandinavia east across Russia, while the white-spotted races *L. s. cyanecula* and *L. s. namnetum* breed in southern and central Europe, and western France, respectively. European birds winter around the Mediterranean and in the Sahel zone of Africa. 4,541 records for Britain 1968–2003, with an average of 85 per year 2000–2003; considered by the BOU as a passage migrant rather than a nationally scarce migrant.

Though recorded quite regularly at bird observatories and many other well-known migration watch-points along the east coast of Britain, Bluethroat is an extreme rarity on Lundy. There have been just eight records, with four of these in May, three in September and one in October. Available information allows only three birds to be assigned to a subspecies (see below). The four most recent occurrences have all been in late spring:

1949 14 Sep – one of the red-spotted race (*L. s. svecica*).
20 & 22 Oct – one, different to the September individual.
1956 19 & 21 Sep – a first-year male trapped and ringed on 19 Sep.
1964 2 Sep – one, caught and ringed.[124]
1985 20 May – one, caught and ringed.
1993 27 May – one of the red-spotted race watched catching insects on a dung heap at the top of the High Street during the late afternoon.[125]
1995 10 May – a male of the red-spotted race at Stoneycroft.
2004 23 May – a female near Quarter Wall.[126]

In addition, the 1959/60 *LFS Annual Report* states "one probable on 27th September". This record is included without any qualification in the 1960 *Devon Bird Report*, but discounted by Dymond (1980). Given the doubt that clearly applied to the original report, we have also excluded it here.

Three Bluethroats had been ringed on Lundy by the end of 2006, but there are no controls or recoveries involving the island.

Red-flanked Bluetail *Tarsiger cyanurus*

British vagrant.

Breeds from Finland eastwards across Russia, wintering in south-east Asia. 34 records for Britain 1950–2005.

There is one Lundy record, also the first for Devon:

2005 14 Oct – a first-year bird (thought likely to be a female) mist-netted in St John's Valley and ringed, seen subsequently in Millcombe.

The following is an extract from Richard Castle's account in the 2005 *Devon Bird Report*:

"...we were due to start taking down the nets in St Johns Valley around mid-afternoon. Things were starting to quieten down when at 13.40 hrs a brownish chat was seen in a net on the north side of St Johns Valley by one of the group, Lucy James. Upon reaching the bird she realised she had something special when she saw the large area of blue on the rump and tail feathers. She initially identified the bird as a Red-flanked Bluetail and brought it back to the base (in a rather

Red-flanked Bluetail

excited state) for confirmation and ringing. It turned out to be a first winter bird, and possibly a female due to lack of a blue tinge to the tertials or lesser coverts. After pictures were taken, the bird was released and flew towards Millcombe Valley. It was last seen there a couple of hours later" (Castle 2005).

Remarkably, Devon's second Red-flanked Bluetail (also a first-winter individual, but unringed) was seen at Berry Head in the south of the county, four days after the Lundy bird, on 18 & 19 October.

Black Redstart *Phoenicurus ochruros*

Common late-autumn migrant in small numbers; uncommon spring migrant; has overwintered.

Black Redstarts have a liking for the sidelands and cliff-tops – especially between the Castle and Benjamin's Chair – though they also occur regularly on buildings and drystone walls around the village and Old Light/Stoneycroft. The first recorded occurrence of a Black Redstart on Lundy was one seen by Felix Gade on 28 October 1944 (1944 *Devon Bird Report*).

Small numbers occur during spring migration, which extends from mid-March to mid-June. The two highest counts for each month (1947–2006) are:

March Ten on 25 Mar 1949, six on 26 Mar 2002
April Eight on 24 Apr 2002, three on 12 Apr 1988
May Six on 4 May 1980, two on 10 May 1976 and 8 May 1988
June Single birds only, mostly in the first week.

There have been a handful of sightings between mid-June and mid-September, mostly of single birds. These are likely to include early-returning failed breeders and dispersing first-year birds. However, there is also the possibility that a few of these individuals have been misidentified Common Redstarts, which migrate earlier than Black Redstarts.

More concerted autumn migration sometimes begins with ones and twos in the second half of September, but typically gets under way in October, reaching a peak from the middle of the month and continuing until mid-November. The highest counts for October are 23 on 23 October 1988 and 24 on 23 October 1996, while up to 12 have been seen in November (3rd 1982).[127] However, numbers vary considerably from year to year; for example, there were only three sightings of single birds in October 1997, the year after the highest ever count. This presumably reflects prevailing weather conditions, easterly winds being most favourable for arrivals of this species.

Dymond (1980) noted the occasional occurrence of Black Redstarts on the island in winter. During the 25 years 1981 to 2005, single birds were seen in December in nine years. There were sightings in January and/or February of the following year in at least four cases, strongly suggesting that these individuals had overwintered on Lundy; for example, singles were seen on 16 & 24 December 1994 and 8 January and 21 February 1995. Ornithological coverage is patchy in winter and it would be interesting to see what regular recording would reveal about the species' status at this time of year.

Thirty-five Black Redstarts had been ringed on Lundy by the end of 2006, but there are no controls or recoveries involving the island. Ringing recoveries mapped in *The Migration Atlas* (Wernham *et al.* 2002) suggest that Black Redstarts passing through Britain in the autumn originate mainly from western continental Europe, while birds from central European breeding populations are more likely to occur in spring.

Redstart *Phoenicurus phoenicurus*   [Common Redstart]

Common spring and autumn migrant in small numbers.

The fence lines around the top of Millcombe, at Quarter Wall and along the Upper East Side Path are among the best places to look for migrant Redstarts, especially in warm, settled conditions. Spring migration is mainly confined to April and May, though there are four March records, the earliest being of one on 17 & 18 March 1998 and two on 18 March 1990. The great majority of first sightings for the year have fallen between 10 and 25 April. Daily counts are typically of ones and twos and have only exceptionally reached double figures, the highest being 14 on 17 April 1966 and 15 on 2 May 2004[128] (the latter coinciding with a major 'fall' of other species). Migrants continue to be seen irregularly until the end of May and occasionally into early June, but there are just three reports later than 10th, the last of these being of a female in Millcombe on 28 June 1995. There are no July records.

While the earliest August record is of one bird on 5th (1973), return migration generally commences towards the end of the month, movements usually peaking in late September or early October. Autumn passage is not much more pronounced than in spring and double-digit counts are again highly unusual. The daily maxima recorded for each month are: six on 31 August 1983; 20 on 19 September 1977, 16 September 1984 and 26 September 1986; and eight on 1 October 1988. Small numbers continue to be seen well into October and the last for the year typically occurs in the second half of the month. Redstarts have twice lingered into November: in 1978 a single bird was seen on 8th, while in 2002 one on 16th[129] is the latest record to date.

While this species has never been numerous (at least since LFS records began), there is some suggestion of an increase during the 1980s and early 1990s, followed by something of a decline, especially since 2000. Although the sample size is small and coverage of the island by birdwatchers varies from year to year, these observations are in line with fluctuations in the UK breeding population reported by the BTO (Baillie *et al.* 2007).

Chanter (1871) and Parfitt (1876) listed Redstart as a "summer visitant", the latter adding "occasional breeder" – a designation described by Davis (1954a) as "most improbable".

By the end of 2006, 348 Redstarts had been ringed on Lundy, with one control and one recovery away from the island. An adult female ringed on Lundy on 16 September 1984 was found at Ben Slimane in north-west Morocco on 28 September 1985, while a first-year male ringed on Lundy on 17 September 1986 was controlled as a breeding bird in the county of Møre og Romsdal, western Norway, on 26 June 1987. These cases provide tantalising glimpses of the migratory journeys followed by two of Lundy's autumn Redstarts, with the Norwegian control suggesting that autumn migrants through the island include at least some birds of Scandinavian/continental origin. There are also two spring controls on the island of birds ringed elsewhere, suggestive of individuals returning to breeding grounds in Britain or Ireland: an adult female ringed at Slapton, South Devon, on 17 April 1963 was controlled on Lundy (caught at South Light) just six days later on 23 April; and an adult male ringed at Calf of Man Bird Observatory on 7 May 1978 was controlled on Lundy on 16 April 1979.

Whinchat *Saxicola rubetra*

Uncommon spring migrant; more regular in autumn; occasional records in midsummer.

The warm, mottled brown and buff plumage of a Whinchat provides perfect camouflage for a species that on Lundy occurs mostly in areas of open rough grassland and bracken. Yet its broad pale eyebrow, or supercilium, and regular habit of perching on top of vegetation, a wire fence or fencepost make it quite easy to pick out.

Spring migration through Lundy occurs mainly in the second half of April and May, with odd ones being seen in June in some years. There are two exceptionally early reports on 6 March (in 1996 and 2002[130]). However, given that the average date of first arrival nationally is 16 April (BTO 2006) and the possibility of confusion with Stonechat – for which the main spring migration period is March – there must be some doubt about the accuracy of these observations. The next earliest date is 17 March in both 1955 and 1958, and these are regarded here as the earliest spring records. There are only five instances of 10 or more birds seen in a day, the largest number by far being 30 on 2 May 2004.

There have been June records in 17 LFS years and these are spread throughout the month, making it difficult to distinguish between late northward-bound migrants and itinerant, non-breeding birds or early-returning migrants, possibly including failed breeders from the populations on Exmoor and in the mountains of South Wales. There are July records for 15 LFS years, spread between the first and last day of the month, by which time juvenile dispersal merges with more concerted southward movements.

Autumn migration occurs principally from the second half of August to the end of September, peaking in early September, with small numbers on a few days in October in some years, very rarely

Whinchat

into November. There is an undated November record for 1955 and Felix Gade reported seeing one on 10 November 1952, while single birds were present on 2 November 2001 and 5 November 2004. Whinchats are more numerous in autumn, and though usually seen in ones and twos, counts may sometimes reach double figures. The maximum is 25 on both 14 September 1958 and 6 September 1972.

The available data suggest that numbers passing through Lundy, especially in autumn, are lower now than formerly and it is noticeable that the two highest autumn counts are from more than 30 years ago. Whinchats underwent a significant range contraction between the 1968–1972 and 1988–1991 BTO breeding atlases and are probably in long-term decline. The English breeding population declined by a third between 1994 and 2004, while the overall UK population fell by 15% (Baillie *et al.* 2006).

In his original history of Lundy, Chanter (1871) listed Whinchat as an "occasional visitant", but his later monograph (1877) stated "resident all the year". It is likely he was influenced by Parfitt's 1876 listing of Whinchat as a breeding resident. This led D'Urban & Mathew (1895) to suggest that "this species and the Stonechat have been probably confounded", which seems certain to be the case. Loyd (1925) mentioned that nearly all of the early observers – Davenport in 1897, Blathwayt in 1900, Ross in 1908 and Hendy in 1914 – saw Whinchats on Lundy, some of them in June, giving rise to speculation that the species might be breeding.

By the end of 2006, 111 Whinchats had been ringed on Lundy, but there are no controls or recoveries involving the island. Unlike Stonechats, which are only partially migratory, Whinchats are long-distance migrants, British breeding birds overflying the Sahara to winter in cultivated land, savanna grassland and forest clearings, and returning to breed in mainly upland areas in northern and western Britain (Wernham *et al.* 2002).

Stonechat *Saxicola torquatus* [Eurasian Stonechat]

Stonechat

Breeds occasionally; uncommon spring migrant and regular autumn migrant; irregular in winter.

Stonechats seldom remain hidden for long, their constant alarm calls and habit of perching prominently on the nearest clump of vegetation or fence-line quickly drawing attention, especially when family parties of still-fluffy juveniles are encountered.

Migrant Stonechats occur regularly in small numbers in spring, mostly in March; the highest counts in a day are 12 on 1 March 1976 and 14 on 16 March 2006. Occasionally very small numbers occur even earlier, with an exceptional influx of 42 on 26 February 1977. In non-breeding years odd ones and twos pass through in April and May, exceptionally in June and July. Higher numbers migrate through the island in autumn. Stonechats are uncommon in August except in breeding years; the main passage occurring from mid-September through October, with small numbers on a few days in November, and occasionally to the middle of December. The highest counts recorded on a single day are 50 on 7 October 1973, all of which had gone two days later, and more than 70 on 10 October 1984.

Parfitt (1876) described Stonechat as an "occasional visitant" and "occasional breeder". Earlier, Chanter (1871) stated "resident all the year" but amended this to "occasional visitant" in his 1877 revision in which Stonechat and Whinchat were transposed – see Whinchat, page 181. Davis (1954a) stated that the species "seems to have bred regularly until 1942, at times in considerable numbers": Loyd (1922) estimated about 20 breeding pairs, Wynne-Edwards & Harrisson (1932) recorded 28 pairs in 1930, and Perry (1940) found 15 pairs in 1939, though only five pairs were noted by Lack (1934) in late June 1934.

There are no records of breeding between 1943 and 1950. One pair bred annually from 1951 to 1953 and there were between four and six pairs from 1960 to 1962. Twenty-eight years elapsed until breeding was recorded again, a pair on the East Side near Tibbett's raising two broods in 1990. Since then Stonechats have bred in at least nine years up to (and including) 2007, fluctuating between one and a peak of seven pairs in 1996, when at least four nests were successful. Most breeding territories are along the East Side, from Halfway Wall Bay to Gannets' Combe, occasionally also on Ackland's Moor and south of Pondsbury. In the first week of May 2007, pairs were established on the sidings below St Helen's Combe, along the Lower East Side Path near Tibbett's Point, on the gorse-covered slopes of Tibbett's Hill and in Gannets' Combe. Breeding birds are summer visitors to the island, rather than resident, and most have probably left by the time the main autumn migration begins in mid-September. Stonechats breeding in Britain are of the race *S. t. hibernans*, which also occurs in Brittany and western Iberia.

Although insectivorous and therefore vulnerable to cold weather when food is scarce, Stonechats are sometimes recorded on the island in winter. It is rare to see more than one or two at a time, but five were present on 27 December 2000 and there was a count of nine on 18 February 2007.

There are two reported instances of 'Siberian Stonechat', *S. t. maurus*. The 1948 *LFS Annual Report* mentions one on 14 September but acknowledges that "it cannot be asserted with confidence on the basis of a sight record only". The 1979 *LFS Annual Report* gives two on 4 October (whereas the original logbook shows just one) but the record appears not to have been submitted to the BBRC. There are two accepted Devon records, both in 2001 (Langman *et al.* 2007).

A total of 194 Stonechats had been ringed on Lundy by the end of 2006, but there are no controls or recoveries involving the island. Ringing studies show that some of the breeding birds in southern England migrate to southern Iberia, while those wintering in Britain establish territories two or three times the size of their breeding territories to ensure sufficient food supplies (Wernham *et al.* 2002).

Wheatear *Oenanthe oenanthe* [Northern Wheatear]

Summer visitor; breeds; common spring and autumn migrant.

Take the main track and head north in spring, summer or autumn and before long there will be a Wheatear on a wall, fence, rock, gorse bush or perched precariously on top of bracken. The males in particular are spectacular in their blue-grey and creamy-buff breeding plumage, the broad white supercilium conspicuous, and the white rump obvious as they flit from perch to perch. Song-flighting Wheatears – males bouncing into the air and letting rip with a torrent of scratchy notes before coming back to earth – are one of the characteristic sights and sounds of the West Side in spring.

Chanter (1871) and Parfitt (1876) listed Wheatear as a "summer visitant", Parfitt adding "constant breeder". Davenport (1897), Ross & Rousham (1909) and Hendy (1914) reported Wheatears as "numerous" but without any indication of breeding numbers. Loyd (1925) recorded up to five pairs in 1922 and one pair in 1923, and nesting also occurred in 1927 to 1934 – Wynne-Edwards & Harrisson (1932) recording 12 pairs during their census of June 1930 – and almost annually from 1942 until the start of LFS recording in 1947. Estimates since then have put the population at between three and six pairs in most years, up to eight pairs in three years and 10 pairs or territory-holding birds in 1952, 1959, 1981 and 1996. The only years when it is considered that breeding was doubtful were 1965 and 1967 (Dymond 1980). Given their liking for holes in walls or under rocks, it is not surprising that nesting birds have been found all over the island. They have a particular affinity for the rocky, boulder-strewn West Side, and of 10 territories in 1996, most were located here. More recent surveys suggest a much higher breeding population: complete island surveys in May 2000 (Davis & Jones unpublished) and May 2004 (Lock 2004) both located 20 territories in broadly similar areas, with 11 and 12 respectively distributed along the West Side.

After early-arriving birds in March, spring passage builds up during April, with the main movements from the end of the month until mid-May. Early peaks in late March and the beginning of April consist mainly of British and Irish breeders of the nominate race, whereas peaks later in April until mid-May are attributable mainly to the later-migrating Greenland race, *O. o. leucorhoa* (Wernham *et al.* 2002). Slightly larger and brighter – though very difficult to distinguish without a practised eye – they are frequent in both spring and autumn. Occasionally, spring passage extends into June, when it becomes hard to separate late migrants from breeding residents. The earliest arrival date noted by the LFS is 5 March (1983 and 2003) but 3 March (1940) is the earliest on record (Davis 1954a). Spring peaks

Wheatear

have fluctuated between 10 (in 1968, a year of low observer coverage) and highs of 250 on 23 April 1989 and at least 300 on 2 May 2004.

Autumn passage, from late July, can be prolonged and is not well defined, with counts of 100 or more between mid-August and the end of September. Most if not all of the island's breeding birds have departed by early September. Smaller numbers of migrants occur during October, though peak autumn counts have occurred twice during the month: 60 on 25 October 1967 and 76 on 16 October 1990. These later peaks are likely to involve birds of the race *leucorhoa*, which do not leave the breeding grounds in Canada, Greenland and Iceland until late August (Wernham *et al.* 2002). Two hundred or more Wheatears in a day have occurred in four years: 200 on 7 September 1977 and 19 September 1987, 250 on 22 September 1982 and the highest count of 300 on 15 September 1974. Stragglers have occurred in November in six years, the latest date being 16 November (1957).

Of 429 birds ringed on Lundy by the end of 2006, none has been controlled or recovered. The only control of a bird ringed elsewhere is a juvenile of the *leucorhoa* race ringed in Greenland in 1958 and trapped in the Tillage Field on 8 May 1959 – the only conclusive evidence linking Lundy and Greenland.

Black-eared Wheatear *Oenanthe hispanica*

British vagrant.

Breeds in southern Europe, wintering in sub-Saharan Africa. 47 records for Britain 1950–2005.

There are two Lundy records, both of single birds:

1974 14 May – a male near Pondsbury.[131]
1984 3 Jun – a male near Quarter Wall Pond.

A record in the 1987 *LFS Annual Report* of a bird on the West Side north of Jenny's Cove from 6 to 15 May was rejected by the BBRC.

Desert Wheatear *Oenanthe deserti*

British vagrant.

Breeds in North Africa, the Middle East and central Asia; most populations are migratory, wintering in Africa south to the Sahel and in south-west Asia. 86 records for Britain 1950–2005.

There is one Lundy record of a single bird:

2003 26 Oct – a first-year male[132] seen feeding near the Devil's Limekiln was later trapped and ringed. There were nine other accepted British records in 2003, the second highest annual total to date, following 17 in 1997.

White's Thrush *Zoothera dauma*   [Scaly Thrush]

British vagrant.

Breeds in northern and eastern Russia, migrating to wintering grounds in south and south-east Asia. 38 records for Britain 1950–2005.

Listed by Chanter (1871) and Parfitt (1876) as "reported but not accurately identified" and therefore regarded by Chanter as doubtful. One LFS record of a single, long-staying bird:

1952 15 Oct to 8 Nov – one in Millcombe, feeding in the grass among the trees and on the open terrace in front of Millcombe House, but fleeing into nearby rhododendrons and hydrangeas when disturbed and staying hidden for long periods (Davis 1953d).

Swainson's Thrush (Olive-backed Thrush) *Catharus ustulatus*

British vagrant.

Breeds in North America, migrating to winter in Mexico and South America. 24 records for Britain 1950–2005.

184

There are three Lundy records, all in October:

1986   27 Oct – one found dead in Millcombe.
1987   15 to 31 Oct – one in and around Millcombe, caught and ringed on the first date.
1995   9 Oct – one in Millcombe was caught and ringed.[133]

The 1980 *LFS Annual Report* refers to an Olive-backed Thrush (the former name of Swainson's Thrush) on 14 April 1980 but the record appears not to have been submitted to the BBRC and is therefore discounted here.

Grey-cheeked Thrush *Catharus minimus*

British vagrant.

Breeds in north-east Siberia and northern North America. 46 records for Britain 1950–2005.
    The two Lundy records are both of single birds in October:

1985   11 Oct – one trapped and ringed in Millcombe.[134]
1986   26 Oct to 2 Nov – one in the St Helen's/Tillage Field area close to the Upper East Side Path.

A bird found dead and decaying in Millcombe on 27 October 1986 was thought, from its wing measurements, to be a Swainson's Thrush and was submitted as such to the BBRC, with a later re-submission as Grey-cheeked Thrush following further research on wing measurements. After due consideration, the BBRC report for 1989 included the following passage:

> "The biometrics of a corpse found on Lundy, Devon, on 27th October 1986 indicated that it was almost certainly of this species [Grey-cheeked Thrush], but its condition and the general circumstances of examination left an element of uncertainty as to whether Swainson's Thrush *C. ustulatus* was completely ruled out."

Veery

Veery *Catharus fuscescens*

British vagrant.

Breeds in North America, migrating to winter in South America. 7 records for Britain 1950–2005.
    There are two Lundy records of single birds, one in autumn and one in spring:

1987   10 Oct to 11 Nov – one, caught and ringed on 10th, remained in the area of Millcombe and St Helen's Field. It was extremely elusive for the first two weeks but then fed regularly in the open and was seen by hundreds of birdwatchers. The second British record.
1997   14 May – one in Millcombe, caught and ringed, and later watched feeding amongst leaf litter. Some 60 birdwatchers arrived on the island the following day in the hope of seeing the bird but, unlike its predecessor, it was never seen again.

Ring Ouzel

Ring Ouzel *Turdus torquatus*

Uncommon but regular spring and autumn migrant in small numbers.

Lundy's wild and rugged landscape provides a fitting staging area for a species synonymous with remote uplands and mountains. Whether feeding quietly on rowan berries, searching for worms in one of the fields, or chacking loudly in wildly dashing flight, Ring Ouzels are always exciting to see. They have been recorded in both spring and autumn in virtually every year since LFS recording began, though numbers vary greatly and there is some evidence of recent decline.

Spring migration generally commences in late March or early April, although in six LFS years the first birds were seen in the first half of March. The earliest by far was a male present from 8 to 10 February 1989. Peak spring passage is in April, with the highest daily counts being 18 on 10 April 1949 and 23 on 7 April 1966.[135] There have been a few other instances of 10 or more in a day, but the highest spring count for the 10 years 1998 to 2007 is five along the East Side on 19 April 2007 (coinciding with a notable national influx). While movements often continue into early May, there are just a handful of records after the middle of the month. Ring Ouzels have been recorded in June in only one year, single birds seen on 14, 15 & 30 June 1998. While a singing male was heard on 12 April 1948, there has never been any suggestion of breeding.

Until the mid-1960s, the first returning migrants were regularly seen in the last week of August (earliest: 23 August 1965) with passage usually peaking in September and often continuing into October, occasionally until the first week in November. However, there has not been an August record

186

since 1965, while from the 1980s onwards the highest numbers have most often been noted in mid to late October. These apparent changes may reflect a shift in the origin of the majority of Ring Ouzels passing through Lundy. Wernham *et al.* (2002) indicated that the main autumn migration of British Ring Ouzels is in September and that a late October peak is more likely to reflect arrivals of birds from Fennoscandian breeding grounds. The highest autumn count is 20, on 2 & 3 October 1951 and again on 18 October 2005. Peaks of 10 or more occurred in six other LFS years, four of these before 1975, perhaps hinting at a declining trend in recent decades, though the evidence for this is less clear in autumn than for spring migration. There have been November records in 13 years, with the latest sighting being a single bird on 11 November 1993.

There have been significant losses of breeding range and population in south-west England, Wales and Ireland since 1970 (e.g. Gibbons *et al.* 1993) and the remaining core nesting areas in northern England and Scotland are threatened by climate change and habitat degradation. It could therefore be expected that the proportion of British birds passing through Lundy would have declined over the years. Such a conclusion is supported by counts from west-coast bird observatories which show a significant reduction in spring-migrating Ring Ouzels, comparable with that recorded in the breeding areas in Britain (Burfield & Brooke 2005).

Chanter (1871) and Parfitt (1876) listed Ring Ouzel as a "summer visitant", and D'Urban & Mathew (1895) also mentioned this species as visiting the island. Loyd (1925) reported sightings by other observers in August 1905 (Joy 1922) and on 10 June 1910 (Hendy 1922). Davis (1954a) stated pre-LFS early and late spring dates as 16 February 1937 and 10 June 1924.

Thirty-five Ring Ouzels had been ringed on Lundy by the end of 2006, but there are no controls or recoveries involving the island.

Blackbird *Turdus merula* [Common Blackbird]

Common breeding resident; irregular spring migrant and common late autumn migrant; occasional winter visitor during hard weather.

Turning the corner of the beach road into Millcombe, one of the first landbirds likely to be encountered is Blackbird. For all their seemingly drab plumage, Blackbirds bring the place alive with their gentle chortling song in spring and clacking alarm calls in autumn as they squabble over the best berry-bearing trees and shrubs.

Resident males start to sing in early March and carry on into late June. Most breeding territories are located along the East Side from above the Landing Beach to Gannets' Combe, but with a distinct concentration in and around Millcombe. In years of high numbers, nesting pairs may also be found on the west, north and north-east sidelands. The breeding population has fluctuated considerably, ranging from a low of five pairs in 1965 to about 25 pairs in 1972 and 1973, and between 25 and 30 pairs in 1962. Blackbird numbers, like those of other resident passerines, may crash during particularly hard winters. From the high breeding population in 1962, numbers fell to six or seven pairs in 1963 following the big winter freeze during which large numbers were found dead. Thirty-four adult males were counted in May 1984, 22 pairs were present in May 1985, and the two most recent surveys located 20 territory-holding birds in 2000 (Parsons 2002) and 24 in 2004 (Lock 2004).

Prior to LFS recording, there is little information on Blackbirds. Chanter (1871) and Parfitt (1876) listed them as "resident all the year", Parfitt adding "and breed there". The Heaven Diaries mentioned nests on 6 April 1879 and 16 May 1884, with "unusual numbers" noted on 3 November 1877, 11 to 13 October 1884 and 19 November 1903 (Boyd 1950). Wynne-Edwards & Harrisson (1932) estimated 34 breeding pairs but Davis (1954a) considered this questionable. Perry (1940) recorded 12 pairs in 1939.

Spring passage in late February and early March is irregular and generally involves very small numbers, apart from an exceptional passage reaching an estimated 1,000 birds on 11 March 1962. Autumn passage, however, from late September through to November and occasionally early December, can be spectacular, especially when large numbers of other thrushes arrive at the same time. In 1973, for example, a heavy passage of Blackbirds began with 150 on 2 October, rose to 250 on 24th and peaked at 2,000 on 25th, numbers then tailing off before 600 arrived on 17 November. In the 10 years 1997–2006, peak counts have been between 37 and 410 birds (the latter on 28 October 2003). However, autumn passage can be almost negligible in some years; for example, peak daily counts of just 15 between September and December 1998, most of which were likely to have been resident birds.

In winter, resident Blackbirds are sometimes joined by cold-weather influxes that have numbered up to 100 birds (e.g. 75 on 15 January 1981, 100 on 1 February 1972).

Between 1947 and 2006, 4,008 Blackbirds were ringed on Lundy. Yet for the many thousands that have migrated through the island, there has been just one control of a bird ringed elsewhere: one ringed at Eksel, Belgium, on 8 September 1975 was found dead on Lundy on 16 January 1977. However, there have been 33 controls or recoveries of Lundy-ringed birds away from the island: in Britain (8), Ireland (1), France (7), Belgium (1), The Netherlands (5), Germany (7), Denmark (2) and Norway (2). Of these, 31 were ringed on Lundy in the autumn and two were spring migrants: one ringed in February 1952 found dead in Yorkshire almost two months later, and one ringed in March 1954 found alive and released in Maarsbergen, The Netherlands four years later in April 1958. An autumn migrant ringed on Lundy on 26 November 1955 was controlled migrating along the Essex coast at Foulness Island five years later on 5 November 1961. The spread of recoveries tallies with the findings of Wernham *et al.* (2002) that continental Blackbirds ringed in Britain in the autumn belong to both wholly migratory northern populations in most of Scandinavia and Finland and partially migrant populations in The Netherlands, Germany and southern Scandinavia.

The longevity record for a resident Blackbird (based on ringing recoveries but not considering retraps) stands at eight years, four months – a juvenile ringed on the island in September 1954 and found in January 1963 (the age record nationally is 14 years, two months). Resident it may have been, but did it ever take a trip off the island? Possibly not, but we'll never know for sure.

Blackbirds ringed on Lundy and controlled or recovered elsewhere

Age/sex	Date ringed on Lundy	Place found	Date controlled or recovered	Speculation about date/place of finding
Adult F	19 Feb 1952	Barlow, nr Sheffield, Yorkshire	06 Apr 1952	On spring migration
1st-year F	16 Oct 1952	Enniger, Nordrhein-Westfalen, **Germany**	30 Jun 1957	In breeding area
Adult M	17 Oct 1952	Manche, **France**	03 Feb 1954	In wintering area
1st-year	15 Nov 1952	St Just in Roseland, Cornwall	10 Feb 1953	In wintering area or on spring migration
1st-year	17 Nov 1953	Kiel, Schleswig-Holstein, **Germany**	20 Nov 1954	On autumn migration
Adult M	19 Nov 1953	Nr Langeso, Fyn, **Denmark**	15 Jul 1954	In breeding area
Adult F	23 Mar 1954	Maarsbergen, Utrecht, **Netherlands**	20 Apr 1958	On spring migration
1st-year	08 Nov 1954	Nr Drammen, Buskerud, **Norway**	27 Aug 1955	In breeding area
Adult F	24 Oct 1955	Stratford-on-Avon, Warwickshire	20 Mar 1957	On spring migration
1st-year	26 Nov 1955	Foulness Island, Essex	05 Nov 1961	On autumn migration
1st-year F	14 Oct 1956	Waalre, Noord-Brabant, **Netherlands**	18 Apr 1957	On spring migration
Adult M	11 Oct 1957	Venlo, Limburg, **Netherlands**	13 Mar 1961	On spring migration
1st-year M	14 Oct 1957	Nord, **France**	14 Feb 1960	In wintering area or on spring migration
Adult	24 Oct 1958	Münster, Nordrhein-Westfalen, **Germany**	02 May 1960	In breeding area
1st-year	01 Dec 1958	Nr Pordic, Côtes d'Armor, **France**	25 Dec 1960	In wintering area
1st-year	03 Oct 1959	Köln, Nordrhein-Westfalen, **Germany**	03 May 1960	In breeding area
Adult F	30 Oct 1960	Skalaskog, Sveio, **Norway**	19 Dec 1965	Overwintering (in breeding area?)
1st-year M	16 Oct 1966	Coesfeld, Nordrhein-Westfalen, **Germany**	15 Jun 1967	In breeding area

continued opposite...

Age/sex	Date ringed on Lundy	Place found	Date controlled or recovered	Speculation about date/place of finding
Adult F	24 Oct 1966	Auchy-les-Hesdin, Pas-de-Calais, **France**	04 Jan 1970	In wintering area
1st-year	24 Oct 1966	Wierden, Overijssel, **Netherlands**	24 May 1967	In breeding area
Adult F	17 Oct 1975	Sjaelland, **Denmark**	24 Jun 1976	In breeding area
1st-year M	16 Oct 1979	Lüneberg, Niedersachsen, **Germany**	23 Apr 1981	On spring migration
1st-year F	25 Oct 1987	Nr Dunkerque, Nord, **France**	13 Apr 1988	On spring migration
1st-year F	26 Oct 1987	Sapignies, Pas-de-Calais, **France**	12 Nov 1989	On autumn migration
Adult F	17 Oct 1988	Camberley, Surrey	11 Mar 1989	On spring migration
1st-year F	24 Oct 1988	Westacre, King's Lynn, Norfolk	28 May 1990	In breeding area
Adult F	26 Oct 1989	Ballindangan, Mitchelstown, Co. Cork, **Ireland**	11 Mar 1991	On spring migration
1st-year M	13 Oct 1992	Nr Lüneberg, Niedersachsen, **Germany**	28 Mar 1996	On spring migration
1st-year F	31 Oct 1992	Notre-Dame-de Gavendron, Seine-Maritime, **France**	09 Jun 1993	In breeding area
1st-year F	18 Oct 1993	Castricum, Noord-Holland, **Netherlands**	08 Oct 1994	On autumn migration
Adult F	26 Oct 1993	Ludchurch, Narberth, Dyfed	27 Feb 1995	On spring migration
1st-year F	27 Oct 1997	Wellen, Limburg, **Belgium**	20 May 1998	In breeding area
Adult M	21 Oct 2001	Milton Abbot, Tavistock, Devon	26 Mar 2003	On spring migration

A further 29 birds ringed on Lundy have subsequently been recovered on the island.

Fieldfare *Turdus pilaris*

Common migrant in early spring and, especially, late autumn; winter visitor in variable numbers, with occasional hard-weather influxes.

The Fieldfare's rapid *chack-chack-chack* call is as familiar in late autumn and winter as it is different to that of the Redwing. From first light until mid-morning along the East Side, large movements of Fieldfares and other thrushes can bring the island to life in late autumn. Once migration has died down, birds can be found gorging on berries in Millcombe and the other vegetated combes, or in flocks feeding in St Helen's, Tillage and Brick Fields.

Spring movements occur mainly in the second half of February and March, most daily counts being in single figures but numbering 10 or more in 27 of the 60 LFS years up to 2006. Spring counts of over 100 birds have been made in just three years (1953, 1973 and 1977), the highest being 300 in early March 1973. Small numbers occur in April in most years (maximum 50 on 24 April 1973), with occasional singles in May (maximum 10 on 1 May 1973) and even one on 7 June 1962 – the latest spring date and the only June record.

Fieldfares are far more numerous in autumn, the first migrants arriving in September in most years, though the earliest date is 27 August (1983). The main passage occurs from mid-October to mid-November, maximum numbers being 950 on 2 November 1982, 1,170[136] on 2 November 1986 and 1,500 on 4 November 1981. Late migrants continue to pass through until mid-December in some years, usually in small numbers, with a high of 500 on 1 December 1981.[137]

Both Chanter (1871) and Parfitt (1876) listed the species as an "autumn and winter visitant". D'Urban & Mathew (1895) wrote that "in the long and bitter winter of 1860–1861 vast numbers of Fieldfares resorted to Lundy Island, where their starved and frozen bodies were lying on the ground in all directions". Hard winter weather on the mainland often brings Fieldfares to the island, though numbers rarely rise above 50. The highest numbers recorded are 200 on 21 January 1985 and 1,000 on 8 January 1982.

Fieldfares and Redwings

Surprisingly, only 26 Fieldfares have been ringed on Lundy, of which just one has been recovered: a first-year female ringed on 30 October 1993 was killed – probably in its breeding area – by a cat at Notodden, Telemark, south-east Norway, on 15 May 1997. This lone recovery tallies with the finding in *The Migration Atlas* (Wernham *et al.* 2002) that Norwegian birds migrate in a south-westerly direction to winter in Britain, Ireland, north-west France and north-west Iberia. Finnish Fieldfares are also known to winter in south-west Britain or further south, so it is likely that birds from Finland also migrate through Lundy.

Song Thrush *Turdus philomelos*

Resident in small numbers, breeding in most years; common migrant in early spring and late autumn; winter influxes during hard weather.

A Song Thrush in full voice in Millcombe, especially when competing against a neighbouring bird in St John's Valley or St Helen's Combe, is always worth stopping for – and there are many vantage points in Millcombe on which to sit and soak up the sound. Yet for all the strength in their song, Song Thrushes have a tenuous hold on Lundy as a breeding bird.

Chanter (1871) and Parfitt (1876) listed Song Thrush as "resident all the year", the latter adding "and breed there". Davis (1954a) reported that the species bred regularly until at least 1943, varying from four to five pairs in 1922 and 1923 (Loyd 1925), nine pairs in 1930 (Wynne-Edwards & Harrisson 1932) and one to two pairs from 1948 to 1951. Perry (1940) reported six nesting pairs in 1939. Subsequently, breeding took place from 1957 to 1959 (one pair), in 1962 (three or four pairs), 1975 (two pairs) and 1978 (one pair). The next breeding record was not until 1987, but since then nesting has taken place annually (up to 2006), with one to three pairs holding territories in Millcombe and St John's Valley, St Helen's Combe and the east sidelands as far as Quarter Wall and the Terrace.

190

Nationally, the scale of Song Thrush passage is smaller than for other migrant thrushes (Wernham *et al.* 2002) and this is evident on Lundy where migration in both spring and autumn is generally modest and irregular. Spring passage occurs from February to April, though late February to early March is the peak period. Movements are usually light and counts exceeding 20 birds have been recorded in only 12 LFS years (up to 2006). Nevertheless, a spectacular record was set on 11 March 1962 when an estimated 700 Song Thrushes passed through the island.

The extended autumn passage may start as early as July, with ones and twos (presumably dispersing juveniles), and runs through to November, occasionally into early December. October to November is the peak period, with maximum daily counts ranging from 16 to 100 for the 10 years 1997–2006. Counts of 100 or more in a day have been made in 14 LFS years. The largest movement on record took place in October 1973, with peaks of 350 on 3rd, 400 on 24th, at least 500 on 25th and 250 on 27th,[138] falling to smaller numbers until a further 250 passed through on 17 November.

End-of-year counts are usually in single figures, but the presence of 15 or more birds in some years indicates that resident birds may be joined by winter visitors (e.g. up to 60 in January 1980). Hard weather on the mainland usually produces small influxes. Even so, some 600 on 12 December 1981 was an exceptional number, 200 on 8 January 1982 being the next highest count, while "large numbers" were found dead during freezing temperatures in early 1963. The Heaven Diaries (1870–1905) recorded many "thrushes" (possibly a mixture of Song Thrushes, Redwings and Fieldfares) on 3 November 1877 and again in early March 1886 when a large number died during hard weather (Boyd 1950).

A total of 857 Song Thrushes had been ringed on the island by the end of 2006, with nine subsequent recoveries elsewhere: six in Britain, one in France, one in Portugal and one in Spain – see table. While most British Song Thrushes (*T. p. clarkei*) are resident and stay close to their natal areas (Wernham *et al.* 2002), the recovery on the mainland of a Lundy-ringed nestling suggests that some birds, probably young of the year, disperse from the island. Despite the many thousands of Song Thrushes that have passed through Lundy, there are as yet no controls of birds ringed elsewhere, so the birds' origins remain unclear – a fact underlined in *The Migration Atlas* (Wernham *et al.* 2002), which concluded that "the main unknowns concern the numbers and ultimate destinations of passage migrants through Britain in autumn". Seven 'continental' Song Thrushes (*T. p. philomelos*) were reported from South West Field on 10 October 2002, with three present the following day. The observers noted in the LFS logbook that the birds' plumage was "distinctive, cold grey on mantle and wings with no hint of rufous. In flight almost resembled pale charcoaly blackbird rather than song thrush". It seems likely that continental migrants regularly pass through the island undetected. Tony Taylor (personal communication) has commented that "there have been times when birds trapped in autumn have looked 'different', but judging a bird's colour in the hand without a direct comparison is remarkably difficult, so no-one has committed themselves on paper".

Song Thrushes ringed on Lundy and recovered elsewhere

Age/sex	Date ringed on Lundy	Place found	Date recovered	Speculation about date/place of finding
Adult	23 Feb 1951	Nr Barry, Glamorgan	15 Jul 1951	In breeding area
Adult	20 Feb 1952	Burton-on-Trent, Derbyshire	20 Sep 1952	On autumn migration
Full-grown	15 Nov 1954	Nr Penzance, Cornwall	08 Mar 1956	Returning from wintering area
Full-grown	09 Nov 1955	Pampisford, Cambridgeshire	21 Jun 1958	In breeding area
Adult	04 Apr 1975	Leiria, Centro, **Portugal**	25 Jan 1976	In wintering area
Full-grown	29 Nov 1975	East Clandon, Guildford, Surrey	01 Mar 1976	Returning from wintering area
Nestling	31 May 1978	Porlock, Somerset	01 Oct 1978	Dispersing juvenile
Adult	22 Oct 2001	Ecija, Sevilla, Andalucía, **Spain**	08 Dec 2001	In wintering area
1st-year	05 Oct 2005	Lacanau, Gironde, **France**	03 Nov 2005	On autumn migration

Redwing   *Turdus iliacus*

Common migrant in early spring and late autumn; winter visitor in variable numbers, with occasional hard-weather influxes.

The thin, high-pitched *tseeep* of migrating Redwings is often heard at night during October and November, perhaps when walking back from an evening in the Tavern. During daylight hours, particularly early in the morning, there may be large movements accompanied by other thrushes and Starlings. As for Fieldfare, Brick, Tillage and St Helen's Fields are among the best areas to search for feeding flocks when the supply of berries in Millcombe has been exhausted.

Autumn movements normally begin in early October, though there are September records for nine years, the earliest being three birds on 19 September 1981. Numbers vary considerably from year to year, but peak daily counts of several hundred are regular throughout October and November. Counts of 500 or more have been made in 19 LFS years (to the end of 2006), including nine years for which the daily maximum exceeded 1,000. The highest total to date was 2,500 passing north-west on 24 October 1974. Movements often continue into December, with variable but generally small numbers sometimes present until the end of the year, and occasional larger influxes; for example, the arrival of 375 Redwings on 29 December 2000.

The irregular presence of small flocks and sporadic influxes is also typical of January and February. While there are few or no midwinter records in some years, in others Redwings have been seen almost daily. Counts of more than 50 are unusual and most often associated with cold weather. For example, many died during a cold snap in late January/early February 1954 (Davis 1954b); harsh conditions at the end of January 1972 preceded the arrival of at least 200 on 1 February; and on the night of 22/23 February 1979, during a large cold-weather movement, some 2,000 Redwings were attracted to the South Light between midnight and 04:00 hours and 12 were found dead. One thousand were present on 8 January 1982.

Chanter (1871) and Parfitt (1876) listed Redwing under "autumn and winter visitants". Loyd (1925) stated, "D'Urban and Mathew record that great numbers perished on the island during the bitter winter of 1860–1861" but while D'Urban & Mathew (1895) certainly wrote of "vast numbers of Fieldfares" having died in this way, they make no mention of Redwing. There is no other published information prior to the commencement of LFS recording in 1947.

In some years it is difficult to distinguish between late-staying winter visitors and spring migrants, but the main migratory movements seem to occur from late February to mid-April, reaching a peak in March, though late birds are occasionally seen in May. Numbers are generally much smaller than in autumn, with relatively few daily counts of more than 100 birds; in some years, only a handful have been seen. Higher counts have included 200 on 3 March 1982, 300 in early March 1973 and 14 March 1991, 350 on 11 March 1983, and 1,600 on 22 March 1976.[139] However, these figures are eclipsed by the 2,000 Redwings recorded on 11 March 1962 (most of which were gone by 13th). There have been May sightings in 15 LFS years, mostly early in the month, with the latest on 28 May (1961).

Redwings ringed on Lundy and recovered elsewhere

Age/sex	Date ringed on Lundy	Place found	Date recovered	Speculation about date/place of finding
1st-year	25 Oct 1953	Liège, **Belgium**	22 Dec 1954*	In wintering area or late migrant
1st-year	15 Nov 1958	Ladva, Karelia, NW **Russia**	11 Aug 1960	In breeding area
Adult	08 Oct 1993	Acalá de los Gazules, Cádiz, Andalucía, **Spain**	14 Jan 1994	In wintering area
Adult	02 Nov 1995	Asbo, Gastrikland, Gavleborg, **Sweden**	01 May 1996	In breeding area

*Finding date accurate to within one week.

Between 1947 and 2006, 823 Redwings were ringed on Lundy, of which four have subsequently been recovered – see table. The highest number ringed in any one year was 84 in 2003. There have been no controls or recoveries on the island of birds ringed elsewhere. The birds found in Sweden and Russia give a clue to the breeding grounds of some of the Redwings reaching Lundy in autumn, while the Spanish recovery shows that onward migration to eventual wintering grounds may be over considerable distances. The bird recovered in Belgium may have been wintering but could also still have been moving south. Wernham *et al.* (2002) demonstrated that the same individual may winter in widely separated locations from one year to the next. A few of the birds trapped for ringing have also shown the characteristics of the Iceland-breeding race *T. i. coburni* (Tony Taylor, personal communication) though as yet there are no recoveries or controls involving Icelandic birds.

Mistle Thrush

Mistle Thrush *Turdus viscivorus*

Rare spring migrant; uncommon autumn migrant; rare summer and winter visitor; has bred.

Mistle Thrushes are sufficiently unusual on Lundy that every sighting, often preceded by a burst of the unmistakable rattling call, is notable. While nesting occurred on the island during the first half of the twentieth century, this species is now a scarce but annual visitor during spring and autumn migration, occurring most often in October and November, though there are records for all months. There has been an unbroken run of sightings in every year since 1972 up to and including 2006. This species is notably absent from the lists compiled by Chanter (1871) and Parfitt (1876).

Spring records are less than annual and almost all are of single birds, with two being the highest count. Most occur in March and April, though there have been about a dozen sightings in May. Hendy (1922) heard "one in song" on 11 June 1914. Davis (1954a) stated that "one pair bred in most years between 1929 and 1941 (F.W. Gade), though not apparently in 1930 (Wynne-Edwards) or 1939 (Perry)". Gade (1978, pp. 278–279) recalled that in 1943 a pair of Mistle Thrushes "built a nest in a sycamore tree quite close to [Millcombe] house, and laid four eggs" but that the birds deserted, nested again close by and successfully raised four young. While the 1947 *LFS Annual Report* refers to "several birds about throughout the season", it also states "no nest found or suspected". There has been no hint of nesting in any subsequent year.

Mistle Thrushes breed commonly in Wales and south-west England; for example, there is a significant population on Exmoor. Sporadic occurrences on Lundy during the summer months, from late June to the end of August, are perhaps most likely to be of young birds dispersing from these areas. Both the number of records and the number of birds involved are very small. From 1980 up to and including 2006 there were just two records in July and one in August,[140] all of single birds.

193

It is during the autumn movements of other thrush species that Mistle Thrushes are most likely to be encountered on Lundy and though a few have been seen in September, most occur in the last three weeks of October and the first half of November, with occasional later records to the end of the month and rarely in early December. Numbers vary considerably from year to year, with ones and twos in some seasons and small flocks in others. Even so, the highest daily total ever reached, on 15 November 1958, was only 20 and there are just four other records of 10 or more. During the 10-year period 1997–2006 the peak count was six, on 17 October 2002 and 5 November 2003.

Midwinter sightings of Mistle Thrush are as sporadic as those in midsummer, with half-a-dozen or so records in each of the three months December to February. Again these are mostly of single birds, but five were present on 16 February 1976 and four in the last week of December 2001 (26th to 31st).

Four Mistle Thrushes had been ringed on Lundy by the end of 2006, but there are no controls or recoveries involving the island.

American Robin *Turdus migratorius*

British vagrant.

Breeds throughout much of North America, wintering in parts of the USA (particularly towards the south), Bahamas, Cuba, Mexico and Guatemala. 22 records for Britain 1950–2005.

There are three Lundy records, including the first for Britain, all of single birds and all between late October and mid-November:

1952   27 Oct to 8 Nov – a first-winter bird caught in the Terrace Heligoland trap and ringed on 27 Oct was the first for Britain. It was later seen at Quarter Wall and elsewhere on the island plateau (Davis 1953a, 1953b). An unconfirmed sighting suggested it had been present since 25 Oct.

1962   7 Nov – one on Castle Hill.

1982   14 to 18 Nov – one near the top of the High Street.

Describing the first occurrence for Lundy and Britain, Davis (1953b) wrote:

"The bird was probably first seen on October 25th by one of the islanders, on top of the island near Quarterwall Pond. On the 27th I found it feeding voraciously on blackberries in a gully north of the Terrace Trap. Later it was taken in the Terrace Trap, and after examination and ringing was shown to F.W. Gade and other residents, photographed and released near the Hotel. The next day it was back on the Terrace, half a mile away,

American Robin

but the remainder of its stay was spent on the open grassland near Quarterwall, where it fed with Redwings and Blackbirds."

Cetti's Warbler *Cettia cetti*

Lundy vagrant.

Since arriving in Britain in 1961, this species has colonised suitable wetland nesting habitat, mainly in southern England and south Wales. The most recent published assessment of the British breeding population was 534 pairs in 1996 (Baillie *et al.* 2007). The number of singing males in Devon was estimated at about 69 in 2005 (2005 *Devon Bird Report*), with the vast majority of these on the south coast and only a handful in North Devon. There are two Lundy records, presumably birds dispersing from one of the established English or Welsh breeding sites:

2003   27 Oct – one trapped and ringed in Millcombe was seen subsequently in the willow clumps in St John's Valley on 28 & 29 Oct. One, presumed the same, was seen in lower Millcombe on 12 Nov.

2006   19 to 26 Oct – one in lower Millcombe, at one time seen briefly together with a Subalpine Warbler (*Sylvia cantillans*); caught and ringed on 23 Oct.

Grasshopper Warbler *Locustella naevia*   [Common Grasshopper Warbler]

Common spring migrant; uncommon autumn migrant.

The extraordinary mechanical 'reeling' song of Grasshopper Warblers can quite often be heard in Millcombe or St John's Valley in April and May, as passage migrants stopping off on the island establish temporary territories. Singing males typically stay hidden in dense cover but will occasionally sit in full view, particularly at dawn and dusk. On other occasions, in both spring and autumn, visitors may be aware of a brown mouse-like bird scuttling or flying low across the ground, seemingly from beneath their feet, before disappearing with a characteristic jink of the tail into a tussock. This is an adaptable species on migration, able to find sufficient cover among granite walls and boulders, as well as in the tiniest patch of vegetation, and can therefore be encountered anywhere on the island from South West Field, to Pondsbury, to the North End.

The earliest arrivals in spring have been singles on 9 April (1981 and 1990). Ten were present on 10 April 1961, a year in which an unusually early movement of Grasshopper Warblers was noted at other British and Irish bird observatories (Lundy was then part of the bird observatories network). The main movements are in late April and early May. Up to 100 were recorded on 9 May 1991 and, while this was an exceptional fall, other high counts have included: 24 on 24 April 1990, 25 on 5 & 6 May 1972, 30 on 4 May 1992 and 1 May 1999, and 40 on 29 April 1967. One heard singing on 21 June 1976 perhaps qualifies as the latest spring record, whereas the status of one on 3 July and two on 9 July, both in 2002, is open to debate.

Autumn passage regularly commences in the last ten days of July, continuing to be noted irregularly until early October, and reaching a modest peak in mid to late September. Numbers are typically lower than in spring and while the highest daily count was 25 on 23 September 1965, single figures are the norm. Of three recorded on 7 October 1959, one was caught at night at the South Light. The latest date for a Grasshopper Warbler is one on 20 October (1969).

The only known sightings of Grasshopper Warbler prior to the first LFS record in 1948 were made by Richard Perry on 26 April and 20 May 1939 (Perry 1940).

Grasshopper Warbler is a 'red-listed' species (of high conservation concern), having undergone significant range contraction and population decline in the UK (Baillie *et al.* 2007). The birds passing through Lundy most likely come from breeding areas in Wales, Ireland, northern England and Scotland. While 354 had been ringed on Lundy by the end of 2006, there are no controls or recoveries involving the island – perhaps not surprising given the species' secretive habits. Grasshopper Warblers winter in sub-Saharan West Africa but little is known in detail about their range and movements outside the breeding season (Wernham *et al.* 2002).

Aquatic Warbler *Acrocephalus paludicola*

Nationally scarce migrant.

Breeds in wetlands of central and eastern Europe, wintering in sub-Saharan Africa, including Senegal. Small numbers occur in southern Britain every year, mainly at reedbeds during autumn passage. 1,221 records for Britain 1958–2003, with an average of 15 per year 2000–2003. Considered by the BBRC until the end of 1982.

There are four Lundy records, all except the first being of single birds:

1949 15 Sep – two perched on brambles in marshy vegetation in St John's Valley, one also sitting for a short time on fence-wire.

1956 31 Aug – one.

1963 13 Sep – one trapped and ringed.

1973 10 Aug – one in Millcombe.[141]

A record of a bird on 3 May 1963, published in the 1963-64 *LFS Annual Report* but not mentioned by Dymond (1980), appears not to have been submitted to the BBRC and is therefore discounted here.

Sedge Warbler

Sedge Warbler *Acrocephalus schoenobaenus*

Common spring and autumn migrant, generally more numerous in spring; has bred.

There is a period for a few weeks each spring when migrant Sedge Warblers, stopping off on Lundy to feed and rest, may be heard chuntering away from suitable cover anywhere on the island. It is not unusual for several to sing or sub-sing simultaneously in Millcombe or St John's Valley, each bird delivering a jumble of scratchy notes as it slips furtively through low vegetation, affording occasional glimpses of a creamy supercilium or an orangey-brown rump.

Spring passage usually commences in the third or fourth week of April; single birds seen on 7 April 1940 (Davis 1954a), 9 April 1961 and 12 April 2007 have been the only arrivals before the middle of the month. Peak numbers are most often concentrated into a narrow window covering the last few days in April and the first two weeks in May. There have been numerous counts of 10 to 30 birds, while the highest daily count has been between 40 and 60 in seven years and 100 or more in eight years, the latter all from 1990 onwards, perhaps suggestive of a recent population increase. BTO data show steep declines in the UK breeding population between 1965 and 1985, with a partial recovery since (Baillie *et al.* 2006). The three highest spring counts are 200 on 2 May 2004, 250 on 1 May 1999 and 300 on 9 May 1998. "Apparently exceptionally large numbers" occurred from 7 to 11 May 1989, when 87 individuals were ringed, but no overall estimate was recorded (1989 *LFS Annual Report*). Numbers tail off rapidly after mid-May, with odd stragglers into June, the latest being one on 30 June 2002.

There is a very short gap between the tail-end of spring movements and the start of post-juvenile dispersal and autumn migration, with the first birds being seen in late July or early August. The earliest date is 20 July (1952[142]). Passage may continue throughout August and September, with odd ones and twos into October. The latest sighting is of a single bird on 21 October (2006). The pattern of migration is less regular than in spring, with peak daily counts in single figures for most years, but influxes of 25 or more in eight autumns and exceptional falls of 100 or more on three occasions: 100 on 15 September 1991, 130 on 30 July 1965 and at least 150 on 10 August 1967.

Alexander *et al.* (1945) and Davis (1954a) reported F.W. Gade's observations of a breeding pair in both 1934 (raising a family of six young) and 1935 – constituting the only known instances to date of breeding. The second report of the Devon Bird Watching & Preservation Society, published in 1930, lists "one seen, Lundy Island, June 8th [1930]" observed by V.C. Wynne-Edwards and cited as a new species record for the island.

Sedge Warbler is the tenth most ringed passerine and the thirteenth most ringed species overall on Lundy, with 2,117 individuals ringed between 1947 and the end of 2006. The highest number ringed in any one year was 163 in 2000 and there have been five other years (all since 1989) when more than 100 have been ringed. Reflecting this high rate of capture, particularly in recent years, there are now 31 controls and recoveries showing movements to and from the island – see tables (a) and (b). In summary, there have been spring or autumn Sedge Warbler movements to or from Lundy involving: elsewhere in Britain (8), Ireland/Northern Ireland (5), Channel Islands (1), France (12), Spain (2), Morocco (1) and Senegal (2). Remarkably, more than a third of these controls and recoveries were generated from just a few days' ringing on Lundy: 29 April to 12 May 1990, 1 May 1999 and 26 to 29 April 2000.

The high number of movements to/from France is consistent with Sedge Warbler ringing data for the UK as a whole. Birds are thought to move in relatively short hops from their breeding grounds to feeding areas in the wetlands of southernmost England and western France where they fatten up for the main migration south, perhaps reaching sub-Saharan Africa in a single flight (Wernham *et al.* 2002). There are five movements to/from a single wetland: l'Etang du Trunvel, near Tréogat on the west coast of Brittany; happily, this site is managed as a nature reserve by the Breton Society for the Study and

(a) Sedge Warblers ringed on Lundy and controlled or recovered elsewhere

Age/sex	Date ringed on Lundy	Place found	Date controlled or recovered	Speculation about date/place of finding
Adult	12 May 1956	Gironde, **France**	01 May 1960	On spring migration
Adult	19 Aug 1965	Middleton, Co. Cork, **Ireland**	15 Aug 1966	On autumn migration
Adult	17 May 1985	Stodmarsh, Kent	18 Aug 1985	On autumn migration
Adult	18 May 1985	Jersey, Channel Islands	09 Aug 1986	On autumn migration
Adult	10 May 1989	Charente-Maritime, **France**	12 Aug 1889	On autumn migration
Adult	28 Apr 1990	Djoudj National Park, **Senegal**	24 Jan 1993	In wintering area
Adult	29 Apr 1990	Djoudj National Park, **Senegal**	29 Jan 1991	In wintering area
Adult	09 May 1991	Tréogat, Finistère, **France**	23 Aug 1996	On autumn migration
1st-year	30 Aug 1994	Poole Harbour, Dorset	02 Sep 1994	On autumn migration
Adult	05 May 1996	Loire-Atlantique, **France**	29 Jul 1997	On autumn migration
1st-year	05 Aug 1998	Tréogat, Finistère, **France**	19 Aug 1998	On autumn migration
Adult	01 May 1999	Seine-Maritime, **France**	16 Aug 1999	On autumn migration

(b) Sedge Warblers ringed elsewhere and controlled on Lundy

Age/sex	Date ringed	Place ringed	Date controlled on Lundy	Speculation about date/place of ringing
1st-year	19 Aug 1973	Sussex (location unknown)	16 Aug 1975	On autumn migration
Adult	16 Apr 1975	Tangier, **Morocco**	18 May 1975	On spring migration
1st-year	04 Aug 1988	Southampton Docks, Hampshire	17 May 1991	On autumn migration
1st-year	01 Aug 1989	Loire-Atlantique, **France**	05 May 1990	On autumn migration
1st-year	23 Aug 1989	Tréogat, Finistère, **France**	07 May 1990	On autumn migration
Adult	06 May 1990	Morbihan, **France**	12 May 1990	On spring migration
1st-year	23 Jul 1990	Lough Neagh, Co. Armagh, Northern Ireland	18 May 1991	On autumn migration
1st-year	01 Oct 1990	Tréogat, Finistère, **France**	04 May 1992	On autumn migration
1st-year	02 Sep 1995	Youghal, Co. Cork, **Ireland**	01 May 1999	On autumn migration
Adult	03 Aug 1996	Ballycotton, Co. Cork, **Ireland**	01 May 1997	On autumn migration
Adult	15 May 1997	Great Saltee Island, Co. Wexford, **Ireland**	01 May 1999	On spring migration
Adult	20 Apr 1998	Alava, País Basco, **Spain**	29 Apr 2000	On spring migration
1st-year	09 Aug 1998	Tréogat, Finistère, **France**	01 May 1999	On autumn migration
Adult F	07 Aug 1998	Radipole, Weymouth, Dorset	26 Apr 2000	On autumn migration
Adult	29 Jul 1999	Loire-Atlantique, **France**	26 Apr 2000	On autumn migration
1st-year	31 Aug 1999	Christchurch, Dorset	28 Apr 2000	On autumn migration
Adult M	28 Jul 2002	Chew Valley, Avon	23 Apr 2006	On autumn migration
Adult	24 Apr 2004	Palencia, Castilla y León, **Spain**	12 May 2004	On spring migration
1st-year	30 Sep 2004	Icklesham, Sussex	24 Apr 2006	On autumn migration

In addition, individuals bearing Spanish and French rings were controlled on Lundy on 2 May 2007 and 3 May 2007 respectively. At the time of going to press, details of ringing dates and places were not yet available.

Protection of Nature. The two birds wintering in Senegal were ringed within a day of each other on Lundy and trapped at the same Senegalese National Park (and 'Ramsar' wetland of international importance), almost 4,000 kilometres south, in late January, albeit in different years. These two records represent the furthest known movements to date of any migrant to/from the island. In spring, returning birds stop to refuel in North Africa and Iberia (Wernham *et al.* 2002), as shown by the one Moroccan-ringed and two Spanish-ringed birds controlled on Lundy. There is no conclusive evidence of where the birds passing through Lundy actually breed, though the five movements to/from Ireland and Northern Ireland may provide a strong hint. Others are perhaps likely to nest further north in Britain.

Marsh Warbler *Acrocephalus palustris*

Nationally scarce migrant and very rare breeding species in Britain.

Breeds from France and Norway to north-east Turkey and Kazakhstan. Winters in south-east Africa. 912 records for Britain 1986–2003, with an average of 44 per year 2000–2003, excluding breeding birds.

There are four Lundy records. With the exception of the most recent occurrence, all have been birds trapped and ringed in autumn:

1962 2 Sep – one, trapped and ringed.
1967 12 Oct – one, trapped and ringed, remained until 16 Oct.
1984 17 Sep – one, trapped and ringed.
1997 26 May – one seen and heard singing near Stoneycroft.

The 1985 *LFS Annual Report* states that three Marsh Warblers were trapped and ringed on 8, 11 & 12 September respectively. These birds were later re-identified as Reed Warblers (*A. scirpaceus*).

Reed Warbler *Acrocephalus scirpaceus*   [Eurasian Reed Warbler]

Uncommon spring and autumn migrant.

While there isn't a single reed to be found on Lundy, Reed Warblers occur in very small numbers during both spring and autumn migration periods, when they are typically seen skulking in dense vegetation. Many are only recorded when they turn up in ringers' mist-nets. Most have occurred in Millcombe and St John's Valley, but there have been instances in other parts of the island, including Stoneycroft, Quarter Wall and the Terrace/quarries.

Parfitt (1876) and Chanter (1877) listed Reed Warbler as "reported, but not accurately identified" and therefore regarded by Chanter as doubtful. There were three reported occurrences before LFS recording began: one in May 1937 (F.W. Gade, reported by Dymond 1980) and two separate individuals on 13 & 15 May 1944 (F.W. Gade, reported by N.V. Allen in Palmer 1946). However, Allen stated that the two 1944 birds were the first for the island, a statement apparently verified by Gade, so there must be an element of doubt about the 1937 record.

The first LFS record was of one seen by then LFS warden Hugh Boyd on 27 August 1948. This was followed by irregular records of ones and twos during spring or autumn migration (occasionally both) through to 1979. There seems to have been a modest increase from 1980 onwards, with records for every year (up to and including 2006), and both spring and autumn occurrences in most years. Taking all records into account, the earliest spring Reed Warblers were two on 20 April (1971) and the latest, one on 29 June (1988). There have been about 14 records in April, approximately 35 in May and 14 in June, these mostly early in the month. The great majority of spring occurrences involve single birds and no more than two have been recorded in a day.

In autumn Reed Warblers have occurred between 4 August (1954) and 4 November (1982). It is impossible to know precisely the number of individuals involved, but there have been more than 20 in August, probably in excess of 50 in September, and more than 40 in October. As in spring, most records are of single birds, with occasional instances of two in a day. The highest daily counts are three on 13 October 1995 and four on 9 October 2006. A striking feature of this species' occurrence is that there have been 10 very late records, involving at least 11 birds, between 20 October and 4 November.

By the end of 2006, 94 Reed Warblers had been ringed on Lundy, with one subsequent control: an adult ringed on 1 June 2001 was caught on the Ile d'Ouessant, off the Brittany coast (north-west France), on 24 July 2002. There are two controls of birds ringed elsewhere: a first-year bird ringed at Lapscheure, West-Vlaanderen, north-east Belgium, on 6 September 1996, was controlled on Lundy just over two weeks later on 23 September 1996. A bird trapped on Lundy on 29 October 2004 had been ringed as a first-year bird at Getteron, on the southern coast of Sweden, 1,282 kilometres north-east of Lundy, some seven weeks previously on 9 September 2004. This suggests that at least some of the late-autumn migrants reaching Lundy have covered considerable distances. Nationally, about a quarter of foreign-ringed Reed Warblers found in Britain have originated from north-east Europe, including Scandinavia (Wernham *et al.* 2002).

Icterine Warbler *Hippolais icterina*

Nationally scarce migrant.

Breeds in central and eastern Europe, wintering in sub-Saharan Africa. 3,660 records for Britain 1968–2003, with an average of 71 per year 2000–2003. Considered by the BBRC until the end of 1962.

First recorded on 28 August 1949,[143] by the end of 2006 there had been records in 25 years, involving a total of at least 48 individuals, the vast majority in autumn. Like the closely related Melodious Warbler, Icterine Warblers are much rarer in spring than in autumn and there are just two records: one on 8 May 1995 and one on 8 June 1988, in line with this species' generally rather late northward migration. Autumn occurrences have been spread over a much longer period, from 10 August (1975)[144] to 26 October (1949), but with a clear peak, involving over 80% of records, from the second half of August to the end of September (only five have occurred in October). There were four records in both 1951 and 1988, while the highest number recorded on a single day was three on 11

199

Icterine Warbler

September 1960. There are five instances of two in a day, but most records are – unsurprisingly – of single birds. The vast majority have been seen in Millcombe and St John's Valley, though one was seen at Jenny's Cove on 10 August 1975.

The following details the 13 accepted records for the 20-year period 1987–2006:

1987 16 & 21 Sep – one; in addition, an unidentified *Hippolais* warbler, presumably the same bird, was seen on 19 Sep.

1988 8 Jun – one (first spring record for Lundy).
9 to 12 Sep – one, with two present on 10 Sep.
25 & 29 Sep – one.
25 Oct – one.

1990 12, 15 & 16 Aug – one on the Terrace.
2 Sep – one in Millcombe.

1995 8 May – one in Millcombe.
19 to 22 Aug – two; one trapped and ringed in St John's Valley on 19th.

1997 8 to 14 Sep – two in Millcombe, one remaining to 16 Sep when it was seen in St Helen's Combe.

2002 23 Aug – an adult trapped and ringed in St John's Valley.

2003 22 & 24 Sep – one, first seen in Millcombe, trapped and ringed on 24th.

2005 18 Sep – one in Millcombe.

Seventeen Icterine Warblers had been ringed on Lundy by the end of 2006, but there are no controls or recoveries involving the island.

Melodious Warbler *Hippolais polyglotta*

Nationally scarce migrant.

Breeds in southern and western parts of continental Europe, migrating to wintering grounds in sub-Saharan Africa. 1,143 records for Britain 1968–2003, with an average of 26 per year 2000–2003. Considered by the BBRC until the end of 1962.

Melodious Warblers are rare autumn migrants to Lundy and even rarer in spring, usually turning up in Millcombe and St John's Valley and occasionally on the Terrace, though one was also seen in Gannets' Combe. There have been records in 30 years (to the end of 2006) involving at least 50 individuals, the first being caught in the former Garden Trap at the Old Light on 30 July 1951. The overwhelming majority have been recorded during autumn dispersal and migration between 28 July (1987) and 24 October (1990), although almost half the occurrences have been in August, with most of the remainder in September and only a handful of records in October. There have been just two occurrences in spring: one by the Old Light on 25 May 1973 of a bird that was trapped and ringed, and the above-mentioned Gannet's Combe bird on 17 May 1974.[145]

There are only three instances of more than one bird on the same day: two on 21 August 1967, 30 August 1972 and 24 October 1990.

Melodious Warblers breed primarily to the south of Britain, whereas Icterines breed mainly to the north and east. With a higher rate of occurrence in Britain than Melodious Warblers, albeit with a more easterly bias, it might be expected that Icterines would have outnumbered Melodious over the years, but in fact the number of occurrences are virtually identical. The fact that almost twice as many Melodious Warblers have been caught for ringing (30 against 17) suggests that they may be the more commonly occurring of the two species on the island, and that without the ringing effort many would otherwise have passed unnoticed. The peak arrival period for Melodious Warblers is during August, slightly earlier than the September peak in arrivals of Icterine Warblers. In both cases it seems likely that most of the birds reaching Lundy early in the autumn are dispersing juveniles and that occurrences are greatly influenced by weather conditions from year to year.

The following is a complete listing of 16 accepted records for the 20 years 1987–2006:

1987	28 Jul & 1 Aug – one.
	16 Aug – one in Millcombe/St John's Valley, trapped and ringed.
	19 Aug – one in Millcombe, trapped and ringed.
	5 Sep – one.
1988	16 Sep – one.
1989	28 Aug – one in Millcombe.
	1 Oct – one in Millcombe.
1990	10 to 24 Oct – one in Millcombe, trapped and ringed; a second, unringed bird was also present on 24 Oct.
1991	20 Sep – one in Millcombe.
1993	11 Oct – one, trapped and ringed.
1995	16 Aug – one.
2000	12 Aug – one in St John's Valley, trapped and ringed.
2003	14 & 15 Aug – one in St John's Valley.[146]
2004	29 Aug – a first-year bird on the Terrace, trapped and ringed.
2005	29 Aug – one trapped and ringed in St John's Valley was present the following day.

Thirty Melodious Warblers had been ringed on Lundy by the end of 2006, but there are no controls or recoveries involving the island.

Melodious-Icterine Warblers: Unidentified *Hippolais* warblers were recorded in 1954 (one in September), 1959 (singles in May, September and October), 1961 (one in late August and at least one in September), 1962 (one or two in September), 1963 (at least one in September), 1966 (at least two in late August[147]), 1980 (one in May and two in August), 1981 (one in August and one in September), 1987 (one in September) and 1988 (one in May and one in September). The record of an Icterine Warbler on 26 September 1968 published in the 1968 *LFS Annual Report* appears in the *Devon Bird Report* for that year under Melodious-Icterine Warbler, as "one, perhaps Icterine".

Blackcap *Sylvia atricapilla*   [Eurasian Blackcap]

Common spring and autumn migrant; occasional in midsummer and winter.

Blackcaps have been recorded on Lundy in all months of the year except February, though they are scarce outside the main migration periods of April to June and August to November. There has been a very marked increase since the late 1970s and early 1980s, reflected in both the numbers of birds seen and those trapped for ringing. This has coincided with a significant increase in the British breeding population (Baillie *et al.* 2006) and growing numbers of birds from continental Europe wintering in Britain.

Blackcap

The first spring migrants are usually seen in early or mid-April, but there are March records in nine LFS years, including six of the 10 years 1997–2006. This may indicate a trend towards earlier arrival dates, possibly linked to climate change. The earliest date is 17 March (2003). Until the late 1970s the highest spring count was 21, on 16 April 1966; even this modest number being exceptionally high compared with other years. Since 1978, however, when 30 were seen on 2 May, there have been five counts of more than 50, including 120 on 2 May 2004, 150 on 26 April 1987 and the maximum to date, at least 200 on 29 April 2000 (of which 40 were trapped and ringed). Following peak movements in late April or early May, migration slows during the second half of May, though stragglers occur regularly in June, especially early in the month.

"Black-cap Warbler" was listed by Parfitt (1876) and Chanter (1877) as "reported, but not accurately identified" and therefore regarded by Chanter as doubtful. Cummings (1909) suspected breeding but saw only one bird in June 1909. Lewis (1924) suspected breeding in 1924, as did Wynne-Edwards & Harrisson (1932) in 1930, while Harrisson (1932) listed Blackcap as an "erratic breeder". However, Davis (1954a) stated that "this belief was based merely on the presence of a singing bird in June, a phenomenon which has since proved in no way unusual". There continue to be scattered records in late June and July (e.g. a singing male on 27 June 2004 and a male on 1 July 2005) but there is still no indication that breeding has ever been attempted.

Autumn movements begin in late August or, more usually, in early to mid-September. The highest counts are usually recorded in October and migration continues well into November, with scattered records in December and January. As for spring, there has been a dramatic rise in the numbers of migrant Blackcaps recorded in autumn during the last 25 to 30 years. Until 1982 the highest count was 50 on 27 September 1972. Sixty were seen on 2 November 1982 and there have been 11 further counts of 50 or more, including 100 on 14 October 1992 and 28 September 2004, 130 on 11 October 1993, 150 on 12 October 1988, at least 200 on 23 October 1991 and an exceptional influx estimated at 200–300 birds on 10 October 1984. During that one day – which is described in detail by King (1985) – 58 Blackcaps were ringed; almost all had left the island the following day. The analysis presented by Wernham *et al.* (2002) suggests that peak emigration of British breeding Blackcaps occurs in September and that the significant movements recorded on Lundy from mid-October to early November are more likely to be birds of continental origin. This conclusion is supported by King (1985) in relation to the October 1984 fall and by Blackcap movements to and from Lundy shown by ringing (see below).

There are seven records in the first half of December, mostly of single birds (though three were seen on 5 December 1989) and mainly in the first week of the month. One or two remained through much of December 1976, one was seen on Christmas Day 2005, and there have been two January sightings: a female on 2 January 1978 and three birds on 13 January 1997. However, there is no known instance of an individual Blackcap spending the whole winter on the island, with no sightings at all between 14 January and 16 March inclusive.

Between 1947 and 2006, 4,140 Blackcaps were ringed on Lundy, of which 14 have subsequently been controlled or recovered – see table (a). A further eight birds ringed elsewhere have been controlled on the island – see table (b). In summary, these 22 movements involve: elsewhere in Britain (9), Ireland (1), Belgium (6), Germany (1), Switzerland (1), France (2), Spain (1) and Algeria (1). There was a huge increase in the number of Blackcaps ringed from the late 1970s, with 155 ringed in 1984 being the first time the annual total exceeded 100. However, there have been 17 such years since (up to and including 2006), with the maximum being 380 in 1993.

Two adult females ringed on Lundy on 7 May 1984 were controlled at the bird observatories on Calf of Man (a few days later) and Bardsey (the following May), and were presumably heading for breeding grounds in northern Britain or Ireland. This conclusion is supported by other movements to or from Cumbria, Strathclyde and Cork. The finding of Lundy-ringed birds in western France, southern Spain and North Africa is consistent with the conclusion by Wernham *et al.* (2002) that the vast majority of Blackcaps breeding in Britain and Ireland winter in Iberia and north-west Africa. However, over half of the foreign Blackcap controls and recoveries involving Lundy do not fit this

(a) Blackcaps ringed on Lundy and controlled or recovered elsewhere

Age/sex	Date ringed on Lundy	Place found	Date controlled or recovered	Speculation about date/place of finding
Adult M	28 Oct 1967	Riksingen, Limburg, **Belgium**	05 Jul 1968	In breeding area
Adult F	07 May 1984	Calf of Man, Isle of Man	11 May 1984	On spring migration
Adult F	07 May 1984	Bardsey Island, Gwynedd	13 May 1985	On spring migration
Adult M	28 May 1985	St Martin, Ile de Ré, Charente-Maritime, **France**	01 Apr 1987	On spring migration
1st-year M	05 Oct 1986	Mühlheim am Main, Darmstadt, Hesse, **Germany**	20 Apr 1987	On spring migration or in breeding area
1st-year M	20 Oct 1988	Laufen, Basel, **Switzerland**	28 May 1990[148]	In breeding area
1st-year M	26 Oct 1991	Río Guaro, Periana, Málaga, Andalucía, **Spain**	18 Mar 1995	On spring migration
1st-year M	14 Oct 1992	Artannes sur Indre, Indre-et-Loire, **France**	24 Nov 1993	On autumn migration
1st-year F	22 Oct 1995	Ballincollig, Co. Cork, **Ireland**	01 Jun 1996	In breeding area
1st-year M	29 Oct 1995	Congresbury, Bristol, Avon	03 Feb 1996	In wintering area
1st-year F	02 Nov 1995	Stewarton, Strathclyde	16 Jul 1998	In or close to breeding area
Adult F	29 Apr 2000	Grande Kabylie, northern **Algeria**	01 Feb 2003	In wintering area
1st-year M	21 Oct 2001	Upton-upon-Severn, Worcester	29 Oct 2005	On autumn migration
1st-year M	29 Oct 2001	Tacolneston, nr Norwich, Norfolk	10 Jan 2002	In wintering area

(b) Blackcaps ringed elsewhere and controlled on Lundy

Age/sex	Date ringed	Place ringed	Date controlled on Lundy	Speculation about date/place of ringing
1st-year M	01 Jul 1986	Great Corby, Carlisle, Cumbria	18 Apr 1988	In breeding area
1st-year M	24 Sep 1989	Icklesham, Sussex	01 Jun 1991	On autumn migration
1st-year M	29 Sep 1992	Sandwich Bay, Kent	30 Oct 1992	On autumn migration
1st-year F	29 Aug 1993	Boitsfort, Brabant, **Belgium**	11 Oct 1993	On autumn migration
1st-year M	15 Oct 1995	Semmerzake, Oost-Vlaanderen, **Belgium**	01 Nov 1995	On autumn migration
1st-year M	14 Sep 1999	Asse ter Heide, Brabant, **Belgium**	26 Oct 1999	On autumn migration
1st-year M	29 Sep 2003	Ingooigem, Oost-Vlaanderen, **Belgium**	28 Oct 2003	On autumn migration
1st-year F	03 Oct 2004	Bellem, Oost-Vlaanderen, **Belgium**	27 Oct 2004	On autumn migration

pattern. In particular, there is a remarkable series of controls of Belgian-ringed Blackcaps showing westward migration to Lundy in late autumn. A bird ringed at Sandwich Bay, Kent, in September showed a similar movement, reaching Lundy in late October, and had perhaps arrived in Kent from the near continent. It seems likely that these birds were heading for wintering grounds in western Britain and Ireland; but do they all originate from breeding areas in Belgium (as hinted at by the single movement in the other direction) or from elsewhere in continental Europe?

The recoveries in Germany and Switzerland indicate that at least some birds passing through Lundy in October come from more central areas of western Europe. Two Blackcaps ringed on Lundy in late autumn and recovered in subsequent winters near Bristol and Norwich respectively are highly likely also to have been continental birds overwintering in Britain; Wernham *et al.* (2002) reported only one instance of a known British breeding Blackcap found in Britain during the winter. Indeed, all of these movements to/from Lundy are consistent with the national picture, which shows that Blackcaps wintering in Britain originate mainly from breeding populations in the Low Countries and Germany (Wernham *et al.* 2002).

Garden Warbler *Sylvia borin*

Regular spring and autumn migrant, usually in small numbers; has bred.

Garden Warbler is one of the later spring migrants on Lundy, with the first arrivals usually occurring towards the end of April. The earliest date shown by LFS records is 7 April 2007, with only two other reports in the first half of the month (9 April 1947 and 10 April 1988). While passage continues throughout May and late birds are regularly seen in June, the main movements are typically in the first half of May. Until 1985 no more than six had been recorded in one day in spring, but between 1985 and 2004 there were six instances of more than 10 in a day, including by far the highest count to date: 50 on 1 May 1999. The latest spring record is of one on 26 June 1972.

Loyd (1922) quoted Ross (presumably Rousham & Ross 1909) as stating that Garden Warbler bred on Lundy but gave no further detail. Alexander *et al.* (1945) and Davis (1954a) mentioned F.W. Gade's observations of a nesting pair in 1934 – also reported in the 1934 *Devon Bird Report* as the "first nesting record for Lundy" – and a pair present "throughout the season" in 1938. Though passage migrants are often heard singing in spring, there has been no subsequent indication of breeding.

Autumn migration is mostly within the period mid-August to late October, but there have been occasional sightings in early August, and the earliest by more than two weeks was one on 17 July 1992. Peak movements usually occur between mid-September and mid-October and numbers tend to be rather higher than in spring, with daily counts reaching 10 or more birds in 15 LFS years (to the end of 2006). The highest number yet recorded is 30, on both 23 September 1965 and 22 September 1982. Migration normally continues well into October (e.g. 20 on 16th 1979), with late birds often occurring right up to the end of the month. Stragglers have been seen during the first week of November in six LFS years, while the latest by a considerable margin was one in Millcombe on 27 November 1994.[149]

A total of 759 Garden Warblers had been ringed on Lundy by the end of 2006, but there are no controls or recoveries of these birds. A bird ringed at Gibraltar Point Bird Observatory, on the Lincolnshire coast of The Wash, on 1 September 1981 was controlled on Lundy 27 days later on 28 September; the time and place of ringing is suggestive of a migrant recently arrived from continental Europe. More than 50% of the birds ringed on Lundy were caught during the 10-year period 1980–1989, with between 44 and 65 trapped annually between 1984 and 1988. BTO data indicate that the UK population increased significantly during this period, but now appears to be showing a long-term decline (Baillie *et al.* 2006).

Barred Warbler *Sylvia nisoria*

Lundy vagrant.

Breeds in central and eastern Europe, migrating south-east in autumn to wintering grounds in East Africa. 5,184 records for Britain 1968–2003, with an average of 199 per year 2000–2003. Considered by the BOU as a passage migrant rather than a nationally scarce migrant.

Barred Warbler

There are Lundy records for 20 years to the end of 2006, from the first occurrence on 10 October 1949 to the most recent in September/October 2005. In most years only a single bird was involved, but two were seen in 1960, 1975, 1982, 1988 and 2001, with an exceptional six birds between 18 September and 23 October 1967, four of which were trapped and ringed.[150] All records are for autumn, with over 80% falling between 20 September and 20 October. The earliest and latest dates are 21 August (2002) and 27 October (2001). All individuals that have been aged, either in the field or in the hand, have been first-winter birds. A total of 10 had been ringed by the end of 2006, but there are no controls or recoveries involving the island.

The following is a complete list of accepted records for the 20-year period 1987–2006:

1988 20 Sep – one in Millcombe.
           26 Oct – one.
1989 23 Sep to 5 Oct – a first-winter bird in Millcombe.
1995 29 Sep – a first-winter bird in Millcombe, trapped and ringed.
1996 14 to 17 Oct – one.
1997 7 to 19 Oct – one in Millcombe, trapped and ringed on 14th.
1999 29 Sep – one in Millcombe.
2001 13 Oct – one in St John's Valley, first seen in the scrub behind Brambles Villa.[151]
           27 Oct – one between the Ugly and St Helen's Combe.
2002 21 Aug – a first-winter bird caught and ringed in St John's Valley and seen again on 23 Aug.[151]
2005 28 Sep to 1 Oct – a first-winter bird in the garden at Stoneycroft.[152]

Lesser Whitethroat *Sylvia curruca*

Uncommon but annual spring and autumn passage migrant; one recent breeding record.

There has been a significant increase in Lesser Whitethroat records since Nick Dymond's *Birds of Lundy* was published in 1980. From the beginning of LFS recording in 1947 until the early 1970s, the species occurred in very low numbers and there were eight years with no records at all. Since 1977, however, Lesser Whitethroats have been seen every year, mainly in spring.

The earliest date is 16 April (1980), but spring migration typically commences in the last week of April or first week of May, with most records occurring in early to mid-May. The highest count is 10, recorded daily from 11 to 13 May 1996. There have been several other April/May counts of between five and eight birds in a day, all since 1989, though most sightings involve ones and twos. Migrants continue to occur irregularly to the end of May, with a few records into June. The latest date is 12 June (1977), though summering/breeding birds have remained until later (see below).

In 2002 came the first evidence of Lesser Whitethroat summering on the island, with one seen on six dates between 5 June and 14 July. The following year a pair was seen feeding young in Millcombe in mid-June, and feeding a second brood on 12 August. This is the first and – to date – only breeding record for Lundy. This apparent increase in spring/summer records belies a moderate decline nationally, thought to be caused by pressures during migration and on the East African wintering grounds (Baillie *et al.* 2007). A range extension into Wales (and also the first Irish breeding record) between the first (1968–1972, Sharrock 1976) and second national breeding bird atlases (1988–1991, Gibbons *et al.* 1993) may be the reason for the Lundy increase.

This is a species that is scarcer in autumn than in spring and there continue to be occasional blank years (e.g. 1998 and 2000). Most records are from mid-September and October and usually involve single birds. The highest daily count in autumn is four, on 16 September 1988, while three occurred on 23 October 1995 and there have been several records of two birds. The earliest date is 5 August (1966) and the latest 19 November (1954). Birds apparently showing the characteristics of the Siberian race, *S. c. blythi*, have been reported twice: on 28 October 1994 and 29 October 1999. However, while *S. c. blythi* is currently recognised as a scarce migrant by the BOURC, a recent *British Birds* paper points out that some experts no longer regard *S. c. blythi* as a valid subspecies. The author underlines that "the taxonomy and identification of the Lesser Whitethroat complex is a particularly thorny topic", as a result of which the BBRC has put all claims of eastern races of Lesser Whitethroat 'on hold', pending further research (Kehoe 2006; see also Langman *et al.* 2007).

Ninety-two Lesser Whitethroats had been ringed on Lundy by the end of 2006, but there are no controls or recoveries involving the island.

Whitethroat *Sylvia communis*   [Common Whitethroat]

Common migrant in spring and autumn; formerly bred in small numbers.

Although Whitethroats have not bred successfully on Lundy since 1978, singing birds can still be heard during spring migration, especially in areas of bramble, gorse and blackthorn scrub such as St John's Valley and Millcombe.

Whitethroat was listed by Chanter (1871) and Parfitt (1876) as a "summer visitant", Parfitt adding "occasional breeder". Loyd (1922) stated that "a few pairs" bred but contradicted himself later (Loyd 1925) by saying "many" pairs bred in 1922 and 1923. Wynne-Edwards & Harrisson (1932) listed 10 breeding pairs in 1930. Perry (1940) found one breeding pair in 1939, while Davis (1954a) put the breeding population at usually "fewer than ten pairs". Confirmed breeding took place in 19 LFS years between 1947 and 1978, mostly involving one to two pairs, but three pairs bred in 1953, 1968, 1971 and 1977, and eight pairs bred in 1952. Coincident with a population crash throughout Britain and Ireland – attributed to a long period of drought in the species' African wintering grounds south of the Sahara – none nested in 1969 and numbers passing through the island that year were miniscule (only two birds were seen in spring). The last successful nesting was in 1978 when an adult was seen carrying food on 21 June and four chicks were ringed on 23 June. However, the presence of birds in summer in many years, including a singing male from 10 to 13 June 1996 and an apparent territory-holding bird in 2000, are encouraging signs that Whitethroats may again breed successfully on the island in future.

The main spring passage takes place in late April and early May, with a few late migrants in early June in some years. The earliest arrival date is 7 April (1947) but there are only 10 other LFS years in which birds have arrived in the first half of April. Peak numbers vary considerably from year to year. The highest spring count prior to the 1969 population crash was in excess of 400 birds on 5 May 1953, followed by 200 on 30 April 1959 and 12 May 1960, and with counts of 100 or more in a further five years. Between 1969 and 2006, peak counts have generally been in the low tens, and in single figures in eight years. However, highs of 80 on 1 May 1999, 100 on 9 May 1990, 150 on 29 April 2000 and at least 300 during an astonishing fall of spring migrants on 2 May 2004 have also occurred.

Autumn passage starts with a few birds in late July, though the main migration takes place between early August and late September, followed by a scattering of birds in October. In fact there have been records into October in 33 LFS years, including nine of the 10 years 1997–2006. The only November occurrence is also the latest autumn date: one on 5 November 1959. Numbers are usually smaller in autumn but include two enormous falls. On 16 September 1958, observers "woke to find the whole island covered with warblers. A conservative estimate put the number of Whitethroats present at over 1,000 in company with almost as many other warblers. By the following day almost all had gone – only three Whitethroats were seen" (1958 *LFS Annual Report*). In 1959, four influxes of 100 or more birds in August and early September were followed by a huge fall on 8 September when 900 were estimated. Counts of 100 or more birds have only occurred in three other years: over 100 on 24 August 1967, 120 on 18 September 1954 and 350 on 11 September 1982.

By the end of 2006, 2,977 Whitethroats had been ringed on Lundy, of which nine had been controlled or recovered – see table (a). In addition, there have been three controls on Lundy of birds ringed elsewhere – see table (b). The Whitethroat ringed at Dungeness was trapped and released at Lundy's North Light four years later and was on at least its fifth southward migration to Africa.

(a) Whitethroats ringed on Lundy and controlled or recovered elsewhere

Age/sex	Date ringed on Lundy	Place found	Date controlled or recovered	Speculation about date/place of finding
Adult	05 May 1952	Listowel, Co. Kerry, **Ireland**	24 Jul 1952	Found in breeding area
Juvenile	08 Sep 1952	Bragança, Norte, **Portugal**	24 Sep 1952	On autumn migration
Adult F	17 May 1956	Cardigos, Centro, **Portugal**	09 Oct 1956	On autumn migration
Juvenile	21 Aug 1958	Sandwich Bay, Kent	27 Aug 1958	On autumn migration
Adult	07 May 1959	Alto Alentejo, Alentejo, **Portugal**	18 Sep 1959	On autumn migration
Juvenile	31 Aug 1959	Centro, **Portugal**	28 Dec 1959	Passage bird probably long dead when found
Adult M	11 May 1965	Soulac Medoc, Gironde, **France**	24 Sep 1966	On autumn migration
1st-year	23 Aug 1966	Nr Castlebar, Co. Mayo, **Ireland**	13 Jun 1967	Found in breeding area
Adult F	30 Apr 1976	Newton Abbot, Devon	09 May 1976	Spring migration (re-oriented overshoot?)

(b) Whitethroats ringed elsewhere and controlled on Lundy

Age/sex	Date ringed	Place ringed	Date controlled on Lundy	Speculation about date/place of ringing
Unspecified	17 Aug 1952	Jersey, Channel Islands	06 May 1953	On spring migration
Adult M	17 Aug 1952	Dungeness, Kent	11 Sep 1956	On autumn migration
2nd-year	07 May 2001	Great Saltee Island, Co. Wexford, **Ireland**	11 May 2004	On spring migration

Dartford Warbler *Sylvia undata*

Lundy vagrant.

There are only six LFS records (to the end of 2006) and none previously:

1951 28 Oct – a first-winter bird frequenting gorse-covered slopes in St John's Valley.
1963 26 & 28 Mar – one.
1988 18 Apr – one seen at Quarter Wall was later trapped and ringed.
1994 21 Oct – one seen briefly in Millcombe.
2004 29 Oct – one in the Quarter Wall area.
2005 13 Oct – a male above Pilot's Quay.[153]

The dates for the 1963 record given in Gade (1978, p. 444) – who wrote: "My wife sighted a bird on March 25th which could not have been anything but a Dartford warbler. It was confirmed on March 27th by Michael Jones, the Field Society warden" – differ from those published in the 1963-64 *LFS Annual Report*, which are used here. The 1963 *Devon Bird Report* gives 26 March only. Unfortunately the original LFS data for the year in question no longer exist.

Dartford Warblers have expanded their breeding range in southern England in recent years and now nest in suitable heathland habitat along the coastlines of North Devon and Somerset, as well as the Gower and Pembrokeshire in South Wales. The UK population has also increased from 420 pairs in 1984 to 1,890 pairs in 1994, and 3,208 pairs in 2006 (national survey by BTO, Forestry Commission, Natural England, RSPB). If this trend continues it is likely that occurrences on Lundy will become more regular in future.

Rüppell's Warbler

Rüppell's Warbler *Sylvia rueppelli*

British vagrant.

Breeds only in parts of Greece, Turkey and Syria, migrating to wintering grounds in sub-Saharan Africa, mainly Chad and Sudan. 5 records for Britain 1950–2005.

There is one Lundy record of a single bird, the second for Britain, two years after the first on Shetland in August/September 1977:

1979 1 to 10 Jun – a singing male present along the Terrace and around the quarries was trapped and ringed on 4 Jun.

The warbler was first seen in the mouth of the Terrace Heligoland trap by David Carey, a visiting birdwatcher from Oxford, in the late afternoon of 1 June. By nightfall all but one of the 20 or so birdwatchers on the island had seen it at close quarters in the willows in the small quarry (now known among many regular Lundy birdwatchers as 'Rüppell's Quarry') some 100 metres north of the trap. Well before daybreak the following day, three birdwatchers (Richard Campey, Keith Mortimer and a fretful Tim Davis – the sleep-deprived soul who had missed the bird the day before) were gathered by the quarry. At 6.30am the warbler appeared on top of the willows, around which it stayed for virtually the entire day before dropping over the side of the Terrace at dusk to roost. It sang for much of the day, at one time disputing ownership of the willows with a male Whitethroat. News of the warbler's presence on the island soon got out and hundreds of birdwatchers came to see it over the duration of its stay, the 100 or so remaining boat tickets for the Lundy Field Society's annual excursion to the island selling out almost overnight.

Subalpine Warbler *Sylvia cantillans*

British vagrant.

Breeds in southern Europe and North Africa, migrating to winter in sub-Saharan Africa. 536 records for Britain 1950–2005. Considered by the BBRC until the end of 2005 (from 1 January 2006 only records of the eastern subspecies *S. c. albistriata* are dealt with by the BBRC).

There are 12 accepted Lundy records (and two pending), all of single birds. All except one have occurred in spring and all since 1985, reflecting increased frequency in Britain generally. Of the five caught and ringed, none has been controlled or recovered subsequently.

1985 3 Jun – a male near the Terrace trap.
1987 31 May to 4 Jun – a singing male in lower Millcombe.[154]
 9 & 17 Aug and 5 Sep – an adult male, trapped on the Terrace and ringed.
1988 22 Apr – a male caught in Millcombe and ringed.
1992 6 May – a male in Millcombe.
1993 3 May – a male trapped in St John's Valley and ringed.
1994 2 to 7 May – an adult female in the vicinity of VC Quarry.
1995 14 May – a probable female was watched feeding in Millcombe.
1997 2 May – a first-summer male trapped in Millcombe and ringed.[155]
 15 & 16 Jun – a male singing in Millcombe (presumed different to the May individual).
2005 17 & 18 Jun – a male in Millcombe.
2006 10, 12 & 13 Oct – a first-winter male trapped and ringed in Millcombe was relocated on 19 Oct and still present on 20 Oct. This record was submitted to the BBRC as relating to the eastern sub-species *S. c. albistriata* but was considered by the committee to be attributable only to species.
2007 11 Apr – a male in Millcombe.
 19 & 20 Apr – a male on the north side of the Ugly.
 (Both 2007 records subject to acceptance by the Devon Birds Records Committee.)

A record of a singing male on the Terrace from 15 to 20 May 1988, though included in the 1988 *LFS Annual Report*, appears not to have been submitted to the BBRC and is therefore discounted here. In addition, a female was trapped, ringed and photographed in Millcombe on 6 May 1990; however, it appears that this record was never submitted to the BBRC and is therefore also excluded.

Subalpine Warbler is listed by Chanter (1877) as an "occasional visitant" but with the addition of a question mark against both the common name and the (then) scientific name, *Sylvia subalpina bonelli*. In the text Chanter stated: "It is not only the variety, but the comparative rarity of many of the birds which frequent this curious Island…which is most deserving of notice; some of them, such as the subalpine warbler, almost new to British ornithology."

Sardinian Warbler *Sylvia melanocephala*

British vagrant.

Breeds around the Mediterranean basin. Partly migratory, with wintering grounds extending into Africa. 73 records for Britain 1950–2005.

There are two Lundy records of single birds, both in late spring, including the first occurrence of Sardinian Warbler in Britain:

1955 10 May – an adult male, trapped and ringed (Whitaker 1955c).[156]
1988 8 Jun – a female on the Terrace.

Greenish Warbler *Phylloscopus trochiloides*

British vagrant.

Breeds in eastern Europe from the Baltic eastwards across western Russia, Siberia and parts of Asia. Evidence of westward spread, with an increase in British records of singing birds in spring. European birds migrate to wintering grounds in Nepal, India and Bangladesh. 441 records for Britain 1950–2005. Considered by the BBRC until the end of 2005.

There are two Lundy records, the more recent being of a singing male in summer:

1958 2 & 3 Nov – one in Millcombe was mist-netted and ringed on the latter date. The 1958 *LFS Annual Report* states "a second bird present on the Terraces on the following day, with a more conspicuous wing bar, was also probably of this species".[157]

1978 14 & 15 Jul – one singing in Millcombe.[158]

8 Aug – one, perhaps the same bird but treated as different by the BBRC.

A record in the 1973 *LFS Annual Report* of a bird trapped on the Terrace on 22 June 1973 was subsequently rejected by the BBRC. Similarly, a record in the 1980 *LFS Annual Report* of a singing male in Millcombe on 16 May 1980 (and 17th according to the LFS logbook) was also rejected.

Arctic Warbler *Phylloscopus borealis*

British vagrant.

Breeds from north-easternmost Scandinavia eastwards across Russia. Migratory, wintering in southern south-east Asia. 262 records for Britain 1950–2005.

There are three Lundy records, all in September and October:

1959 6 Sep – one trapped and ringed.[159]

1981 5 Oct – one in St Helen's Copse.

1985 19, 22 & 23 Sep – a first-winter bird, trapped and ringed on 19th.

Pallas's Warbler *Phylloscopus proregulus*   [Pallas's Leaf Warbler]

Nationally scarce migrant.

Breeds in northern and eastern Asia, wintering in south and south-east Asia. Formerly a rare vagrant to Britain but now annual. 1,783 records for Britain 1958–2003, with an average of 110 per year 2000–2003. Considered by the BBRC until the end of 1990.

There are four Lundy records, all since 1993, reflecting the national trend of more regular occurrence in recent years, and all in late October or November – again typical of records nationally.

1993 11 & 12 Nov – one watched feeding on the Terrace.

1994 25 Oct – one watched feeding in Millcombe, later mist-netted and ringed.

1997 31 Oct – one seen on the Terrace.

2003 27 Oct – one trapped and ringed in Millcombe.

Yellow-browed Warbler *Phylloscopus inornatus*

Nationally scarce migrant.

Breeds in eastern Russia, migrating south to wintering grounds in south and south-east Asia. 9,093 records for Britain 1968–2003, with an average of 434 per year 2000–2003. Considered by the BBRC until the end of 1962.

One of the most beautiful and easier to identify of the 'little green jobs', Yellow-browed Warblers on Lundy are most often seen feeding in the canopy of trees in Millcombe, St Helen's Copse and Quarter Wall Copse. This frequently results in severe neck-ache as observers strain to catch glimpses of a tiny bird flitting between sycamore leaves high above their heads.

When Nick Dymond published his *Birds of Lundy* in 1980, there had been fewer than 20 occurrences of Yellow-browed Warbler since the first LFS record on 6 & 7 October 1949. From 1980 onwards sightings have been almost annual in autumn, with around 12 individuals in 2005 alone and a total of at least 81 birds to the end of 2006. Adding a minimum of 17 birds between 1949 and 1979, the overall total is at least 98. The earliest and latest dates are 16 September (1988, 1999 and 2006) and 30 November (1986, one at Halfway Wall), with the overwhelming majority occurring in October. The

Yellow-browed Warbler

highest daily count was of five birds between 8 & 11 October 1986. The greater frequency of records in recent years reflects the national trend, which has also been sharply upward.

There are no confirmed spring records, though one was reportedly seen by F.W. Gade on 26 April 1944 (Davis 1954a).

The following is a complete list of records for the 10-year period 1997–2006 (not recorded in 2000 or 2002):

1997 3 Oct – one, caught and ringed in Millcombe.
14 Oct – one in Quarter Wall Copse.
1998 9 Oct – one on the Terrace.
1999 16 Sep – one in Millcombe.[160]
2001 13 Oct – between four and six in Millcombe, St Helen's Combe and (one seen) near the Castle.
29 to 30 Oct – two in Millcombe, with one ringed on 1 Nov remaining until the following day.
2003 23 to 26 Sep – one in Millcombe and St Helen's Copse.
21 to 27 Oct – two in Millcombe and St Helen's Copse, with one remaining to 30 Oct when it was caught and ringed.
2004 12, 14, 15 & 19 Oct – one in the Terrace area.
26 Oct – two ringed in St John's Valley, with one of these seen at Quarter Wall on 29 Oct.
2005 18 Sep to 23 Oct – about 12 in Millcombe, St John's Valley, St Helen's Copse and Quarter Wall Copse, with six caught and ringed (including a total of five on 22 & 23 Oct).[161]
2006 8 Oct – one in St Helen's Copse.
24 Oct – one in lower Millcombe gardens, trapped and ringed.
27 & 28 Oct – one in lower Millcombe, trapped and ringed on 28th.

Hume's Leaf Warbler *Phylloscopus humei* (generally referred to by birdwatchers as Hume's Warbler) was split from Yellow-browed Warbler and added to the *British List* in 1997 (BOURC 1997; Sangster *et al.* 2002). There were 83 British records to the end of 2005 (including pre-1997 individuals that had previously been assigned to the race 'Hume's Yellow-browed Warbler' *P. i. humei*). There is no evidence that any of the 'Yellow-browed Warblers' seen on Lundy prior to the taxonomic split showed the characteristics of Hume's Warbler, but the possibility cannot be excluded. This is perhaps one of the species most likely to be added to the Lundy list in the near future.

Forty-eight Yellow-browed Warblers had been ringed on Lundy by the end of 2006, but there are no controls or recoveries involving the island.

Radde's Warbler *Phylloscopus schwarzi*

British vagrant.

Breeds in Russia (from southern Siberia eastwards), northern Mongolia, north-east China and North Korea. Migratory, wintering in south-east Asia. 270 records for Britain 1950–2005, all in autumn. Considered by the BBRC until the end of 2005.

The sole Lundy record was the second for Devon following one at Prawle Point in November 1991:

1996   30 Oct – a first-year bird trapped in a mist-net below Brambles Villa and ringed.

Radde's Warbler

Western Bonelli's Warbler *Phylloscopus bonelli*

British vagrant.

Breeds in south-west Europe and North Africa, wintering in sub-Saharan Africa. 75 records for Britain 1950–2005.

There is one Lundy record:

1976   9 Apr – one feeding around blackthorn and flycatching in the (then) Manor Farm Hotel garden was trapped and ringed.

The first 'Bonelli's Warbler' on Lundy – caught and ringed on 1 September 1954 and only the second record for Britain (Whitaker 1955a) – long pre-dated the 1997 splitting of 'Bonelli's Warbler' into two separate species: Western Bonelli's Warbler *P. bonelli* and Eastern Bonelli's Warbler *P. orientalis* (BOURC 1997). The 1976 Lundy bird was assigned upon review, post-split, to Western Bonelli's Warbler on the basis of its wing formula. However, the description of the 1954 bird did not permit unequivocal allocation to one of the two 'new' species. Consequently, the 1954 record now stands as Western or Eastern Bonelli's Warbler (Rogers 1998; 1997 *Devon Bird Report*).

An entry in the 1959/60 *LFS Annual Report* concerning two birds on 26 Aug 1960, details of which were also published in the 1960 *Devon Bird Report*, appears not to have been submitted to the BBRC. It was excluded by Dymond (1980) and is also discounted here. In addition, a record published in the 1980 *LFS Annual Report* of a bird on 13 May 1980 appears to have been included in error as the original sighting is crossed out in the LFS logbook, and there is no trace of the sighting having been accepted or rejected by the BBRC.

Eastern Bonelli's Warbler *Phylloscopus orientalis*

British vagrant.

Breeds in south-east Europe and western Asia, wintering in sub-Saharan Africa. 4 records for Britain 1950–2005.

This species was split from 'Bonelli's Warbler' *P. bonelli* (now Western Bonelli's Warbler) and added to the *British List* in 1997 (BOURC 1997). There has been one Lundy record, only the fourth for Britain:

2004   26 Apr – one feeding very actively from a defunct electric fence and the drystone wall on the southern side of the Tent Field above Benjamin's Chair. There was a cold and blustery north-east wind blowing and both the warbler and its four observers were sheltering in the lee of the wall. Although the bird did not call – differences in call being a key feature for separating Western and Eastern Bonelli's Warblers – the prolonged, close-range views permitted the taking of a detailed description and an excellent series of photographs. Examination of these photographs enabled the tentative field identification to be confirmed and acceptance of the record by the BBRC.

Wood Warbler *Phylloscopus sibilatrix*

Uncommon spring and autumn migrant; declining.

A bird "in vivid yellow and green and pure white underparts, contrasting with the smaller (willow) warbler both in size and colouring and especially in its broad yellow eyestripe". So wrote Mrs F.E. Carter of Bude, Cornwall, on seeing the first Wood Warbler to enter LFS records on 6 October 1947. Unsurprisingly for a bird most at home in the canopy of broadleaved trees, Millcombe is where most Wood Warblers are seen, and their trilling song, often culminating in a slow, soft, descending *tew-tew-tew*, is occasionally heard on the island.

Wood Warbler was first recorded on Lundy by Felix Gade on 24 April 1932 (Palmer 1946). Gade also noted one on the exceptionally early date of 7 April 1944 and another on 24 July 1943 (Dymond 1980).

Between 1947 and 1970 there were nine years in which Wood Warblers were not recorded. Since then, however, they have been seen in every year. From 1983 to 1991 the species was recorded in higher numbers than previously and in both migration seasons, with averages of six or seven birds in spring and four in autumn. Since 2000 those averages have fallen to one in spring and less than one in autumn.

This fall-off in occurrence reflects a 65% decline in the UK's Wood Warbler population between 1994 and 2005 (Eaton *et al.* 2006), with declines also evident across north and west Europe (BirdLife International 2004). The species is currently 'amber-listed' (of medium conservation concern) but could be 'red-listed' in the not too distant future. National surveys have shown declines in other woodland-nesting long-distance migrants, such as Redstart and Spotted Flycatcher, so factors on the African wintering grounds or on migration routes may be involved. Other causes could include the effects of climate change and abandonment of traditional management in many British woodlands.

There are about a third more spring records (approximately 150 individuals to the end of 2006) than autumn ones (about 100). Spring migration peaks from late April to mid-May, extreme dates in LFS years being 12 April (1980 and 1999) and 29 June (1988). An entry in the LFS logbook of three on 31 March 1999, included in the *LFS Annual Report* for that year, must be considered as highly doubtful. Most records are of single birds. About 14 individuals occurred in spring 1987, including the highest ever daily total of eight on 26 April 1987 during a major influx of Willow Warblers.

Most autumn birds pass through during the second half of August and the first half of September. Extreme dates are an exceptionally early 17 July (1990) and 14 October (1984), with a maximum count of six on 20 August 1959. One bird was seen at North End – presumably an exhausted migrant – on 27 September 1971.[162]

Forty-six Wood Warblers had been ringed on Lundy by the end of 2006, but there are no controls or recoveries involving the island.

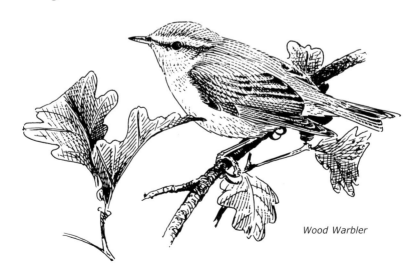

Wood Warbler

Chiffchaff *Phylloscopus collybita*

Common spring and autumn migrant; occasional in midsummer and winter; breeds sporadically.

One of the earliest signs of spring is the unmistakable *chiff-chaff chiff-chaff* song of the eponymous bird; on Lundy usually first heard in Millcombe on a March morning. Given this prominent self-announcement of male Chiffchaffs, it is surprising that there is an almost complete absence of any information about the species on Lundy prior to formation of the LFS. Chiffchaff is missing from the lists of both Chanter (1871) and Parfitt (1876), while Loyd (1925) noted tersely, "stated by Ross to breed, but no authority is given". Nowadays, Chiffchaffs have been seen in all months of the year and are particularly common during spring and autumn migration.

Chiffchaff

Overwintering birds have been recorded in January and February, with spring migrants typically beginning to arrive in early to mid-March; but if weather conditions are unfavourable it may be the end of the month before Chiffchaffs are seen or heard. Small influxes of several tens can occur at any time between late March and early May, but the main movements and larger falls are most often recorded in April. The highest daily counts have been 200 on 28 April 2000 (when 50 were ringed) and 400 on 15 April 1987.[163] Passage drops away markedly after the beginning of May, though double-figure counts can continue throughout the month.

In most years small numbers of Chiffchaffs are seen in June and July, with males often holding territory well into the summer. Despite this, there have been only six instances of confirmed breeding: one pair in 1965 (location unknown) and 1967 (Millcombe), and single pairs seen feeding young in July 1976, July 1988 and July 1994 (all in Millcombe) and carrying food on 24 May 1977. Breeding landbird surveys in June 2000 and June 2004 recorded zero and three Chiffchaff territories respectively, but with no confirmation of breeding in 2004 (Lock 2001, 2004). It seems likely that the patchy midsummer coverage of the island by birdwatchers means that a number of successful nesting attempts have been missed over the years.

Chiffchaffs continue to be seen in small numbers during July and August (probably birds dispersing from the nearby mainland), but it is late August or more often into September before true autumn passage gets under way. Peak movements usually occur between mid-September and early October but migration extends well into November in most years. The highest daily counts are usually lower than those recorded in spring, but notable falls occur from time to time; for example, about 300 on 16 September 1958 (600 *Phylloscopus* warblers were present that day; ringing totals showed a roughly 50:50 split Chiffchaff:Willow Warbler) and 150 on 24 September 1989.[164]

Wernham *et al.* (2002) reported that significant numbers of continental birds are likely to be involved in movements of Chiffchaffs in Britain during the second half of October and November. On Lundy, individuals thought to belong to one of the eastern races of Chiffchaff, *P. c. abietinus* (from Fennoscandia) or *P. c. tristis* ('Siberian' Chiffchaff) / *P. c. fulvescens* have been reported between October and December in at least 15 LFS years. For example, two Chiffchaffs present from 29 October to 5 November 2001 (both trapped, ringed and photographed – see photograph in 2001 *Devon Bird Report*) were considered to show characteristics of *P. c. tristis*. However, re-evaluation in the light of recent expert opinion on call and plumage criteria (e.g. Kehoe 2006) suggests that racial identification has not been proven conclusively for any of these individuals (M. Langman, personal communication). At the time of writing, the Devon Birds Records Committee is undertaking a comprehensive review of all such occurrences in Devon (Langman *et al.* 2007).

214

There have been December records of one to seven birds (the latter count on 23 December 1985) in at least 19 LFS years, all except three of these from 1975 onwards. While those seen early in the month may be late migrants, others appear to have been overwintering, though there is no ringing evidence to prove that any one individual has spent the whole winter on the island. The first January Chiffchaff record for Lundy was not until 1980 when one was seen from 1st to 12th. While there have been January sightings of one to four birds (the latter on 28 January 1988) in a further seven years, up to and including 1989, there has been none since. There are February records of ones and twos in seven years, all between 1977 and 1989. This raises the possibility that a wintering tradition was established for a short time by a small group of birds that subsequently died out – or have Chiffchaffs been overlooked in more recent winters?

Between 1947 and 2006, Chiffchaff was the seventh most frequently ringed species on Lundy, with a total of 3,979, the most in any one year being 279 in 1988. However, only four (0.1% of those ringed) have subsequently been controlled or recovered – see table (a). A further six birds ringed elsewhere have been controlled on the island – see table (b). Overall, these 10 movements involve: elsewhere in Britain (6), Channel Islands (1), Portugal (1), Spain (1) and Senegal (1). Six show movements within Britain and the Channel Islands during spring migration, with one of these birds taking just two days to reach Lundy from Guernsey. While it can be assumed that these birds were all heading for British or Irish breeding grounds, only the bird found in Nottinghamshire in late July seems likely to have been in its nesting area. The individual found in Portugal was probably still moving south. The Chiffchaff ringed in Senegal in February 1991 and controlled on Lundy just over ten weeks later shows one of the longest known movements of any bird to or from the island (two Lundy-ringed Sedge Warblers controlled in the same Senegalese National Park in which the Chiffchaff was ringed share the record distance of 3,999 kilometres). Given that some British Chiffchaffs winter much closer to home, around the Mediterranean, this example serves as a reminder that many of the birds passing through Lundy also undertake truly long-haul migrations. Indeed, Senegal is recognised as a major wintering area for Chiffchaffs of British and Irish origin (Wernham *et al.* 2002).

(a) Chiffchaffs ringed on Lundy and controlled or recovered elsewhere

Age/sex	Date ringed on Lundy	Place found	Date controlled or recovered	Speculation about date/place of finding
Adult	17 Mar 1966	Oliveira de Azemeis, Aveiro, northern **Portugal**	15 Nov 1967*	On autumn migration
Adult	19 Mar 1966	Skokholm, Dyfed	01 Apr 1966	On spring migration
1st-year	25 Oct 1997	Carburton, Nottinghamshire	24 Jul 1998	In breeding area
1st-year	28 Oct 2004	Massalcoreig, Lérida, Catalonia, **Spain**	19 Feb 2005	On spring migration or in wintering area

*Date of finding accurate to within two weeks (i.e. the bird was found during the month of November).

(b) Chiffchaffs ringed elsewhere and controlled on Lundy

Age/sex	Date ringed	Place ringed	Date controlled on Lundy	Speculation about date/place of ringing
Adult	06 May 1967	Bardsey Island, Gwynedd	17 May 1967	On spring migration
Adult	14 Apr 1983	Vale Marais, Guernsey, Channel Islands	16 Apr 1983	On spring migration
Adult	11 Apr 1984	Portland Bill, Dorset	19 Apr 1984	On spring migration
Adult M	02 Apr 1986	Portland Bill, Dorset	12 Apr 1986	On spring migration
1st-winter	06 Feb 1991	Djoudj National Park, **Senegal**	22 Apr 1991	In wintering area
Adult F	22 Apr 2000	Portland Bill, Dorset	29 Apr 2000	On spring migration

Willow Warbler *Phylloscopus trochilus*

Very common spring and autumn migrant with occasional mass arrivals; has bred.

Given that many Chiffchaffs now winter in Britain, Willow Warbler (along with Wheatear, Sand Martin and Swallow) is perhaps more likely to be regarded as a true harbinger of spring migration, being one of the earliest trans-Saharan migrants to arrive. Given the right conditions, hundreds or even thousands of Willow Warblers may make landfall on Lundy in April or early May, when the island can literally seem to be crawling with them – birds in every tree, bush, bramble and tussock, on every stone wall and even hopping about in open fields. These dramatic mass arrivals or 'falls' generally occur overnight and the birds move on as quickly as conditions allow, typically departing the very next night, or even the same day. Though such events are exceptional – perhaps only once or twice in a lifetime of regular trips to the island – smaller numbers are almost certain to be seen in any mid-spring (or early autumn) visit. The recollection and anticipation of sitting in Millcombe, listening to the liquid song of a newly arrived Willow Warbler on a perfect spring day, the air filled with the scent of flowering gorse, is enough to see even the most hard-bitten birder through the winter.

The first spring birds nowadays tend to arrive in the last few days of March, whereas prior to 1980 the first week of April was the norm. The earliest on record is one on 10 March 1994. Peak movements occur between mid-April and early May when daily counts of up to 50 are commonplace and arrivals of between 100 and 300 are fairly regular. As already mentioned, spectacular falls have occurred in some years, with counts of 500 or more as follows:

1959	Most of the 800 *Phylloscopus* warblers present on 28 Apr were Willow Warblers.
1977	500 on 16 Apr.
1984	500 on 20 Apr.
1985	750–1,000 on 1 May.
1987	3,000 on 15 Apr and 1,000 *Phylloscopus* warblers on 24 Apr, of which most were probably Willow Warblers.
1988	500 on 10 & 11 Apr.
1989	2,000 on 23 Apr, 1,200 on 24 Apr and 1,000 on 2 May.
1990	1,000 on 28 Apr.
1991	1,000 on 9 May.
1992	1,000 on 20 Apr, 5,000 on 29 Apr and 1,000 on 2 May.
1998	1,500 on 26 Apr.
2000	1,000 on 28 & 29 Apr.
2004	500 on 24 Apr.
2006	At least 500 on 23 Apr, of which 201 were trapped and ringed.

It is noticeable that most of these high counts have been since 1980, particularly during the late 1980s and early 1990s. Annual totals of Willow Warblers ringed also showed a marked increase in this period, giving credibility to the unprecedented counts entered in the LFS logbook. Migration continues at a lower level through May, with ones and twos seen well into June in most years. BTO data since 1994 show that while English and Welsh breeding populations have declined, there was a marked increase in numbers in Scotland and Northern Ireland over the same period (Baillie *et al.* 2006). Ringing recoveries (see below) suggest that many Willow Warblers passing through Lundy nest in Scotland and Ireland, so the population increase in those countries could explain the high numbers recently observed on the island.

"Willow Wren" was listed by Chanter (1871) and Parfitt (1876) as a "summer visitant", the latter adding "occasional breeder", while Ross (1908) referred to Willow Warbler as having bred but gave no further detail. Davis (1954a) reported that breeding occurred in most years from 1927 (F.W. Gade) to 1944, with a maximum of four pairs in 1930 recorded by Wynne Edwards & Harrisson (1932). During LFS years, nesting probably occurred in 1947 (Davis 1954a), one or two pairs bred in Millcombe in 1949 and one pair was believed to have nested in 1954. There were no further records of nesting until 1972 when two pairs bred in Millcombe. A single pair bred in each of the following three years, 1973 to 1975 (the 1973 pair rearing six young) and also in 1978 and 1980. There was a further long gap until 1989 when adults were seen feeding young in Millcombe in July. In 1990 a nest with young was found in Millcombe, while an adult was feeding fledged young on 21 July 1992. Breeding has been recorded in three subsequent years: 1997 – fledged young being fed in Millcombe in late July; 2000 – three territories located, one in Millcombe and two along the East Side (Lock 2001); and 2004 – one territory (Lock 2004) and adults feeding fledged young in July.

While odd birds may be present in late June and early July even in non-breeding years, return migration usually commences in the second half of July, reaching a peak during August or early September, dwindling rapidly after mid-September, with stragglers into October and exceptionally as late as November. Significant falls can occur at any time from late July to mid-September, depending on weather conditions, though there appears to be a tendency in autumn for arrivals to be smaller but more frequent than in spring, reflecting a more protracted passage. The highest daily total is 1,000 on 28 August 1989, 8 August 1997[165] and 10 & 11 August 1999. Five hundred were seen on 11 September 1982, and 400 on 2 September 1987, while the daily maximum has been between 100 and 350 in at least 24 other years. There have been November sightings in five years, the latest of these being one on 15 November 1999.

A bird seen on 22 September 2003 showed the characteristics of an eastern subspecies (perhaps *P. t. acredula*), while another on 22 October 2005 was also assigned to *acredula*. Langman *et al.* (2007), however, state that: "Identification is unreliable in the field…The status of *P. t. acredula* [in Devon] is unclear with no confirmed records, but is probably an under-recorded migrant."

Willow Warbler

More Willow Warblers have been ringed on Lundy than any other species: 12,814 between 1947 and the end of 2006, with the highest annual total being 897 in 1989. Twenty have been controlled or recovered – see table (a) overleaf. In addition, there are 19 controls and one recovery on the island of Willow Warblers ringed elsewhere – see table (b) overleaf. These movements involve: elsewhere in Britain (31), Ireland (5), Portugal (1), Morocco (1), Italy (1) and Denmark (1). Of the movements within Britain, there is a fascinating series of exchanges with Portland Bill Bird Observatory in Dorset, as well as west-coast observatories including Bardsey Island, Cape Clear (Ireland), Calf of Man and Walney. This pattern, together with movements to/from mainland Scotland and Ireland indicates that many, if not most, of the Willow Warblers passing through Lundy nest in northern and western Britain and Ireland. However, the fact that some Willow Warblers of continental origin also occur on Lundy is proven by the Danish-ringed bird controlled in September 1993.

Although Willow Warbler is a very common migrant on Lundy, there are significant gaps in the information available from the LFS logbooks and *LFS Annual Reports*. For some years, particularly during the 1960s, Willow Warbler and Chiffchaff counts were lumped together, while in more recent times birdwatchers have often not been present on the island during the peak 'autumn' passage period in late summer. This is also the species most often involved in falls of migrants and there is likely to be great variation between observers in the way in which larger totals are arrived at – from detailed counts of those birds actually seen, to estimated numbers of those seen, to extrapolation for the whole island based on counts from a limited area. In spite of these challenges, it has still been possible to build a fairly detailed picture of Willow Warbler movements.

(a) Willow Warblers ringed on Lundy and controlled or recovered elsewhere

Age/sex	Date ringed on Lundy	Place found	Date controlled or recovered	Speculation about date/place of finding
Adult	22 Apr 1951	Hereford, Herefordshire	04 Jul 1951	In breeding area
Adult	26 July 1952	Izmorene, northern **Morocco**	07 Apr 1954	On spring migration
1st-year	03 Sep 1961	Marinha Grande, Leiria, Centro, **Portugal**	10 Oct 1961	On autumn migration
1st-year	11 Sep 1963	Portland Bill, Dorset	19 Sep 1963	On autumn migration
Adult	19 Apr 1967	Thurles, Co. Tipperary, **Ireland**	19 Apr 1968	On spring migration
Adult	18 Apr 1975	Portland Bill, Dorset	08 Apr 1981	On spring migration
Adult	05 May 1976	South Bishop Lighthouse, nr St David's Head, Pembrokeshire	07 May 1976	On spring migration
Adult	14 Apr 1977	Portland Bill, Dorset	19 Aug 1977	On autumn migration
1st-year	13 Aug 1977	Bridgwater, Somerset	c.20 Apr 1978	On spring migration
Adult	11 Apr 1980	Bickington, Newton Abbot, Devon	25 Apr 1981	On spring migration
Adult	13 Apr 1983	Cape Clear, Co. Cork, **Ireland**	20 Apr 1983	On spring migration
Adult	01 May 1985	Bardsey Island, Gwynedd	04 May 1985	On spring migration
Adult	11 Apr 1988	Great Saltee Island, Co. Wexford, **Ireland**	26 Apr 1990	On spring migration
Adult F	24 Apr 1989	on ship off Point Lynas, Anglesey	30 Apr 1989	On spring migration
Adult	29 Apr 1989	Glen Roy, Lonan, Isle of Man	22 Jun 1989	In breeding area
Adult F	02 May 1990	Prawle Point, South Devon	08 May 1990	On spring migration
Adult	04 May 1993	Doonfoot, Strathclyde	22 Jul 1994	On autumn migration
Adult	04 May 1996	Bardsey Island, Gwynedd	06 May 1996	On spring migration
Adult	27 Apr 1998	Portland Bill, Dorset	06 Aug 1998	On autumn migration
1st-year M	10 Aug 2003	Bardsey Island, Gwynedd	23 Apr 2004	On spring migration

(b) Willow Warblers ringed elsewhere and controlled on Lundy

Age/sex	Date ringed	Place ringed	Date controlled on Lundy	Speculation about date/place of ringing
1st-year	23 Aug 1971	Beachy Head, Sussex	16 Apr 1972	On autumn migration
Adult	16 Apr 1976[166]	Calf of Man, Isle of Man	06 Apr 1977	On spring migration
1st-year	10 Sep 1977	Higher Metcombe, South Devon	08 Apr 1979	On autumn migration
1st-year	21 Jul 1981	Out Head, St Andrews, Fife	05 May 1982	On autumn migration
Adult	27 Apr 1982	Isle of Man (location unknown)	23 Aug 1984	On spring migration
1st-year	03 Sep 1982	Fornaght Bog, Dunmore East, Co. Waterford, **Ireland**	11 Sep 1982	On autumn migration
1st-year	03 Sep 1984	Isle of May, Fife	16 Sep 1984	On autumn migration
Adult	25 Apr 1985	Hengistbury Head, Dorset	16 Apr 1987	On spring migration
Adult	27 Apr 1985	St Agnes, Isles of Scilly	30 Apr 1985	On spring migration
Adult	04 May 1985	Great Saltee Island, Co. Wexford, **Ireland**	26 Apr 1987	On spring migration
1st-year	31 Jul 1985	Powys (location unknown)	27 Apr 1986	On autumn migration
Adult M	17 Aug 1985	Portland Bill, Dorset	07 Apr 1987	On autumn migration
Adult F	08 Aug 1988	Balsarroch, Kirkcolm, Dumfries & Galloway	07 May 1989	On autumn migration
Adult	01 Apr 1989	Calf of Man, Isle of Man	04 May 1990	On spring migration
1st-year	26 Aug 1990	South Walney, Cumbria	22 Apr 1991	On autumn migration
1st-year M	13 Aug 1991	Icklesham, Sussex	29 Apr 1992	On autumn migration
Adult	16 Apr 1992	Castello Barbarossa, Capri, Naples, **Italy**	03 May 1992	On spring migration
1st-year M	04 Sep 1993	Hanstholm, Viborg, **Denmark**	25 Sep 1993	On autumn migration
Adult F	20 Apr 2000	Portland Bill, Dorset	28 Apr 2000	On spring migration
Adult	25 Apr 2001	Nanjizal, Land's End, Cornwall	29 Apr 2001	On spring migration

Goldcrest *Regulus regulus*

Common spring and autumn migrant, most numerous in autumn; has bred; occasional in winter.

During autumn on the East Side it is rare to spend long out of sight or sound of Goldcrests, which can be encountered singly or in small flocks busily searching through the bracken, willow and rhododendron, or scouring what remains of the leaf canopy in Quarter Wall Copse, St Helen's Copse or Millcombe, calling constantly as they zip and tumble through the branches.

There are sometimes one or two overwintering birds present in January and February (seven on 5 January 1988 was an exceptionally high winter count), but in most years it is not until the start of spring migration in March that the first Goldcrests are entered in the LFS logbook. Movements are mainly during the period mid-March to late April, but a few later birds are seen in May or even early June in some years. The numbers involved are almost always much smaller than in autumn, with maximum daily counts having exceeded 30 in just eight LFS years. The highest spring count to date is 75 on 16 April 1972.

"Golden-crested Wren" was listed by Chanter (1871) and Parfitt (1876) as an "occasional visitant", the latter adding "occasional breeder". Loyd (1925) recorded single breeding pairs in 1922 and 1923. During LFS years the only confirmed instances of breeding were in: 1952 – a pair that arrived in mid-April had reared and fledged young by early July; 1971 – a used nest found on 15 October; 1978 – one pair bred, rearing two broods; and 2000 – at least one, possibly two pairs held territory, and a male was seen feeding two fledglings on 23 July. In 1995 a juvenile was seen on 11 & 12 July, while in 1996 there were scattered sightings in May, June and July, so it is possible that there have been other, undetected, breeding attempts. There have also been occasional records of ones and twos in July of other years when Goldcrests were not known to have nested; these are most likely to have been dispersing young from breeding areas on the nearby mainland.

Autumn migration generally gets under way in late August or early September, usually peaking between late September and late October. Until the 1980s the highest count was 180 on 7 October 1973. However, 200 were present on 5 October 1980 and there followed an astonishing series of high counts: 400 on 10 October 1984, 1,500 on 20 October 1988 and 29 September 1995, and 2,000 on 11 October 1987 and 1 October 1990. Numbers have reached 200 to 300 in six other years since 1990 (to the end of 2006). Movements continue into November but tail off rapidly after mid-month. Small numbers – usually ones and twos, but as many as six – have been seen in December, some remaining through the winter. Wernham *et al.* (2002) noted that migratory tendencies are stronger in years when numbers are high, and point out the importance of local weather conditions in precipitating major falls at coastal sites. While there are fluctuations from year to year, the BTO Breeding Bird Survey recorded a 60% increase in the UK breeding population from 1994 to 2004 (Baillie *et al.* 2006).

Goldcrest has been one of the most frequently ringed species on Lundy, second only to Willow Warbler, with 8,353 ringed between 1947 and 2006. Not surprisingly for such a tiny bird, the rate of subsequent controls or recoveries has been very low, with just 13 cases over the years – see table (a) overleaf – or less than a fifth of one per cent of those ringed! There have also been six controls on Lundy of birds ringed elsewhere – see table (b) overleaf. Most were both ringed and found during autumn or spring migration periods, but there are indications of one wintering in Dorset, while a bird ringed on Lundy in September 2001 was found freshly dead on the island, during bad weather, in early January 2002 – confirming that some autumn arrivals may attempt to overwinter.

Taken together, it is striking how the ringing and finding locations of these birds are concentrated in western Britain and Ireland. Movements away from Lundy in autumn are primarily to the south and east, while birds arriving in autumn have come from the north and west, including one which flew the 172 kilometres from Great Saltee Island, off the Wexford coast of Ireland, to Lundy in a single day. There are two spring movements, one from Scilly to Lundy and the other from Lundy to Bardsey Island. All of this ringing data is suggestive of birds of northern British and Irish origin migrating through the Irish Sea to wintering grounds in southern England, or perhaps slightly further afield in France. While large numbers of Goldcrests of continental origin arrive in eastern Britain in autumn, and some penetrate as far west as Irish Sea coasts (Wernham *et al.* 2002), there is no evidence of continental birds being involved in any of the Lundy ringing movements. One ringer familiar with continental birds on the Suffolk coast has ringed regularly on Lundy in autumn and has never seen a Goldcrest showing continental-type plumage on the island. Furthermore, a comparison of wing-length data from Lundy with that from an October fall at Landguard, Suffolk, showed that Lundy's Goldcrests were in the typical range for British breeding birds, with none in the higher, continental range of measurements (Tony Taylor, personal communication).

(a) Goldcrests ringed on Lundy and controlled or recovered elsewhere

Age/sex	Date ringed on Lundy	Place found	Date controlled or recovered	Speculation about date/place of finding
Full-grown M	12 Oct 1967	Bridgwater, Somerset	24 Mar 1968	On spring migration
1st-year F	24 Sep 1984	West Christchurch, Dorset	01 Feb 1985	In wintering area
1st-year F	15 Sep 1987	Bideford, North Devon	16 Sep 1987	On autumn migration
1st-year M	16 Sep 1988	Hartland Point, North Devon	20 Sep 1988	On autumn migration
1st-year F	16 Sep 1988	Mumbles, Swansea, Glamorgan	29 Oct 1988	On autumn migration
1st-year M	30 Sep 1988	Bolberry Down, Marlborough, South Devon	12 Oct 1988	On autumn migration
1st-year M	20 Oct 1988	Brixham, South Devon	27 Oct 1988	On autumn migration
1st-year	19 Oct 1990	Chew Valley Lake, Avon	03 Nov 1990	On autumn migration
1st-year F	07 Oct 1993	Westward Ho!, North Devon	24 Oct 1993	On autumn migration
1st-year F	28 Sep 1995	Prawle Point, South Devon	15 Oct 1995	On autumn migration
1st-year F	29 Sep 1995	Lannacombe Valley, Start Point, South Devon	04 Nov 1995	On autumn migration
1st-year F	02 Oct 1997	Bardsey Island, Gwynedd	20 Mar 1998	On spring migration
1st-year M	06 Oct 1999	Higher Clovelly, Bideford, North Devon	02 Nov 1999	On autumn migration

(b) Goldcrests ringed elsewhere and controlled on Lundy

Age/sex	Date ringed	Place ringed	Date controlled on Lundy	Speculation about date/place of ringing
1st-year F	01 Sep 1987	Cape Clear, Co. Cork, **Ireland**	30 Sep 1988	On autumn migration
1st-year F	22 Oct 1989	St Martins, Isles of Scilly	23 Oct 1989	On autumn migration
1st-year F	30 Sep 1990	Great Saltee Island, Co. Wexford, **Ireland**	01 Oct 1990	On autumn migration
2nd-year	27 Mar 1996	Nanjizal, Land's End, Cornwall	17 Oct 1996	On spring migration
1st-year M	21 Sep 1997	Eskmeals, Bootle, Cumbria	02 Oct 1997	On autumn migration
1st-year M	05 Oct 1999	Calf of Man, Isle of Man	25 Oct 1999	On autumn migration

Firecrest *Regulus ignicapilla*

Uncommon spring passage migrant, more regular and more numerous in autumn; has wintered.

Trees and bushes in Millcombe, St John's Valley, St Helen's Copse, Quarter Wall Copse and along the Terrace are prime places to locate the diminutive but brightly coloured Firecrest. Chanter (1871) and Parfitt (1876) listed "Fire-crested Wren" as an "occasional visitant", but this species was not reliably recorded on the island until 1949, and then only sporadically until the mid-1960s. Since 1966, Firecrests have occurred every year up to and including 2006, with the single exception of 1991. There is a very small spring migration between mid-March (earliest 9 March 1983, but overwintering has occurred in some years) and early June (latest 5 June 1981), with most occurrences in April and May. The highest spring count is of four on 29 March 1972, but most records are of single birds. In 1996 one was present from 28 May to 2 June and was heard singing in Millcombe on the last day; and a male present from 31 May to 3 June 1980 was heard singing on 1 June.

Firecrest

In autumn there are occasional records in late August (earliest: three on 22 August 1998) and the first half of September, but the main migration period begins in late September, peaking in October. Movements continue at a reduced level into the first half of November, dwindling rapidly after the middle of the month. Numbers vary significantly from year to year and in good seasons it is often difficult to estimate accurately the number of birds present given the species' size and mobility. The maximum daily count is 12 on 30 October 1980 and again on 13 October 1995. Eight were counted on 28 October 1999, and six on 10 October 2006. At least 28 different individuals were thought to have passed through in the autumn of 1972.

Firecrests have occasionally overwintered; for example, one ringed in early November 1972 was still present on 20 December, one or two were seen frequently between December 1979 and February 1980, and up to three were present in December 1982 (three on 28th and one or two on three other dates). There have been scattered sightings between December and February in nine other LFS years.

Of 202 birds ringed by the end of 2006, there have been two recoveries (see table), both in The Netherlands during the spring after ringing on Lundy, and two of only a handful of British-ringed Firecrests to be found abroad (Wernham *et al.* 2002). In addition, there has been one control on the island of a bird ringed elsewhere: a first-year female ringed at Beachy Head, Sussex, on 15 October 1988 was controlled on Lundy 11 days later on 26 October.

Firecrests ringed on Lundy and recovered elsewhere

Age/sex	Date ringed on Lundy	Place found	Date recovered	Speculation about date/place of finding
1st-year M	06 Oct 1979	Zuid-Holland, **The Netherlands**	31 Mar 1980	On spring migration
1st-year F	29 Oct 2003	Oranjezon, Vrouwenpolder, Zeeland, **The Netherlands**	13 Apr 2004	On spring migration

Spotted Flycatcher

Spotted Flycatcher *Muscicapa striata*

Common spring and autumn passage migrant; irregular breeder.

Migrant Spotted Flycatchers feed wherever there are sheltered but relatively open areas with suitable perches. Depending on the wind, favoured areas include Millcombe, St John's Valley, the fence line around the top of Millcombe and along the Upper East Side Path, Quarter Wall, the Terrace and the East Side copses. In easterlies, the shelter of the West Side is often preferred and birds can sometimes be seen flycatching from rocks or boulders.

Chanter (1871) and Parfitt (1876) listed Spotted Flycatcher as a "summer visitant", Parfitt adding "occasional breeder". Hendy (1933) saw three birds in September 1930. Harrisson (1932) and Wynne-Edwards & Harrisson (1932) stated that the species did not breed on Lundy, basing their finding on a five-day survey in June 1930, three years after Felix Gade found an empty nest in Millcombe (Davis 1954a).

During LFS years Spotted Flycatchers have primarily been passage migrants, though breeding has occurred from time to time. Single pairs nested in Millcombe in at least five years from 1956 to 1963. There was no further evidence of breeding until 1984 when a pair was seen nest building in Millcombe. One or two pairs then bred in most years up to and including 1997, using sites in Millcombe and along the Terrace (especially VC Quarry), some pairs probably rearing two broods. Although 'Spot Flys' have continued to be reported off and on during the summer months, and four apparently territorial pairs were noted in May 2004 (Lock 2004), there has been no further confirmation of breeding (whether attempted or successful) up to and including 2006.

The first spring migrants usually arrive in the last week of April or first week of May, the earliest by some days being two on 12 April 1987. Ten of the 12 earliest arrivals have occurred since 1980. Passage continues until mid-June, peak numbers typically occurring during the latter three weeks of May, though significant arrivals of more than 30 birds have occurred well into June. The highest spring count is about 200 on 22 May 1959, following strong easterly winds, and there have been peaks of 100 on at least six other occasions between 9 and 27 May, most recently on 22 May 1997. However, the average spring maximum for the 10 years 1997–2006 is just over 30.

Autumn passage usually begins in the first half of August, and peak numbers may occur at any time until about the third week of September, though most annual maxima fall between mid-August and mid-September. The highest daily count is 270 on 9 September 1969, while 200 occurred on 16 August in both 1971 and 1973, and there have been at least nine other counts of between 100 and 150. These numbers are exceptional though, the average maximum autumn count for the 10 years 1997–2006 being 36. Migration continues at a lower level until the end of September or first half of October. In most years the last one or two birds have passed through by 15 October, though occasional stragglers have occurred to the end of the month. There are three exceptionally late records for November: a single bird on 1 November 1996, two on 5 November 1983 and one on 13 November 1982, the latest sighting to date.

Of 1,240 Spotted Flycatchers ringed on Lundy between 1947 and 2006, four have been recovered – see table. Three had reached southern Spain or North Africa within a month of being ringed – on their way to wintering grounds south of the Sahara – when they were shot or trapped by hunters. Most of the Spotted Flycatchers passing through Lundy probably nest in Britain and Ireland (Wernham *et al.* 2002). This species is currently 'red-listed' (of high conservation concern), the UK breeding population having declined by more than 85% since the late 1960s (Baillie *et al.* 2007).

Spotted Flycatchers ringed on Lundy and recovered elsewhere

Age/sex	Date ringed on Lundy	Place found	Date recovered	Speculation about date/place of finding
1st-year	15 Sep 1953	Nr Rabat, **Morocco**	c.15 Oct 1953	On autumn migration
1st-year	19 Aug 1965	La Rioja, **Spain**	08 Sep 1967	On autumn migration
1st-year	23 Sep 1982	Cadiz, **Spain**	17 Oct 1982	On autumn migration
1st-year	10 Sep 1983	Málaga, **Spain**	c.28 Sep 1983	On autumn migration

Red-breasted Flycatcher *Ficedula parva*

Nationally scarce migrant.

Breeds in central and eastern Europe, migrating south-east in autumn to wintering grounds in south and south-east Asia. 3,367 records for Britain 1968–2003, with an average of 108 per year 2000–2003.

The treed areas of Millcombe, St Helen's Copse and Quarter Wall Copse are the most likely places to encounter a Red-breasted Flycatcher (though after more than 30 years of birdwatching on Lundy, one of the authors of this book has yet to catch sight of one!). Dymond (1980) listed Red-breasted Flycatcher as a very rare autumn migrant, with 25 occurrences between 20 October 1950 (the first Lundy record) and 1978. The species remains scarce but is now virtually an annual autumn migrant, with records from all except three years (1989, 1990 and 2005) between 1980 and 2006, involving at least 51 individuals. Most records are from a five-week period between late September and the end of October, the earliest and latest dates being 4 September (1985) and 8 November (1972). There has been one spring record, in June 2003 (see below).

Most records are of single birds, but there are more than a dozen instances of two on the same day, while three on 29 October 1985 is the highest count (to the end of 2006). 1985 was an exceptional year for this species on Lundy (though not especially notable nationally), with at least eight different birds seen, including the earliest ever and the maximum daily count.

The following is a complete list of accepted records for the 10 years 1997–2006 (only 2005 was blank):

1997 31 Oct – one.
1998 1 Oct – one in Millcombe.
1999 25 Sep – one.
2000 6 to 8 Oct – a first-winter bird in Millcombe, trapped and ringed on 6th.

Red-breasted Flycatcher

2001 20 to 24 Oct – a first-winter bird originally seen in Quarter Wall Copse and from 21st in St Helen's Combe where it was trapped and ringed.

2002 25 Sep – two, one on the Terrace and one in Millcombe; two (possibly the same birds) present on 28 Sep and singles on 29 Sep, 5, 6, 12 & 28 Oct.[167]

2003 11 Jun – a female in Millcombe.

2004 25 Sep – one in St Helen's Combe.
13 Oct – a first-winter bird in Quarter Wall Copse.
19 Oct – an adult male in Millcombe.

2006 5 to 10 Oct – one in Millcombe, caught and ringed on 10th.

Taiga Flycatcher (*Ficedula albicilla*) was split from Red-breasted Flycatcher in 2004 (Sangster *et al.* 2004) and added to *The British List* by the BOURC in 2005. There have been two British records (to mid-2007), in Yorkshire and Shetland. There is no evidence that any of the Red-breasted Flycatchers on Lundy prior to the taxonomic split showed characteristics of Taiga Flycatcher, but the possibility cannot be excluded.

Twenty-one Red-breasted Flycatchers had been ringed on Lundy by the end of 2006, but there are no controls or recoveries involving the island.

Pied Flycatcher *Ficedula hypoleuca* [Eurasian Pied Flycatcher]

Uncommon spring migrant; common autumn migrant, usually in small numbers; occasional records in midsummer.

Pied Flycatchers on Lundy prefer the wooded East Side combes, though they are sometimes encountered feeding from walls, fences or rocky outcrops, and odd ones and twos can turn up anywhere. The first spring migrants typically occur in the second half of April, though there have been several 'firsts for the year' between 8 and 14 April, and the earliest ever sighting was of one in St John's Valley on 31 March 1992, coinciding with a significant arrival of Chiffchaffs and Willow Warblers. There is some suggestion that 'Pied Flys' now arrive earlier than they used to, given that the eight earliest dates have all been since 1980. Spring passage is usually light and sporadic (there are even a few blank years in spring), typically peaking in late April or early May. Maximum daily counts are nearly always in single figures, but there are three records of 10 – on 2 May 1978, 2 May 2004 and 4 May 1992. Hence, the 60+ that arrived on 26 April 1987, along with large numbers of other migrants, represented an exceptional influx and is by far the highest spring count to date (up to and including 2007).

Small numbers continue to pass through the island during the remainder of May and into early June, and there have been a handful of sightings in the second half of June and during July; perhaps failed breeders or dispersing young from nesting sites as close as the North Devon coast. Usually only ones and twos are involved, but seven were seen on 23 July 1989.

The main autumn passage usually gets under way by the second or third week of August, the majority of annual peak counts falling between 15 August and 15 September. There have been at least 15 daily counts of 30 or more birds, the maxima being 70 on 24 August 1973, 80 on 6 September 1959 and 100 on 2 September 1990. Numbers tend to decline after mid-September, though 30 were seen on 25 September 1989 and 25 on 6 October 1958. *The Migration Atlas* (Wernham *et al.* 2002) suggests that these later migration peaks, which are more frequent at east-coast bird observatories, may involve mainly continental birds. On Lundy, last records for the year have occurred mostly in the first half of October, though ones and two have sometimes been seen until 24th. After that, there have been two exceptionally late sightings, both of single birds: on 1 & 2 November 1977 and 4 to 6 November 1962.

Chanter (1871) and Parfitt (1876) listed Pied Flycatcher as an "occasional visitant", the latter adding "occasional breeder" but without giving any further details. D'Urban & Mathew (1895) stated: "A pair were shot on Lundy Island in May 1861, and passed into the collection of the late Dr. Woodforde of Taunton, and are now at Taunton Castle museum." The first documented twentieth century record was of a male seen by Felix Gade on 4 May 1927 (Harrisson 1932). Hendy (1933) reported seeing a female and an immature between 2 and 7 September 1930. Palmer (1946) stated: "Recorded as a passage migrant…from Lundy in September, 1937." And Perry (1940) reported Pied Flycatcher as a northward-bound passage migrant in spring 1939.

By the end of 2006, 730 Pied Flycatchers had been ringed on Lundy, with five subsequent controls/recoveries, along with six controls on Lundy of birds ringed elsewhere. Evidence from ringing suggests that many of the birds passing through Lundy in spring are from relatively nearby breeding populations in south-west England, Herefordshire and mid-Wales, though there may be some bias given that there has been particularly intensive ringing of Pied Flycatchers using nestboxes in these regions. Nestlings ringed in June in Herefordshire (in 1979), Dyfed (1982) and Powys (1977 and 1986) were controlled on Lundy in either April or May of the year following ringing and were presumably returning to their breeding areas. A further nestling, ringed in Dyfed in June 1988, was controlled on Lundy on 22 April 1992 during its fourth return migration. A first-year bird ringed on Lundy in May 1989 was controlled at Lanhydrock, Cornwall, in June 1992, while an adult ringed on Lundy in May 1999 was controlled near Bovey Tracey, Devon, in May 2000.

Three recoveries or controls involving Pied Flycatchers moving through Lundy in autumn suggest that birds from a much wider area may occur at this time of year. An adult ringed on Lundy at the end of August 1961 was controlled in Brittany on 1 September 1962, while a first-year bird ringed on Lundy on 23 August 1966 was caught as an adult in the Moscow region of Russia on 5 June 1967. The first of these could well have been a British breeding bird moving south, but the timing of the Moscow recovery strongly suggests it was breeding in Russia. That Pied Flys may reach Lundy rapidly from considerable distances to the east is underlined by a first-year bird ringed on the Baltic island of Bornholm, Denmark, on 2 September 1982 and controlled on Lundy just 12 days later.

Long-tailed Tit *Aegithalos caudatus* [Long-tailed Bushtit]

Very rare autumn migrant and exceptional in spring/early summer; two winter records.

Although it is hard to conceive of Long-tailed Tits flying over mile upon mile of open sea, they have reached Lundy surprisingly often. A flock of five on 12 November 1932 constitutes the first island record, and eight were also present on 13 & 14 October 1944 (F.W. Gade, reported by Palmer 1946). There are LFS records for 16 years between 1947 and the end of 2006, involving single birds on nine occasions, one record of two together, and 16 sightings of small flocks of between three and 22 birds.

There have been just five spring/early summer records: two in March, one in May and two in June (latest date, 15 June 1999). With one exception these have all been of single birds seen on one or two days only, the exception being a flock of five that arrived in early March 1973, remaining until 12th.

More than half of all occurrences have been in October (12 records involving 76 individuals), with larger flocks including 11 on 26 October 1999, about 12 on 17 October 1958 (which flew in from the north-west, landed on the Old Light tower for a few minutes and flew off high to the south-east), 15 on 18 October 1975 and 22 seen flying high to the south-west, over Benjamin's Chair, on 24 October 1973. There are five November records totalling 27 individuals, including a flock of 10 in Millcombe on 3 November 1989. The latest date is four on 6 November (2000). There are two winter records of single birds on 9 December 1995 (in Quarter Wall Copse) and 7 January 1984.

Thirteen Long-tailed Tits had been ringed by the end of 2006, but there are no controls or recoveries involving the island.

Blue Tit *Cyanistes caeruleus*

Uncommon autumn migrant and rare spring migrant; occasionally overwinters; exceptional in midsummer.

Though records were sporadic in the first 25 years of LFS recording (1947 to 1971), there were almost annual sightings from 1972 to 2006, with only four blank years during this more recent period, making Blue Tit the most regularly recorded tit species on Lundy. Even so, this is an uncommon bird for the island and all sightings are noteworthy. Millcombe and St John's Valley, St Helen's Copse, Quarter Wall Copse and along the Terrace are the most likely places to see any of the tit species, though they may be encountered anywhere on the island during autumn movements.

The overwhelming majority of records have been in autumn, and of these most are for the month of October. There are seven September sightings, all except one being from the 15th onwards. In October there are records throughout the month, mostly of one to three birds, with only seven years in which the maximum daily count was higher: four in 1981 and 1993, six in 1949, seven in 1975 and 1983, 14 in 1997 and a phenomenal 80 in 1957, the year of a massive irruption of Scandinavian Blue Tits into the UK, mostly to the east and south coasts (Wernham *et al.* 2002). On Lundy, up to four were seen between 26 September and 3 October, with about 80 present on 4 October, 65 on 5th, then between 10 and 40 up to 16th and four to six birds daily thereafter until 23rd (Whitaker 1957).

There have been many fewer sightings in November, with most being of single birds. There are about a dozen December records, again mainly of lone individuals, but four were present on 16 December 1975 and 2 December 1985. There have been at least 10 years in which Blue Tits appear to have overwintered on the island, often remaining well into March or April; for example, following the four in December 1975, two were seen regularly between January and early April 1976. Mostly ones and twos are involved, but "two or three pairs" were reported as "present in winter" in 1957/58, following the big autumn influx of 1957, "decreasing in numbers during April, and last seen on the 28th [April]" (1958 *LFS Annual Report*).

Other than late-staying overwintering birds, spring sightings of Blue Tits are rare and mostly of single birds in March or April, though six were recorded on 7 April 1950. Occurrences are extremely rare from May to August: one from 4 to 8 June 1950, one on 15 May 1972 and one from 9 to 11 & 27 May 1996. There are no July records and only one in August: two on 15th 2005.

Chanter added "Tom Tit" to the 1877 revision of his list of "occasional visitants". The first dated record was of four birds on 16 November 1943 (Gade, reported by Davis 1954a).

By the end of 2006, 122 Blue Tits had been ringed on Lundy, but there are no controls or recoveries involving the island.

Great Tit *Parus major*

Uncommon and irregular spring and autumn migrant; rare in winter.

Of the three most familiar tit species (Great, Blue and Coal), this is the scarcest on Lundy, with records for 36 years between 1947 and the end of 2006, mostly of single birds. The majority of sightings have been in March/April and October/November.

There are March records for seven years and April records for 11 years. The maximum during this period was five in April 1958. The exact date is unknown due to the loss of the original data for that year, but the 1958 *LFS Annual Report* notes that up to five birds were seen on nine days to 20 April "mainly on the west sidelands". There have been May occurrences of one to two birds in three years, including a male that stayed from 4 May to 18 June 1996.[168] There are no other records for the period June to August (up to the end of 2006).

In autumn there have been three sightings of single birds between 10 and 30 September, most recently on 16 September 1998. October is the peak month, with sightings in 17 years, mostly involving one to three birds, but daily maxima of four or more were recorded in 1952 (four on 17th), 1954 (six on 27th), 1957 (10–15 from 9th to 15th), 1959 (four on most days from 3rd to 19th) and 1983 (eight on 21st). During the exceptional tit influx of 1957, Great Tits were seen daily from 4 to 23 October.

Ones and twos have been seen during November in at least 11 years, with four records of single birds in December. A female was seen regularly in Millcombe and St Helen's Copse from 12 January to 14 March 1992, and overwintering may have occurred in 1977/78 (one present November/December and the first half of February). There have been January or February sightings in three other years.

Thirty-five Great Tits had been ringed on Lundy by the end of 2006, but there are no controls or recoveries involving the island.

Coal Tit *Periparus ater*

Uncommon autumn migrant; very rare spring migrant; occasional in winter.

There are Coal Tit records for 32 years between 1947 and the end of 2006, which is slightly fewer than for Great Tit, but the overall number of birds involved is significantly higher.

There are March or April records of mostly single birds from at least 10 years, though some of these refer to late-staying overwintering individuals rather than to spring migrants. More recent isolated spring occurrences have been singles on 16 & 17 March 2004 (two on 17th), 2 & 6 April 1993, 4 April 1996, 17 & 21 April 1997 (Millcombe), and 16 & 21 to 23 April 2006 (two on 22nd). The only May sightings are of one on 15th 1970, followed by one on 19th and two on 21st 1975 (Millcombe). None has been seen on Lundy during the months of June to August and there are only two September records, both at the very end of the month: one on 28th 1971 and two on 30th 1949 (all in Millcombe).

The overwhelming majority of records have come in October, with sightings in about 20 years. In most seasons only ones and twos have been seen, but three or more occurred in 1957 (maximum daily count 30 on 11 October), 1975 (seven on 9th), 1988 (15 on 12th, 16th & 18th), 1997 (12 on 4th) and 1999 (six on 26th). During the tit invasion of October 1957 there were daily sightings from 1st to 23rd, with peak counts of 14 on

Coal Tit

7th, 15 on 9th and 30 on 11th. Ringing showed that at least 31 different individuals passed through during the slightly smaller autumn influx of October 1988, when sightings were daily from 5th to the end of the month, with maxima as given above. Between one and four birds have occurred in November in eight years.

Following the influx of October 1957, up to six were present throughout the winter, with the last one seen on 30 April 1958. A bird ringed on the island in the autumn of 1966 stayed until 4 April 1967. There have been December, January or February records of ones and twos in half-a-dozen further years, though none since February 1992 when one was seen in St Helen's Copse on 2nd & 6th.

Sixty-four Coal Tits had been ringed on Lundy by the end of 2006, but there are no controls or recoveries involving the island. The 31 birds caught and ringed in autumn 1988 more than doubled the total of 14 ringed between 1947 and 1987. Although there have been occasional field sightings of birds showing characteristics of the continental European race *P. a. ater* (e.g. one reported on 12 & 13 October 1997[169]), all those trapped and ringed since 1972 appear to have been of the British race *P. a. britannicus* (Tony Taylor, personal communication).

Willow Tit *Poecile montanus*

Lundy vagrant.

There is one Lundy record:

1995 11 May – one observed for 20 minutes by Richard Campey in Quarter Wall Copse.

Willow Tit is 'red-listed' (of high conservation concern), numbers breeding in the UK having declined by around 80% since 1979 (Baillie *et al.* 2007). The Lundy individual is perhaps most likely to have originated from the modest breeding population on the nearby mainland of north-west Devon.

Marsh Tit *Poecile palustris*

Lundy vagrant.

Common and widespread in broadleaved woodland on the nearby mainland, Marsh Tits are highly sedentary. Unsurprisingly, the only record is of a single bird seen by F.W. Gade on 15 & 18 January 1958 (1958 *LFS Annual Report*), making this by far the rarest of the five commoner British tits to have occurred on Lundy. Like the closely related Willow Tit, this species is 'red-listed' due to its rapidly declining UK breeding population (Baillie *et al.* 2007).

Treecreeper *Certhia familiaris*   [Eurasian Treecreeper]

Uncommon late summer and autumn visitor; very rare outside this period.

There are no recorded sightings of Treecreeper on Lundy until one on 18 July 1950 and what was probably the same bird seen nine days later feeding on a sheer rock face to the north of the Devil's Slide. One was subsequently trapped at the Old Light on 23 October 1950. Most, if not all, other Treecreepers have occurred, as would be expected, in Millcombe and the few other treed areas of the island. There have been records in 29 further years to the end of 2006, including in seven of the 10 years 1997–2006. There are records for all months from April to December, with most in September and October, but none between January and March.

There has been one occurrence in April (6th 1968), two in May (2nd 1994 and 18th & 19th 2004), and two in June (4th & 5th 2000 and 27th 1973, the latter staying until 2 July). There are rather more records scattered through July and August, presumably representing dispersal of young from the mainland. Occurrences increase in September, reaching a marked peak in October, but drop sharply to just a handful in November. The latest sightings for the month are of one on 20 November 2003 and two on 25 November 1978, then one or two (presumably the same birds) seen regularly from 10 to 24 December 1978.

The great majority of records are of single birds, but there have been about 10 instances of two in one day. The only higher count is of four seen on 3 October 1988. No fewer than six different individuals were ringed during the autumn of that year, which was also notable for a significant influx of tits to the island.

British Treecreepers belong to the race *Certhia familiaris brittanica*, which is sedentary. *The Migration Atlas* (Wernham *et al.* 2002) indicates that movements of more than five kilometres are exceptional, with only five examples nationally exceeding 20 kilometres. This suggests that most if not all Treecreepers reaching Lundy are from very nearby areas of the mainland. Birds of the continental race *C. f. familiaris* may undertake irruptive movements westward, occasionally reaching the UK, but there is no evidence that any have occurred on Lundy.

Twenty-one Treecreepers had been ringed on Lundy by the end of 2006, but there have been no controls or recoveries involving the island.

Golden Oriole *Oriolus oriolus*   [Eurasian Golden Oriole]

Lundy vagrant.

Summer migrant to Europe and western Asia, wintering in the tropics. 3,100 records for Britain 1968–2003, with an average of 90 per year 2000–2003. Small numbers breed in the UK but most British records are of returning migrants 'overshooting' their continental breeding grounds in late spring. Considered by the BOU as a passage migrant and migrant breeder rather than a nationally scarce migrant.

The heart-stopping flash of yellow as a Golden Oriole flies across one of the tree-lined paths in Millcombe is one of the quintessential late-spring birdwatching experiences on Lundy. Yet, in spite of the species' apparently striking plumage, orioles have a habit of melting into the background, being surprisingly hard to pick out in the dappled light and shade of freshly leafed-up tree canopies, and frequently leading would-be observers on a long and frustrating search.

Golden Oriole was listed by Chanter (1871) and Parfitt (1876) as an "occasional visitant", while D'Urban & Mathew (1895) wrote: "The Golden Oriole...has visited Lundy Island, but the Rev. H.G. Heaven tells us it has not been seen there of late years." There are, however, no dated records prior to 1947 (the start of LFS recording) when "a pair" was seen in May.

Between 1947 and 1984, Golden Orioles were reported in 21 years. Nowadays, the species is a scarce but virtually annual spring migrant, having occurred in every year from 1984 to 2006, with the exception of 1998. The vast majority of sightings occur from early May to mid-June, with a distinct peak in the second half of May. Extreme dates are 20 April (1964) and 13 July (1973). There have been April occurrences in four further years, the most recent a male on 30 April 1994. The only other July records are of one on 2 July 1965 and two on 10 July 2002. There is just one autumn record: an immature bird on 11 October 1967.

Most records are of one or two birds, but three have been seen on several occasions (e.g. 9 May 1987, 4 June 1993, 16 & 22 May 1994 and 16 May 2000). The 1967 *LFS Annual Report* states: "On the evening of May 9th two of the island residents saw five bright yellow birds which they thought were Golden Orioles fly in over the sea and come down in Millcombe Gardens. As at least three were present the next day and up to four including two singing males recorded on subsequent days until 28th, their identification was probably correct".

Golden Oriole

Given this species' elusive nature, the regular occurrence of several birds together and some individuals staying for a few days or even weeks, it is impossible to put a precise figure on the total number seen over the years, but it is probably in excess of 100. Given that Golden Orioles are woodland birds, it is not surprising that most sightings have been in the Millcombe/St John's Valley area and in St Helen's and Quarter Wall Copses, though there have also been several recorded from the Terrace and in the vicinity of Quarter Wall. Males are sometimes heard singing, their rich, mellifluous notes bringing a touch of the tropics to the island.

The following is a complete list of accepted records for the 10 years 1997–2006 (only 1998 was blank):

1997 12, 14 & 15 May – a female, trapped and ringed on 12th, joined by a male on 15th.
26 & 27 May – a female.
1999 10 to 14 May – two, a male and a female; the male was heard singing, and the female was seen taking large caterpillars next to Government House on 14th.
15, 19 & 31 May to 2 Jun – a sub-adult male.
2000 13 & 14 May – two, with a third on 16 May and one on three days to 22 May.
2001 30 & 31 May – a female.
2002 10 Jul – two.
2003 4 & 5 May – an immature male on the Terrace, heard singing on 5th.
29 May – a male.
2004 22 May – two, followed by one near Quarter Wall and in St Helen's copse on 23rd and a female or immature in Millcombe on 29th.
2005 7 to 11 May – a female or immature in Millcombe.
2006 13 May – one in Millcombe and St John's Valley.

Five Golden Orioles had been ringed on Lundy by the end of 2006, but there are no controls or recoveries involving the island.

Isabelline Shrike *Lanius isabellinus*

British vagrant.

Breeds in central Asia, wintering in south-west Asia and sub-Saharan Africa. 68 records for Britain 1950–2005.

There is one Lundy record of a single bird:

2001 28 Aug – one near the Upper East Side Path. The BBRC report gives this bird as a male, age uncertain, while the 2001 *Devon Bird Report* states "a male, age uncertain, of the West-Central Asian race (*L. i. phoenicuroides*)", the latter sometimes called Turkestan Shrike.

At the time of writing, the BBRC is reviewing the racial identity of records of Isabelline Shrike, and an article explaining the Committee's decisions is in preparation (Fraser *et al.* 2007, pp. 92–93; Langman *et al.* 2007). No conclusion has yet been published concerning the Lundy bird.

Red-backed Shrike *Lanius collurio*

Lundy vagrant.

Formerly bred widely in Britain, now virtually extinct as a British breeding species, but nests commonly in continental Europe. 4,102 records for Britain 1986–2003, with an average of 191 per year 2000–2003. Considered by the BOU as a casual breeder and passage migrant rather than a nationally scarce migrant.

Red-backed Shrikes have occurred in many parts of the island, including Gannets' Combe, the Terrace, Millcombe, St John's Valley and the other East Side combes, Middle Park, Quarter Wall and the Brick Field, and are usually seen perched prominently on fence-wires, drystone walls or vegetation. Taking all LFS years into account (1947 to June 2007), there have been some 57 Red-backed Shrikes recorded on Lundy: 24 in spring between 7 May (1995) and 20 June (1988), and 33 in autumn between 17 August (1985) and 4 November (1989). The majority of sightings (21) have been in September. All records involve single birds except for two juveniles seen in St John's Valley on 17 August 1985.

Chanter (1871) and Parfitt (1876) listed Red-backed Shrike as a "summer visitant", the latter adding "occasional breeder". Ross & Rousham (1909) also stated that the species had bred but provided no supporting information. There are five documented pre-LFS records: single birds on 12 July 1870, described in the Heaven Diaries as "a butcher bird so busy" (Boyd 1950), 1 June 1922 (Loyd 1922), 2 September 1927 (C.S. Elton, reported by Harrisson 1932) and 11 & 12 September 1937 (F.W. Gade & H.H. Davis, reported by Dymond 1980), and two birds on 6 May 1938 (F.W. Gade, reported by Dymond 1980). The first LFS record was of a female on 10 June 1949.

Although surviving documentation does not always enable the ages of Lundy birds to be determined, there has been an apparent decrease in autumn records of young birds, perhaps reflecting the demise of Red-backed Shrike as a breeding bird in Britain and the decline of many populations elsewhere in western Europe. There have been only three autumn records in the last 20 years, up to and including 2006 – see below.

Ten birds had been caught and ringed on Lundy by the end of 2006, but there are no controls or recoveries involving the island.

The following is a complete list of accepted records for the 20 years 1987–2006 (a late-spring 2007 sighting is also included):

1987 15 May – one.
1988 20 Jun – a female by Quarter Wall trap.
1989 7 May – a male caught in the Terrace trap was ringed and seen later in St Helen's Copse.
8 May – a second male was caught in Quarter Wall trap and ringed.
4 Nov – a first-year bird.
1993 6 Jun – a female near the Ugly.
1995 7 May – one.
2 Jun – a male at Quarter Wall.
18 & 19 Aug – a female perched on a tree-protection cage in Quarter Wall Copse.
1997 15 May – a male.
1998 13 & 14 May – a male.
1999 14 May – one.
14 Jun – a male on the fence next to Quarter Wall Cottages.
2004 23 & 24 May – one, probably a first-summer male, frequenting the Brick Field fence.
30 Sep – a first-year bird in St John's Valley and Millcombe.
2007 11 & 12 Jun – a male below the Terrace and near Quarter Wall. (Record subject to acceptance by the Devon Birds Records Committee.)

Lesser Grey Shrike *Lanius minor*

British vagrant.

Breeds in south-east Europe and Asia, wintering in southern Africa. 150 records for Britain 1950–2005.

There is one Lundy record:

1961 24 Sep – an adult sitting on a fence to the south of the Old Light was seen by Tony Vickery.

Lesser Grey Shrike

Reports of Lesser Grey Shrike published in the *LFS Annual Reports* for 1958 (one on 14 Sep) and 1963 (one on 26 May) were both rejected by the BBRC.

Great Grey Shrike *Lanius excubitor*

Nationally scarce migrant and winter visitor.

Breeding range extends from central France and Norway eastward across Eurasia to the Bering Sea and across Alaska and northern Canada. Winters in western and central Europe, and similar latitudes across Asia and North America. 2,243 records for Britain 1986–2003, with an average of 110 per year 2000–2003.

There is one Lundy record:

1974 22 Oct – a first-winter female was trapped, ringed and photographed on the Terrace.

A Great Grey Shrike was reported near the Devil's Chimney on 15 May 1987. While the description entered in the LFS logbook clearly fits a 'grey' shrike, the details are insufficient to rule out Lesser Grey Shrike, occurrence of which must be equally likely on this date.

Woodchat Shrike *Lanius senator*

Nationally scarce migrant.

Breeds in southern Europe, wintering in sub-Saharan Africa. 717 records for Britain 1958–2003, with an average of 20 per year 2000–2003. Considered by the BBRC until the end of 1990.

Woodchat Shrikes can turn up on fences or walls anywhere on the island, though most have occurred on the East Side between Millcombe and the Terrace, and around Quarter Wall. First recorded on Lundy on 16 June 1949, there have been from one to three records in 27 subsequent years to the end of 2006, involving a total of 44 or 45 individuals. Though occurring in all months from April to October, the vast majority of sightings are in May and June (adults overshooting their continental breeding grounds) and mid-August to the end of September (mainly juvenile/first-winter birds). The earliest

Woodchat Shrike

and latest dates are 10 April (1956) and 3 October (1992). The April record is exceptional, the next earliest spring occurrence being 1 May (1994). There have been three July records, all of adults, probably involving itinerant failed/non-breeding birds. The earliest date for a juvenile is 18 August 1970 when one was watched catching and eating a large beetle at Quarter Wall.

The following is a complete list of accepted records for the 20 years 1987–2006:

1989 3 to 5 May – a female, caught and ringed on 3rd, stayed in the Millcombe area.[170]
28 Aug to 2 Sep – a juvenile at the top of St Helen's Combe.

1991 27 & 28 Jun – a female in St John's Valley and Millcombe. During the early evening of 27 Jun seen perching on trees next to Millcombe lawn, from where it was hunting beetles, on several occasions mobbed by up to five of the resident Chaffinches.[171]

1992 14 May – an adult female just south of the Terrace trap.
22 Sep to 3 Oct – a juvenile in Millcombe, trapped and ringed on 30 Sep.

1994 1 to 9 May – a male along the East Side between Millcombe and Quarter Wall.

1997 15 & 16 May – a female at Quarter Wall.
8 Jul – a female on the East Side.

2002 19 Aug – a juvenile, trapped and ringed in St John's Valley.[172]

2004 16 & 19 Jun – one first seen between Quarter Wall Cottages and the Quarter Wall Heligoland trap, and on 19th in St Helen's Field.
2 to 4 Sep – a first-year bird in the Pondsbury area, watched for two hours on the first date when it was feeding continuously, mainly by vertical flycatching sallies up to six metres above its perch.

2005 27 & 28 May – a female in the vicinity of Quarter Wall ranging as far as the gorse on Ackland's Moor.

2006 12 Sep – a juvenile in St John's Valley; seen again on 15 Sep and still present on 26 Sep.

Records of Woodchat Shrike on 10 to 13 May 1960 and 31 May 1969 were published in the relevant *LFS Annual Reports* and/or *Devon Bird Reports* but were either rejected by the BBRC or apparently never submitted. In addition, a record of a juvenile bird on 22 September 1988, though published in both the 1988 *LFS Annual Report* and 1988 *Devon Bird Report* (the latter stating 19 September) was rejected by the BBRC; the original LFS logbook indicates that an unidentified shrike was seen on 19 or 20 September 1988.

Jay *Garrulus glandarius*   [Eurasian Jay]

Lundy vagrant.

Although they are common and widespread on the nearby mainland, Jays are extremely rare on Lundy. In fact, there have been only three records, fewer than for many species that are national rarities. Red-eyed Vireo, for example, which originates in North America, has occurred twice as often on the island! The second Jay record came more than three decades after the first, but the next was seen only four years later:

1965 26 Sep – one flew across Millcombe (Tony Vickery, personal communication).
1999 17 Jul – one around the quarries.
2003 9 Sep – one in Millcombe.

Magpie *Pica pica*   [Eurasian Magpie]

Lundy vagrant.

In spite of the relative proximity of Lundy to mainland England and Wales, where Magpies are abundant, this species is an extreme rarity on the island, having been recorded in only seven LFS years (1947 to the end of 2006):

1952 12 to 18 Jun – one.
1953 2 Jul – one.
1975 28 Feb – one seen in Millcombe by John Ogilvie.

1981 15 Oct – two seen by Mary Gade, Keith Mortimer, Steve Wing and others.

1984 14 to 17 Apr – two, after which one seen daily from 18 to 25 Apr and again from 29 Apr to 2 May.

1991 13 Feb – one dead, found floating in the Landing Bay among other debris washed up by easterly winds.

1996 5 May – one seen at North End flying out to sea, gaining height and making for the Devon coast.

26 May – one on the ground just north-east of Quarter Wall gate.[173]

There are only five earlier known occurrences of Magpie: one on 30 November 1887 survived until it was shot on 28 February 1888 and sent ashore for stuffing on 14 March! (Heaven Diaries, reported by Boyd 1950). Another long-staying bird remained from March 1930 until the summer of 1932 and was seen nest-building that year; one was seen on 28 February 1934; and single birds were present for several days from 14 July 1938 and from 1 to 3 February 1939 (F.W. Gade, reported by Davis 1954a).

Chough

Chough *Pyrrhocorax pyrrhocorax*   [Red-billed Chough]

Lundy vagrant; formerly bred.

Listed by Chanter (1871) and Parfitt (1876) as "resident all the year", Parfitt adding "and breed there". Choughs bred on Lundy in the nineteenth century and were reported by D'Urban & Mathew (1895) as "fairly numerous" in the 1860s. However, Crespi (1888) found only one or two breeding pairs. Blathwayt (1900) noted: "The Chough, formerly common, has now been quite exterminated. Their final disappearance is said to be due to the persecution they received from the men who some years ago were engaged in quarrying granite on the eastern side of the island. One of the islanders told me that in former years he often saw small flocks of Choughs flying about the fields, but that they no longer nested on the island. The price which may be obtained for the skins and eggs of these birds has done much towards banishing them from many of their former haunts…". Hendy (1922) reported a conversation in 1914 with Walter Heaven (nephew of the then owner of Lundy) who told him he had "seen none for fifteen years, but that before that time they were 'common as crows'." Loyd (1925) wrote that in 1890 "a few were yet to be found" and added that by 1895 Choughs were "only represented by a chance straggler from the mainland at long intervals".

None was seen subsequently until the first LFS record in 1949. There have been a further six records to the end of 2006, five of these since 1990, perhaps reflecting increased numbers on the nearby Welsh coast. Four other reported sightings of single birds in this period (September 1991, June 1998,

234

July 2002 and October 2003) were rightly rejected for inclusion in the *LFS Annual Reports* owing to a lack of supporting information. However, given that Choughs are fairly unmistakable birds, it is very likely that some or all of these sightings were genuine. With nesting having resumed in Cornwall in 2002 (a single pair; increasing to two pairs in 2006) after an absence of many years, the Pembrokeshire population also spreading eastwards along the Bristol Channel coast of South Wales, and recent records from Somerset, the exciting possibility exists that Choughs may one day return to breed on Lundy.

All LFS records to the end of 2006:

1949 18, 20, 21 & 24 Oct – one thought to be a first-year bird seen at Quarter Wall Cottages on 18th and subsequently around the quarries and north of the High Street.

1952 20 Feb to 3 Mar – one.

1990 4 & 10 Feb – one first seen by the Timekeeper's Hut (near Quarry Pond) then later around the Terrace and by the main track south of Halfway Wall.

7 Jun – one perched on a rock at North End "eventually flew off out of sight".

1994 4 May – one flying north along the East Side past the mouth of Millcombe Valley.

1997 29 Mar – one on the eastern side of Ackland's Moor was seen to be ringed on the right leg.

2000 28 Dec – one first seen on Gull Rock then flew north of Tibbett's Point.

Jackdaw *Corvus monedula* [Western Jackdaw]

Rare spring migrant; very rare autumn migrant and winter visitor; may formerly have bred.

The pattern of Jackdaw sightings on Lundy is very similar to that of Rook, involving records from all months of the year, though the great majority are during spring, with sporadic autumn influxes and occasional midwinter occurrences. However, the overall number and frequency of Jackdaw sightings is considerably higher, with records in all except three years for the period 1947 to 2006 inclusive.

Most Jackdaws have been seen between March and June, with a noticeable peak in April. Small groups used to be a fairly regular feature of springtime birdwatching on the island and larger flocks occurred from time to time, the highest daily count being 53 on 25 April 1948. Other peak numbers included 25 on 7 April 1976, 28 on 12 April 1988, 32 on 13 April 1994 and 50 on 29 March 1984.

While there have been many sightings in June and a handful in July and August, there is no firm evidence of Jackdaws nesting on Lundy, certainly for many decades, though Rousham (1908) stated that "fair numbers" were breeding on the high cliffs. Chanter (1871) and Parfitt (1876) listed the species as an "occasional visitant", while Harrisson (1932) felt that the Jackdaw's absence as a nesting species was "one of the most striking and puzzling features of the island". More recently there is an intriguing record of a dead bird being found in one of the chimneys of Millcombe House on 20 November 1991.

Autumn occurrences are less than annual and generally involve only small numbers (one to five birds) for a day or two. However, there have been several notable influxes, including up to 27 on 14 November 1952, 49 on 12 November 1976, 60 on 16 October 1993 and an astonishing 250 on 20 October 1983, which remains the all-time high count. Just six birds were present the next day, though 50 were seen on 24th. However, these figures are dwarfed by the counts of 1,000 and 4,000 in the Isles of Scilly on 23 & 24 October 1983, respectively (Robinson 2003), clearly part of the same overall movement noted on Lundy.

Small numbers (up to five birds, most recently five on 3 February 2007) have occurred occasionally during the winter months since LFS recording began in 1947, but large parties wintered on the island in each of the three winters 1934/35, 1936/37 and 1937/38 (F.W. Gade, reported by Davis 1954a).

As is the case for Rook, Jackdaw sightings have dwindled in recent years, with just a handful of spring records – each involving only one or two birds – in the 10-year period 1997–2006 (and again in 2007) but none at all in 2004 or 2005. Over the same period there have been only four autumn records – again of ones and twos, except for five on 6 November 2004 – and none in winter.

Two Jackdaws had been ringed on Lundy by the end of 2006, but there are no controls or recoveries involving the island.

Rook *Corvus frugilegus*

Rare spring migrant; very rare autumn migrant and winter visitor.

Although they have occurred in every month of the year, Rooks are recorded less than annually on Lundy and any sighting is a notable event. Most have occurred as spring migrants between March and May, the maximum seen in a day during this period being 30 on 3 April 1977.[174] However, the numbers involved are generally much lower than this, more than three being very unusual.

Autumn sightings are even more sporadic, with records in just eight LFS years from 1947 to the end of 2006. However, these included two notable influxes, in October 1976 and October 1983. The 1976 movement began with a single bird on 20 October, followed by three on 25th & 26th, 16 on 27th, 20 on 28th and reaching a peak of 42 on 29 October[175] – this remains the highest number ever recorded on the island. Rooks were then noted almost daily right through the winter until the late spring of 1977; up to 25 in November, 15 in December, 25 in January, 18 in February, 25 in March and 30 in April. By way of contrast, the 1983 influx was very much a one-day wonder, with 40 on 20 October, then just two on 24th, one on 26th and none subsequently. Apart from 1976/77, other scattered winter occurrences have involved mostly ones and twos, exceptionally up to four birds, for short periods only.

The 1976/77 and 1983 influxes were both associated with wider movements that were also noted in the Isles of Scilly, where "autumn 1976 saw the arrival of large numbers, 100 of which remained into March 1977…though all had departed by early June" (Robinson 2003). In October and November 1976, significant movements were also noted as far away as Fair Isle, Shetland (Pennington *et al.* 2004).

There is little historical information concerning Rooks on Lundy. Chanter (1871) and Parfitt (1876) listed them as "occasional visitants"; Oldham (1932) recorded "a dozen in the fields at the south end, daily" between 24 August and 4 September 1907; Harrisson (1932) stated that "some appear to visit the island from the mainland almost daily", recording 12 on 8 June 1930; and Hendy (1933) counted 20 on 2 September in the same year.

The number and frequency of Rook records has declined significantly in recent years, with sightings in only four of the 10 years 1997–2006. There was only one autumn and one winter sighting during this period, both of single birds, while the highest spring count was three on 27 April 1998. Three were also seen together over the village on 28 April 2007. A similar decline in the frequency of migrant Rooks has been noted in Shetland (Pennington *et al.* 2004). British and Irish Rook populations

Rooks

are resident but many breeding in continental Europe move south-west in winter and there are irregular influxes into Britain (Wernham *et al.* 2002). Perhaps climate change means that fewer continental Rooks are now wintering as far west as Britain.

Carrion Crow *Corvus corone*

Breeds; present throughout the year.

Arguably the least popular of the resident birds, Carrion Crows appear to thrive on Lundy, making a living by scavenging on scraps of food around the village and farm, feeding on rabbit carcases or sick and dying animals, and stealing seabird eggs during the breeding season. Gaining an understanding of the dynamics of the Carrion Crow population is difficult as they are highly mobile – one moment scattered in ones and twos or small groups around the island, and then suddenly congregating into a single flock only to split up again shortly afterwards.

The greatest insights were achieved in the late 1940s and through the 1950s when the records kept by the LFS wardens revealed an annual pattern of movements that, despite the sparseness of firm data since the 1960s, appears to have remained unchanged over the years. Resident birds are joined in spring by small numbers of passage birds (e.g. 10 were seen apparently leaving the island, high to the north-east on 29 April 2007); breeding birds establish territories and nest, leaving a non-breeding flock to loaf around the island; the adults and young of the year join up with the non-breeders during summer, occasionally joined by a few visiting birds; numbers build up during late August as passage birds begin to arrive, peaking in September and October, and tailing off as birds depart the island in November, leaving the resident flock to pass the winter. In hard winters it is likely that even the resident birds may move away from the island for a time.

There is little in the way of historical information. Chanter (1871) listed Carrion Crow as "resident all the year", as did Parfitt (1876) who added "and breed there". Crespi (1888) and Davenport (1897) referred to "small numbers" of crows, while Hendy (1922) found "many all over the island" in 1914. Loyd (1925) doubted whether more than six pairs bred at the most (he found one nest eight feet up an East Side cliff). Harrisson (1932) estimated about 16 pairs in 1930 and quoted Gade as believing that in 1931 there were nearly 40 pairs nesting; however, Alexander *et al.* (1945), who had access to Gade's unpublished notes, considered this to be Harrisson's misunderstanding of a count made outside the breeding season. Perry (1940) reported five nesting pairs in 1939, while Davis (1954a) stated "usually fewer than ten pairs" breeding. Summarising LFS records from 1947 to the late 1970s, Dymond (1980) stated that between three and 10 pairs had bred annually.

Full or partial counts of nesting pairs have only been documented six times since 1970, with between one and six pairs holding territories. Three regular territories are situated in the wooded combes of the East Side, where long-established nests can be seen in the tallest trees in Millcombe, St Helen's Combe and Quarter Wall Copse. Other territories involve cliff sites. Among an estimated six territories in 2000, Parsons (unpublished) found two young in a cliff-top nest below Quarry Pond.

Prior to 2007, counts of 50 or more birds had been made on 11 occasions, eight of these between 1951 and 1958, with a maximum of 69 birds on 17 October 1957. Some of these high counts coincided with an outbreak of myxomatosis among rabbits on the mainland and hence bumper breeding seasons owing to an abundance of rabbit corpses, followed by post-breeding dispersal to Lundy. An unprecedented (for winter) 50 were present on 22 January 2004, with high January counts of 30 or more in each of the two subsequent years; 51 were counted on 17 September 2006 and 52 on 17 October 2006, again coincident with an epidemic of disease among the rabbit population, this time on the island itself. This was followed by a series of high counts (in excess of 50 birds) in the spring of 2007, including a flock of 55 on 30 April. With at least eight apparently territorial tree and cliff-nesting pairs also present around the island, this gave a likely total in excess of 70 individuals – which would be an all-time record. Given the predatory nature of this species and the increasing vulnerability of Lundy's auk and Kittiwake populations, this could be deemed "rather too large a population", to quote the 1959/60 *LFS Annual Report* (a time when there were also high numbers).

Twenty Carrion Crows – mostly nestlings – had been ringed on Lundy by the end of 2006 (most recently in 1996), but there are no controls or recoveries showing movements to or from the island.

Hooded Crow *Corvus cornix*

Lundy vagrant, primarily in spring; treated as a separate species by the BOU since 2002, formerly as a sub-species of Carrion Crow.

Dymond (1980) stated that there had been "about 28 records" since 1928, all between March and July, except for one long-staying bird in 1972 which remained until October. Since 1976 (the last year covered by Dymond's analysis for this species), the pattern of occurrence has been broadly similar, with most sightings between April and July. Exceptions are one seen from 23 February to 7 March 1977, a late autumn bird on 3 November 1978 and another long-staying individual seen irregularly from May to October 1981. A bird of intermediate Carrion/Hooded Crow plumage was seen on 4 May 1989. Overall, Hooded Crows have been seen in 24 LFS years, up to and including 2007. The only date on which two have been recorded is 16 May 1972, all other sightings being of single birds.

The following lists all records for the 20 years 1987–2006 (and an additional sighting in spring 2007):

1988 5 to 10 Jun – one; seen on the west side of Quarter Wall on the last day.
1991 23 Apr – one seen perched and in flight near Barton Cottages.
1995 23 Apr – one.[176]
2001 24 & 25 Apr – one on Ackland's Moor and near the village.
2002 16 Apr – one flying north high over the island with 13 Carrion Crows.
         10 Jul – one near South Light.
2003 3 May – one around Ackland's Moor and Quarter Wall.
2007 4 to 19 May – one seen on at least eight days in the vicinity of the Airfield, Ackland's Moor, High Street gate and Tillage Field.

Listed by Chanter (1871) and Parfitt (1876) as an "autumn and winter visitant". D'Urban & Mathew (1895) stated that Hooded Crows visited Lundy in autumn and winter, while the Rev. H.G. Heaven (reported by Blathwayt 1900) noted that a few years prior to 1900 one or two remained and apparently interbred with Carrion Crows; Blathwayt saw several birds that he considered to be hybrids. One Hooded Crow was seen from 30 August to 1 September 1907 (Oldham 1932) and Felix Gade noted one on 25 March 1934 (1934 *Devon Bird Report*).

Though Hooded Crows are resident in Scotland and Ireland, the birds reaching Lundy are more likely to be of continental origin, given that the British and Irish populations are highly sedentary, whereas those in northern and eastern Europe are strongly migratory (Wernham *et al.* 2002). The number of continental Hooded Crows wintering in England has declined, perhaps in response to climate change (Wernham *et al.* 2002) and it seems likely that the species was once a more regular visitor to Lundy.

Raven *Corvus corax*   [Northern Raven]

Breeds; present throughout the year.

To watch a pair of Ravens playing and tumbling together on the wind is one of the great thrills of Lundy birdwatching. Raven territories are spread around the entire perimeter of the island, the long-established nest sites situated in high, inaccessible places. For many years a large, stick-built nest was visible towards the top of the Devil's Limekiln, until the ledge supporting it fell away, forcing the pair to build elsewhere.

Dymond (1980) reported that "the breeding population has fluctuated between one and nine pairs, but is usually between two and four pairs". Unquestionably the most successful Raven years on record were 1966 and 1967 when at least nine pairs bred; one pair in 1967 successfully rearing five young. The only other record of a pair raising five young was at Long Roost (formerly referred to as Long Ruse) in 1955.

Remarkably for such an obvious bird, there has been little documented information on breeding numbers or success since six pairs were recorded in 1977. A count of up to six territories in 2000 appears to be the only full survey since then (Parsons unpublished). Nevertheless, Ravens continue to do well on the island, with Dymond's estimate of between two and four breeding pairs annually still holding at least as good.

Ravens

Breeding adults seem to be resident, while most of the young birds appear to leave the island in their first autumn, a suggestion supported by two recoveries from Somerset and the Devon mainland (see below). Dymond (1980) reported congregations of up to 25 in autumn and winter. However, the disappointingly sparse winter counts in the LFS logbooks since 1990 – most days have a simple tick in the log, denoting presence only – have yielded 10 or more birds on just eight occasions, with a maximum of 25 on 2 February 1992. At other times of year, the highest counts (to the end of 2006) are of 28 birds on 13 October 1991 and 27 on 24 May 1993. Ravens are early nesters; even so, a record of one carrying nest material on 23 November 2003 is unusual, two months before breeding usually starts.

Historically, Chanter (1871) and Parfitt (1876) listed Raven as "resident all the year", Parfitt adding "and breed there". D'Urban & Mathew (1895) witnessed "a daily encounter between a pair of Ravens and a pair of Peregrines" but didn't make any mention of the species' overall status on the island. Crespi (1888) wrote that a pair or two were resident in 1888. Blathwayt (1900) reported that a pair or two were said to nest on Lundy but that he failed to see any during his visit in May that year. He also wrote that "some years ago, it is said, a feud broke out between the Peregrines and Ravens on Lundy, and one of the aerial conflicts which were continually taking place ended in disaster to one of the Ravens, which, failing to evade the Falcon's fatal 'stoop', was struck down into the sea and drowned". Rousham (1908) said that a pair hatched young in 1908 but that the young were shot on the nest. Hendy (1914) reported two pairs, the young of one pair being shot in the nest "owing to their alleged depredations upon sheep". Loyd (1925) stated that four or five pairs nested in 1922 and 1923. Harrisson (1932) recorded four pairs in 1930 and only two pairs the following year.

An alarming encounter!

An entry for 18 September in the 1991 LFS logbook reads: "Raven sitting on rock at first pecking at, and then dropping, and then attempting several times to retrieve but obviously very scared of being attacked by (so eventually giving up) a quartz alarm-clock in a red leather case (still working!)."

Lundy's Ravens show a fondness for seabird eggs and can often be seen carrying eggs in flight in mid to late spring. A note in the 2005 *Devon Bird Report* states that: "A pair worked as a team to prey on Herring Gull eggs; one grabbed incubating bird, pulled it off nest and wrestled with it, while the other nipped in to steal egg; both then retreated to nearby cliff to consume their bounty, and then repeated the process".

Forty-seven Ravens had been ringed on Lundy by the end of 2006. Of two recoveries, a nestling ringed on 24 April 1965 was found at Marsland, Welcombe, near the Devon/Cornwall border, on 26 March 1966; and a nestling ringed on 17 April 1951 was found on Exmoor, at Winsford, Somerset, on 10 June 1953. The metal ring of a nestling Raven ringed near Quarry Beach on 24 April 1965 was read through binoculars 13 years later on 16 April 1978; the bird, a male, would approach people walking in the area of the Devil's Limekiln, where it bred, to within touching distance and take any food offered.

Starling *Sturnus vulgaris* [Common Starling]

Resident; breeds; common spring and autumn migrant, often in large numbers.

Glance at the top of the Church of St Helena, especially towards dusk, and the chances are there will be squadrons of chattering, preening Starlings lined up on the castellated tower. They tend to gather here before heading off to roost in trees and bushes on the East Side.

Chanter (1871) listed Starling as "resident all the year", as did Parfitt (1876), who added "and breed there". Loyd (1925) referred to Westcote's 1646 'Manuscript History of Devon' and "vast multitudes [of Starlings] roosting in the few straggling elders which grew on Lundy" – probably the earliest documented mention of Starlings on the island. Cummings (1909) noted that the species had established itself "within the last twelve years" and reported two pairs as resident in 1909 – a claim disputed by one of the lighthouse-keepers of the time (Loyd 1925). Harrisson (1932) reported Felix Gade saying that several thousands roosted in Millcombe in late winter. Gade reported one pair breeding in 1938, 1942 and 1943 (Davis 1954a) but it was in the mid-1960s that Starlings became established as a regular breeding species.

The first LFS record of breeding occurred in 1962 when at least two pairs nested. None bred in 1963 but a single pair nested in 1964, at Signal Cottage (situated next to the Castle and now demolished). Following another apparently blank year in 1965, Starlings have nested in every year since 1966 (up to and including 2007) when around 14 pairs took up residence. There were about 18 pairs in 1967 and at least 30 pairs in 1972. The locations of many of these nests will remain a mystery since the original LFS data for much of this period have been lost and the *LFS Annual Reports* do not provide this level of detail, except for 1969 when there were nests at the Castle and Old Light. Seven pairs bred in 1984, and in 1985 15 nests were located – at the Castle (3), the Church (5), Signal Cottage (6) and Old Light (1). The next nest count was in 2000 when Davis & Jones (unpublished) recorded seven pairs breeding in May. The only survey since, in 2004, located 10 nests around the farm, including the Church and Old Light (Lock 2004).

Spring movements take place mainly in February and March, with significant passage occurring in some years. Up to 2,000 were counted on 11 & 12 March 1962 and 1,000 passed through on 13 & 14 March 1973 and 22 March 1976. Such figures are exceptional, however, and peak numbers are usually in the low hundreds; for example, over 400 on 11 days in February 2005, falling to around 300 on two

Starlings

days in March and 60 at the end of the month. Passage in April and May is much lighter and largely obscured by the resident birds.

During summer, small groups of mostly young birds visit the island in June, July and occasionally early August. In some years, flocks of a few hundred birds can occur (e.g. 300 in June 1972 and 260 on 16 June 1996).

Autumn movements begin in September, usually towards the end of the month, and continue into late November or early December. Numbers at this time are nearly always substantial – much higher than in spring – especially from the second half of October onwards. Peak counts of 1,000 birds or more in a day are not uncommon and have been recorded in 28 LFS years since 1947 (to the end of 2006). Several spectacular movements have occurred. The first came on 17 December 1953 when at least 10,000 birds flew south over the island. The next, in 1959, is best described by an entry in that year's *LFS Annual Report*:

> "Numbers varied in October, reaching 850 on 11th, but not otherwise above 500 until 29th, when a flock of c.3,000 flew north at 08.00 hours followed by small flocks throughout the day. This was the first of several terrific movements in the late Autumn, over 1,000 birds being recorded on eight occasions in the first three weeks of November. By far the most spectacular was on November 6th when at least 10,000 birds moved south in parties of 50/200 throughout the day, while on the 7th about twice that number flew north in one terrific movement between 07.45 and 08.15. At one time the Airfield and Ackland's Moor, north of the Old Light, was black with Starlings which rested a few minutes before moving on. During these movements up to 500 or more frequently roosted on the island, usually on the Church Tower, occasionally on the Old Light itself and in rhododendrons. Night ringing marked nearly 300 birds before the supply of rings ran out. Many perished in the storms around November 15th, twenty or more being picked up daily while the bad weather prevented them from leaving the island. After a steady decrease about 200 remained at the end of the month."

The only other comparable count, of over 10,000 birds, was on 17 November 1973. By far the highest daily total since was over 6,000 birds on 13 November 2002. Such huge movements are usually transitory, with birds seldom settling on the island for long. While the largest movements are usually of diurnal (day-flying) migrants, several big nocturnal movements have been noticed (e.g. between 20 and 23 October 1952), mainly in the early years of the LFS when an ornithological warden was stationed on the island for a large part of the year.

Starlings ringed on Lundy and controlled or recovered elsewhere

Age/sex	Date ringed on Lundy	Place found	Date controlled or recovered	Speculation about date/place of finding
Adult	11 Oct 1949	Välinge, Nr Helsingborg, **Sweden**	22 Oct 1951	On autumn migration
Adult	22 Oct 1952	Friesland, **The Netherlands**	15 Jun 1953	In breeding area
Adult F	27 Nov 1952	Senlingen, **Germany**	08 Jul 1954	In breeding area
Adult	15 Feb 1953	Nr Nieuport, **Belgium**	28 Oct 1953	On autumn migration
Adult	17 Feb 1953	Caldey Island, Pembrokeshire	02 Mar 1954	On spring migration
Adult	24 Feb 1953	Delabole, Cornwall	15 Dec 1953	On autumn migration or in wintering area
Adult	16 Nov 1955	Nr Amsterdam, **The Netherlands**	18 May 1958	In breeding area
Adult M	21 Nov 1955	Bicester, Oxfordshire	23 May 1957	In breeding area
1st-year	17 Nov 1959	Lüneburg, **Germany**	05 Jul 1960	In breeding area
1st-year M	19 Nov 1959	Rhinow, Brandenburg, **Germany**	23 Jun 1963	In breeding area
1st-year	23 Nov 1959	Karelian Isthmus, Leningrad, **Russia**	12 Jun 1960	In breeding area
1st-year	14 Aug 1967	St Budeaux, Plymouth, Devon	04 Feb 1970	In wintering area
1st-year M	10 Nov 1975*	Werl, Nordrhein-Westfalen, **Germany**	07 Oct 1977	On autumn migration
Adult F	16 Jun 1978	Winchester, Hampshire	02 Mar 1980	On spring migration
1st-year F	22 Oct 1992	Stadskanaal, Groningen, **The Netherlands**	17 May 1993	In breeding area

*The 1977 *LFS Annual Report* incorrectly shows the ringing date as 20 Aug 1976.

The resident population is joined in winter by visiting birds – influxes that are not necessarily associated with hard weather – though it is unlikely that the same individuals stay throughout. Peak winter counts have occasionally reached 500 or more; for example, on 14 January 1955, 28 January 1981 and on six days in late December 2004, with an estimated 700 present on 14 January 1985. However, by far the highest winter total was 2,000 Starlings moving north over the island on 12 January 1977 when snow was lying "thick on the ground".

By the end of 2006, 1,192 Starlings had been ringed on Lundy, with three subsequently found on the island and 15 controlled or recovered elsewhere. Two recoveries demonstrate the mix of resident and migrant birds that occurs: a first-year bird ringed on Lundy on 18 November 1959 was found (long dead) on the island on 20 May 1964, while one ringed five days later on 23 November 1959 turned up 2,383 kilometres away in the Leningrad oblast (region) of north-west Russia, probably in its breeding area, on 12 June 1960. Of the other 14 birds, five were found elsewhere in Britain (Devon, Cornwall, Hampshire, Oxfordshire and Dyfed), one in Sweden, one in Belgium, three in The Netherlands and four in Germany (see table).

Rose-coloured Starling *Sturnus roseus* [Rosy Starling]

Nationally scarce migrant.

Breeds in south-eastern Europe, western and Central Asia, migrating to winter in south Asia. Breeding range has spread irregularly westwards in recent years and the number of British records has increased accordingly. 723 records for Britain 1958–2003, with an average of 92 per year 2000–2003. Considered by the BBRC until the end of 2001.

The first dated Lundy record occurred in 1934, a bird which stayed from 18 to 26 June (H.H. Davis 1934; Lack 1934). It was 45 years until the next was seen in 1979, the first of 12 LFS records (to the end of 2006), involving a total of at least 16 individuals.[177] Eight of the records have been during the period August to October, with four from mid-May to mid-June:

1979   15 May to 1 Jun – an adult on Castle Hill and elsewhere in the south of the island.

1983   25 to 29 Sep – a juvenile seen on four days.[178]

1992   11 to 13 Aug – an adult with the resident Starling (*S. vulgaris*) flock in and around the pig pen, tea garden and incinerator areas.

1994   3 & 4 Oct – a juvenile at the Old Light and seen later around the pig pen and on South West Field.

1999   22 Sep to 4 Oct – a first-year bird in the village area, first seen perched on the Tavern roof with a flock of 60 Starlings.[179]

2000   9 to 14 Jun – an adult around the incinerator and later by the Church and Big St John's.
3 to 12 Aug – an adult, perhaps the same as the one given above, was present in the Tillage Field and elsewhere in the south of the island.[180]

2002   1 to 10 Jun – an adult present in St John's Valley, joined by a second adult on 4 Jun when both were seen on the slope below Big and Little St John's and on the side of Castle Hill. A single bird, probably one of these two, was seen near Quarter Wall Pond on 22 & 27 Jun.[181]
21 to 24 Sep – a juvenile around the campsite.
(2002 was an invasion year when 182 were recorded in Britain; *British Birds* 97: 661.)

2003   5 to 12 Jun – an adult seen in various places in the south-east of the island, including the Lighthouse Field and campsite, joined by another bird, probably second-summer, on 12th, when they were seen together by the Ugly.
8 Sep to 22 Oct – a juvenile, first seen in the Lighthouse Field, then elsewhere around the village.

2004   5 & 6 Sep – three juveniles were seen in the south of the island, one staying to 13 Sep, favouring the Lighthouse Field.

Rose-coloured Starlings were perhaps more numerous in the last decades of the nineteenth century, in line with a previous range expansion. Mathew (1866a) reported that the species "has occurred within the last few years on Lundy island". Chanter (1871) stated that "the beautiful rose-coloured pastor and the hoopoe are frequently met with in spring" and included it in his list of "occasional visitants", as did Parfitt (1876). D'Urban & Mathew (1895) wrote: "In the spring the beautiful Rose-coloured Pastor was once a frequent visitor, and the Rev. H.G. Heaven was wont to declare that he was almost sure to meet with it if he went out to look for it, and at the request of his friend the late Dr. Woodforde, of Taunton, shot a pair, which are now…in the Museum at Taunton Castle."

Rose-coloured Starling

House Sparrow *Passer domesticus*

Common breeding resident; present through the year; possible immigration obscured by resident population.

Lundy's House Sparrows are frequently in evidence from their twittering calls, mostly between the top of Millcombe and the village as far as the barn close to the High Street gate. They make great use of the many nestboxes erected in these areas for breeding, as well as holes in the walls around the farmyard.

Although House Sparrows are nowadays a daily feature of Lundy life in and around the village area, they have been intermittent as a breeding species on the island since the late nineteenth century. Chanter (1871), referring to some of the common passerines of Lundy, added "…but what is strange, the house-sparrow is not found". However, he listed House Sparrow as an "occasional visitant" in his 1877 revision and changed the end of the above quote to read "…the house-sparrow is very rarely found". Parfitt (1876) also listed this species as an "occasional visitant". Crespi (1988) reported breeding in 1888, but none was recorded by either D'Urban & Mathew in their *Birds of Devon* (1895) or Davenport (1897). Blathwayt (1900), Rousham (1908), Cummings (1909) and Hendy (1922) all reported nesting in the early 1900s, and Loyd (1922) found five or six pairs in 1922 but stated that the islanders regarded them as an entirely new addition to the avifauna. One year later Loyd (1923) reported greatly increased numbers breeding. Gade indicated annual breeding from 1926 to 1942 (Davis 1954a), with 22 pairs nesting in 1930 (Wynne-Edwards & Harrisson 1932) and 40 pairs in 1939 (Perry 1940). Davis (1954a) stated: "By 1940 they were proving such a nuisance on the farm that efforts were made to exterminate them", and only one pair remained by 1942 (Alexander *et al.* 1945).

From the advent of LFS recording in 1947 until 1970, House Sparrows did not breed on the island, although odd ones and twos occurred occasionally in spring between 29 March (1953) and 30 May (1956), with two late June records (27th 1951; 30th 1966) and between one and four birds in mid-October in each year from 1956 to 1959. Things changed in 1971 when two birds arrived on 7 April, two or three were present through June and at least six were counted in September. The *LFS Annual Report* for that year records that "a pair nested" but adds, erroneously, that they did so "for the first time for ten years" when in fact it was at least 29 years judging by the available records. House Sparrows have bred annually since, though with few overall counts up to 1990. The highest number of occupied nests in this period was nine in 1985, and the peak counts of individuals were between 55 and 65 from October to December 1990.

An intensive study of the island's House Sparrow population began in 1991 (see opposite), when 80 nestboxes were erected in Millcombe and around the farm. Between 1995 and 2004 the number of breeding females varied from 30 to 40 (1997–1999) to 81 (2004); maximum spring, autumn and winter counts are given in the table. The number of nestboxes had increased to 114 by 2004. The recent significant growth in population size may be due to a range of factors, including milder winters, longer breeding seasons and an increase in the number of domestic chickens farmed on the island (Nakagawa 2006), as well as the introduction of 49 birds in 2000.

House Sparrows

Peak numbers of House Sparrows on Lundy, 1991–2005

Year	Spring (pre-breeding)	Autumn (post-breeding)	Winter (November–February)
1991	30	100	40
1992	40	130	70
1993	no counts	85	50
1994	30	110	30
1995	58	100	110
1996	no counts	100	110
1997	no counts	35	32
1998	20	55	35
1999	20	60	[5]
2000	78	111	no counts
2001	82	170	no counts
2002	99	125	no counts
2003	114	150	59
2004	172	100	[6]
2005	250	400	220
2006	160	135	[56]

Counts are of individual birds. Square brackets indicate incomplete counts.

By chance, we crossed to Lundy on the same day (29 April 2000) as the introduced birds. On release, they flew en masse to bushes at the top of Millcombe where, somewhat startled by the suddenness of their new surroundings and chirruping loudly, they gave the impression of looking either wistfully or mutinously at the distant mainland! It was our turn to be startled a day or so later when, sheltering from a sharp north-easterly breeze behind the South Light on the western side of Lametor, we were suddenly aware of loud chirruping – and there were some of the House Sparrows lined up along the wall. It wasn't long, however, before they and the island birds were socialising and the new genes mingling with those of the resident sparrows.

Between 1947 and 2006, 547 House Sparrows were ringed,[182] but there have been no subsequent controls or recoveries to indicate movements away from the island. Similarly, there are no ringing records showing movements to Lundy from elsewhere.

Studies of the House Sparrow population on Lundy

In 1990 Ian Owens and Terry Burke, then at the University of Leicester, realised that Lundy's House Sparrows would be an excellent population in which to study the process of evolution, given that the population was fairly isolated and sedentary, making it easy to study individuals throughout their lives. In 1991 about 80 nestboxes were erected around the farm buildings and on trees in Millcombe, and within a few years virtually all of Lundy's breeding pairs were using them, allowing breeding attempts to be easily monitored. Simon Griffith (also then based at the University of Leicester) carried out intensive research from late 1994 to 1997. Since then, each individual in the population has been marked with a metal BTO ring and a unique combination of three plastic colour rings, allowing birds to be individually identified without the need to recapture them. The birds have been monitored during the breeding season when the number of eggs and chicks has been recorded and the choice of partners by males and females investigated. Back at Leicester University (the birthplace of DNA fingerprinting) genetic techniques were used to establish the parentage of chicks. It was found that sparrows on Lundy showed a surprisingly high level of monogamy and that, in 99% of cases, the male feeding a brood of chicks was their genetic father. This finding contrasted with the usual pattern in passerines, where an average of about 15% of offspring are sired by an 'extra-pair' male (i.e. not the male who feeds them and rears them as 'his').

A major focus of research has been mate choice and sexual selection. Essentially the study has explored variation in the reproductive success of different males and how this might relate to the sparrow's black throat patch. The throat patch or 'badge' is a sexually selected 'ornament', equivalent to the tail of the peacock; several other studies have suggested that this badge reflects the quality of a male and his parenting ability. If this was the case, females would be expected to use badge size as a cue when choosing their mates. After each moult the badge size of all males was measured and compared to their attractiveness to females and individual breeding success. Contrary to findings in other House Sparrow populations, it appears that on Lundy males with small badges were more successful at attracting mates and produced more offspring. Badge size does seem to reflect an individual's condition, however, and males with large badges have a higher chance of surviving the winter.

The findings during the early part of the study (1994–1997) suggested that the Lundy House Sparrows differed from mainland populations in at least two ways: females on Lundy were more faithful to their partners and preferred small-badged males, rather than the large-badged males preferred in mainland populations. One possible cause of these differences is that the Lundy population was less genetically variable than mainland populations. This was investigated by Nancy Ockendon (based at the University of Sheffield) between 1999 and 2003. In part, her research was kick-started through accidental circumstances.

Warfarin-baited grain, marked with a blue dye, was used to control rats around the village for many years up to 1996. Birds have a very high natural tolerance of warfarin and sparrows fed on the poisoned grain for several years (evident from blue-dyed droppings under winter roosts). Unfortunately, in the winter of 1996/97 the poison was switched to difenacoum, which is highly toxic to birds as well as rodents. The sparrows were decimated and the population crashed to a maximum of 15 breeding pairs in 1997. Between 1997 and 2000 the population was very slow to recover, even though rat control had quickly been switched to use of impregnated wax blocks that are unpalatable to birds. Hence, in spring 2000, Nancy Ockendon introduced 49 adult birds from the mainland (captured near Sheffield, Yorkshire, under licence from English Nature), 29 of which settled on the island. In addition to restoring the population to its normal size, this introduction was a unique experiment that allowed Nancy to investigate whether the behaviour of the sparrows on Lundy was caused by living on an island or whether it was due to the genetics of the old population.

If low genetic variability was responsible for the high levels of monogamy seen among House Sparrows on Lundy, it would be expected that the introduction of mainland birds, carrying new genes, would cause an increase in the rate of extra-pair paternity. Specifically, Lundy females would be predicted to mate with mainland males to obtain greater genetic diversity for their offspring. Accordingly, in 2000, the year in which the mainland birds were introduced, the rate of extra-pair paternity on the island shot up, and over 10% of chicks hatching in 2000 were fathered by males other than the one that raised them. Genetic analysis allowed the true father of the chicks to be identified; surprisingly, it was found that the extra-pair males were all native Lundy birds. This implied that reduced genetic diversity was not responsible for the high fidelity of Lundy females between 1994 and 1997, and social factors related to the introduction were more likely to be responsible for the increase in extra-pair paternity seen in 2000.

During 2000–2002 the investigation into the role of male badge size continued. In 2001 there was little evidence that females used male badge size when choosing a mate, but in 2002 females preferred to mate with males with large badges. Therefore female preferences had reversed since 1996, when small-badged males were more successful in attracting a mate. This is one of the first studies to have shown that female choice for male ornamental traits can vary through time. However, large-badged males were still found to have a better chance of surviving the winter than males with small badges, so badge size does consistently reflect male condition. The ongoing story of the Lundy House Sparrows is now being investigated by Shinichi Nakagawa, who began his research, based at the University of Sheffield, in 2003. Future studies will concentrate on the relationship between breeding success and both climatic change and the island's carrying capacity.

Research on Lundy's sparrows has been funded by the Natural Environment Research Council, the Biotechnology and Biological Sciences Research Council, and the Tertiary Education Commission of New Zealand. The LFS has also provided a grant. By early 2007 seven papers on Lundy's House Sparrows had been published in international scientific journals, with another seven in preparation.

Spanish Sparrow *Passer hispaniolensis*

British vagrant.

Breeds in parts of southern Europe, North Africa and western/central Asia. Complex pattern of nomadic and migratory movements. 7 records for Britain 1950–2005.

There is one Lundy record of a single bird, also the first for Britain:

1966 9 to 12 Jun – an adult male, initially seen perched on a fence near Quarter Wall and later in the Tent Field and near the Church. The bird may have been around on 8th and stayed on the island for about 10 days altogether, though 12th is the last clearly stated date on which it was still present.[183]

Writing in *British Birds* some years later, Cliff Waller, LFS warden in 1966, wrote:

"The Spanish Sparrow kept to itself, not associating with any other species except on one occasion when it flew off with a flock of Linnets, which were noticeably smaller. It was always difficult to locate and when disturbed would fly a great distance, never landing nearby. It showed a preference for perching on fences, never on the old buildings which were in the vicinity" (Waller, 1981).

Tree Sparrow

Tree Sparrow *Passer montanus*   [Eurasian Tree Sparrow]

Lundy vagrant; formerly a regular migrant in small numbers and a sporadic breeder.

Several pairs bred in 1928, while two or three pairs were still present in 1932 (F.W. Gade, reported by Alexander *et al.* 1945 & Davis 1954a). Subsequently, a pair bred in a stone wall along the High Street in 1961, and two pairs nested successfully in the wall of the "Fowls' Run" in 1962 and 1963. The *LFS Annual Report* for 1962 notes that "both [pairs] probably had two broods". There are no other breeding records, and given that Tree Sparrow is 'red-listed' (of high conservation concern) following a catastrophic collapse in the UK breeding population between the 1970s and the 1990s (Baillie *et al.* 2007), further nesting attempts seem highly unlikely.

Following the commencement of LFS recording in 1947, the first record was of a single bird from 14 May to 5 June 1951, with another seen in May and June 1954. From 1958 until 1979 there were almost annual records, particularly in spring and early summer. While ones and twos occurred in some years, small flocks also turned up from time to time; for example, 12 from 2 to 10 June 1958,[184] up to 16 in 1962 (one of the years in which breeding occurred), up to six in September 1963, seven on 10 September 1964, 16 on 29 May 1975 and nine from 30 May to 3 June 1978. The highest count was of 19 on 7 June 1975.

The following is a complete listing for the 30-year period 1977 to 2006; since 1979, sightings have been few and far between, presumably reflecting the UK population crash, and all except one have involved single birds. It is noticeable that 10 of the 15 records have been in May or June:

1977   3 Jan – one.[185]
         1 Jun – one.
         24 & 25 Jun – three.
1978   16 May – three.
         30 May to 9 Jun – nine, with one remaining on 10th.[186]
1979   7 Jun – one.
1984   19 May – two.
         31 May – one.
1989   8 to 16 May – one, first seen in Millcombe.
1991   27 May to 10 Jun – one seen on several occasions in the vicinity of Quarter Wall and the East Side.[187]
1994   30 Sep – one at Stoneycroft, flew off high to the south-west.
1995   5 Aug – one.[188]
1996   26 Feb – one.
         5 May – one at the Old Light flew off high to the north.
2000   29 Jul – one with House Sparrows at Benjamin's Chair.

Red-eyed Vireo   *Vireo olivaceus*

British vagrant.

Breeds across much of the Americas, with North American birds migrating to winter in South America. 103 records for Britain 1950–2005.

There are seven Lundy records of single birds, five of which have been trapped and ringed. All have occurred since 1985 and all during the period late September to mid-October:

1985   5 Oct – a first-winter bird caught in the Terrace trap (together with a Scarlet Rosefinch (*Carpodacus erythrinus*) and ringed.
1988   28 Sep – one caught in the Terrace trap and ringed.
         1 Oct – one caught and ringed in Millcombe.
1990   16 to 18 Oct – a first-winter bird caught and ringed in Millcombe on 16th and seen in St Helen's Copse on the following two days.
1995   9 Oct – one seen in Quarter Wall Copse.
2000   5 Oct – a first-year bird caught and ringed in Millcombe and then present in Quarter Wall Copse from 8 to 12 Oct.[189]
2005   29 & 30 Sep – one in Millcombe; caught and ringed on 4 Oct and still present on 6 Oct.[190]

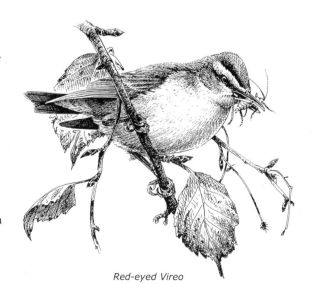

Red-eyed Vireo

A new species for Britain?

D'Urban & Mathew (1895) related the following intriguing story, which might just possibly concern the first record for Britain of Blue-headed Vireo *Vireo solitarius*, formerly known as Solitary Vireo. This is a common and widespread migratory species breeding in eastern North America and wintering in South America. D'Urban & Mathew mentioned the possibility of the "Western form of Solitary Vireo" – now recognised as a species in its own right, Plumbeous Vireo *Vireo plumbeus* – but this is a species of western North America that seems much less likely to reach Europe. The description is probably insufficiently detailed for a definite claim to be sustained, but is fascinating nonetheless:

"From the description sent us by the Rev. H.G. Heaven of a little bird seen by him early in October in 1876, it is probable that the island was visited by a species of *Vireo* ("Greenlets"), a large and widely dispersed North-American genus of small Flycatchers. We copy the very full account given of the bird by Mr. Heaven:–

'Size: about that of the Robin, perhaps slightly more robust in contour, but tail shorter in proportion. Plumage: upper parts of head, neck, back, tail, and wing-coverts uniform ashen grey with an olive-green tint in certain lights; wings and tail umber-brown, but with an ashen-grey tint on them, as though dusted with very fine powder; secondaries and tertiaries tipped with dull white, producing bars on the wings when closed; legs, beak, and eyes black, or very dark brown; the eyes a very marked feature, being very large, full, and brilliant, and set in lids fringed with an edging of the purest white, so that the eye looked like a brilliant jet bead set in a circlet of pearls; the whole of the underparts a pure spotless white, with a lustre upon it very similar to that on the breast of a Grebe, giving almost an iridescence in the sun under certain movements of the bird. I observed it in company with some Flycatchers and Whitethroats, which it much resembled at a distance, but rather exceeded in size apparently. It was very active and lively, and not at all shy, frequently coming within a few yards of where I and my sister were sitting. It was very busy catching insects, sometimes on the wing, sometimes pouncing on them on the ground, and sometimes hunting for them in the bushes, being not unlike a Tit in its restlessness and movements.'

As two examples of *Vireo olivaceus*, the Red-eyed Vireo, have been caught near Derby...there would be nothing unprecedented in another member of the genus, perhaps the Western form of the Solitary Vireo, *Vireo solitarius*, var. *plumbeus*...having paid a visit to Lundy, and it would only be another instance of North-American birds appearing in Devonshire and Cornwall."

Chaffinch *Fringilla coelebs*

Resident, breeding annually in small numbers. Common, at times, abundant, on autumn passage; noticeable spring passage rarely recorded; winter influxes occur in some years.

Lundy's small breeding population of Chaffinches was well monitored from the commencement of LFS recording in 1947 until the mid-1970s. Subsequent information is more patchy, with estimates of the number of pairs only available for six years between 1976 and 2006. The maximum number was about 12 pairs in 1962, but four to eight pairs appears more typical, so the most recent census of nine territories in 2004 (Lock 2004) was above average. Most territories are in Millcombe and St John's Valley, with others along the east sidelands between St Helen's Combe and the Terrace. British Chaffinches, which belong to the race *F. c. gengleri* are highly sedentary (Wernham *et al.* 2002) and it is likely that most of Lundy's breeding birds remain on the island throughout their lives, though occasional dispersal to the adjacent mainland may also occur.

Chaffinch

The British and Irish Chaffinch population approximately doubles in winter due to the immigration of continental birds, mostly of Scandinavian origin, with smaller numbers from Finland and north-west Russia. These birds migrate by day in flocks, most actively in the morning hours, with the main autumn migration occurring from September to November (Wernham *et al.* 2002). This phenomenon is well represented on Lundy in most autumns, when significant, occasionally huge, movements of birds head south. The sight of wave after wave of migrating finches, tucked into the lee of the cliffs, is one of the highlights of regular birdwatching on the island. The first increases in numbers are often reported in late September, but peak movements occur in October and November, particularly between mid-October and mid-November. Several hundred birds seen in a day is commonplace, while peak daily estimates in excess of one thousand were made in at least 27 years between 1947 and 2006, with the following estimates of 5,000 or more in a single day: 7,750 on 25 October 1955; 5,000 on 14 & 30 October 1959; 6,000 on 26 October 1963; at least 5,000 on 25 October 1972; 8,000 on 1 November 1978; 5,000 on 2 November 1979; 15,000 on 28 October 2003; and 11,000 on 27 October 2006. However, even the last-mentioned estimates are dwarfed by the figures for 20 & 30 October 1980 when 35,000 and 20,000 respectively were entered – by experienced observers – in the LFS logbook. On the first date 27,000 were estimated to have passed through the South End between 08.30am and 10.00am.

High counts in the first half of December are perhaps most likely to represent the tail-end of autumn migration (e.g. 150 on 5 December 1976 and 300 on 1 December 1981) and midwinter counts in excess of 30 are exceptional (e.g. about 50 early and late in the year in 1952, 40 on 24 January 1981 and 50 on 24 December 1985). There have been very few winter counts since 1990. However, of 10 daily counts made in January 2007, the highest was 25 on 27th.

Surprisingly, there is little evidence of significant return migration in spring, most of the autumn migrants clearly taking a different route back to the continent. Nevertheless, occasional influxes have been noted between February and April. For example, there were up to 60 birds in March 1962, 70 on 22 March 1967, "small numbers on passage" in mid-March 1973, 50 on 5 April 1981 and 32 on 22 March 1999.

Historically, Chanter (1871) and Parfitt (1876) listed Chaffinch as "resident all the year", the latter adding "and breed there". Loyd (1925) counted about eight resident pairs in 1922 and 1923. Wynne-Edwards & Harrisson (1932) found seven breeding pairs. Perry (1940) reported six nesting pairs in 1939, and Alexander *et al.* (1945) estimated four to five breeding pairs in 1942.

Between 1947 and 2006 a total of 6,885 Chaffinches were ringed on Lundy, with 15 controls or recoveries indicating some of the origins and onward movements of birds passing through the island in autumn – see table (a).

Fennoscandian Chaffinches migrate on a narrow front through Denmark, north-west Germany, The Netherlands, Belgium and north-east France, rather than crossing the North Sea directly. Females migrate before males and first-years before adults. The females tend to move further so that males predominate in winter in The Netherlands, Belgium and Britain, but females are in the majority in Ireland. Westward movement is reportedly very clear in autumn along the north coast of Wales and large numbers pass through Bardsey in October. Many Chaffinches, especially single-sex flocks of females, also occur in the fields of west Wales waiting for the right conditions to cross to Ireland (Wernham *et al.* 2002), while Bull Point, west of Ilfracombe on the North Devon coast, is well known as a Chaffinch migration watch-point in October.

All of the Lundy-ringed birds controlled or recovered elsewhere – see table (a) – were ringed between 16 September and 1 November, with the vast majority having been captured in late October. Recoveries and controls from Belgium (3), The Netherlands (1), Germany (1), Denmark (1) and Sweden (2) are entirely consistent with the overall pattern of migration to/from Britain described above. Measurements of Chaffinches have also shown that many individuals captured on Lundy during autumn migration are of the nominate continental race *F. c. coelebs*. The first-year male ringed on Lundy on 26 October 1997 and controlled in The Netherlands on 19 October 2004 was undertaking its eighth autumn migration.

There have also been three controls on the island of birds ringed elsewhere. Two came from Hartland Point on the North Devon coast (the nearest point of the mainland and another well-known migration watch-point), while the most recent had been ringed on the Baltic coast of the Russian enclave of Kaliningrad just a month before its capture on Lundy – see table (b).

The rings of two first-year females, ringed on Lundy on 23 & 25 October 2005 respectively, were both found on the island in the pellets of an unknown species of predatory bird on 13 March 2006.

(a) Chaffinches ringed on Lundy and controlled or recovered elsewhere

Age/sex	Date ringed on Lundy	Place found	Date controlled or recovered	Speculation about date/place of finding
Full-grown F	30 Oct 1958	Kohlscheid, nr Aachen, **Germany**	15 Oct 1961	On autumn migration
1st-year F	13 Oct 1959	Liège, **Belgium**	14 Oct 1960	On autumn migration
1st-year M	26 Oct 1969	Googstraten, Antwerp, **Belgium**	24 Mar 1973	On spring migration
1st-year M	16 Sep 1984	Bideford, North Devon	15 Mar 1985	In breeding area or on spring migration
1st-year M	26 Oct 1993	Alston Hall, Lancashire	15 Jan 1995	In wintering area
1st-year F	26 Oct 1993	Ottenby, Öland, **Sweden**	08 Apr 1998	On spring migration
1st-year M	29 Oct 1993	Thisted, Jylland, **Denmark**	16 May 1997 & 05 May 1998	In breeding area
1st-year M	26 Oct 1997	Wassenaar Meijendel Sparregat, Zuid-Holland, **The Netherlands**	19 Oct 2004	On autumn migration
Adult F	30 Oct 1997	Oost Vlaanderen, **Belgium**	06 Nov 1998	On autumn migration
1st-year F	24 Oct 1999	Uley Bury, Gloucestershire	22 Dec 2001	In wintering area
Adult F	29 Oct 2001	Cound, Shropshire	16 Dec 2001	In wintering area
1st-year F	01 Nov 2001	Muddiford, North Devon	04 Jan 2002	In wintering area
1st-year M	21 Oct 2002	Tavistock, South Devon	13 Mar 2004	On spring migration
1st-year F	22 Oct 2002	Borlange, Kopparberg, **Sweden**	07 Aug 2003	In breeding area
1st-year M	22 Oct 2002	Bideford, North Devon	15 Mar 2003	On spring migration

(b) Chaffinches ringed elsewhere and controlled on Lundy

Age/sex	Date ringed	Place ringed	Date controlled on Lundy	Speculation about date/place of ringing
Full-grown F	04 Apr 1988	Hartland Point, North Devon	08 Oct 1989	On spring migration
Adult M	23 Apr 1991	Hartland Point, North Devon	28 Oct 1991	On spring migration
1st-year F	26 Sep 2005	Rybachiy, Zelenogradskiy District, Kaliningrad, **Russian Federation**	27 Oct 2005	On autumn migration

Brambling *Fringilla montifringilla*

Uncommon spring migrant; annual autumn migrant in variable numbers; occasional in winter.

The Chaffinch flocks that pour through Lundy in autumn are often accompanied by much smaller numbers of Bramblings that can be picked out when seen from above or the side by their white rumps. More often than not, though, it is the nasal flight call that gives them away. Like other migrating finches, Bramblings sometimes drop into the trees in Millcombe or stop to feed on the ground, perhaps drawn to seed put out by visiting birdwatchers. Numbers vary greatly from year to year, as they do nationally, reflecting this species' nomadic tendency to winter wherever beechmast crops are heaviest.

While there was a handful of apparently blank autumns between 1960 and 1970, Bramblings are best regarded as annual autumn migrants on Lundy, occurring between late September (earliest: two on 25 September 1978) and the beginning of December, with a marked peak between mid-October and mid-November. The highest daily counts are: 100 on 30 October 1980, 200+ on 15 & 18 November 1972, 206 on 25 October 1955, 340 on 17 November 1973 and an exceptional 510 on 25 October of the same year.[191] Between 1981 and 2006, counts of 50 or more occurred in just four years: 1988 (51 on 26 October), 1991 (56 on 23 October[192]), 1992 (56 on 30 October) and 2003 (50 on 27 & 28 October).

Autumn migration continues well into November or even early December and it is sometimes difficult to distinguish late migrants from wintering birds. However, small numbers have been seen occasionally between mid-December and early March (when spring passage commences). For example, up to five were seen during a cold spell in late January 1952, six on 5 January and seven on 14 February 1976, and three from 19 to 21 February 1995. Most other winter sightings have involved ones and twos.

Very small numbers occur in spring, with reports in two out of three years on average since LFS recording began in 1947 (to the end of 2006). Most are seen in March and April, but there have been May records in three years: one on 1 May 1972, with a female present 20 to 29 May that year; one from 28 April to 5 May 1976, heard singing on 2 May;[193] and two on 5 May 1994, with a male seen until 23 May. Most spring sightings are of one to three birds, but five were present on 17 March 1972, six on 9 April 1968 and 15 on 2 April 1998.

Historical information is scanty: Brambling was listed by Chanter (1871) and Parfitt (1876) as an "autumn and winter visitant", while Perry (1940) noted spring migrants from 27 to 31 March 1939.

A total of 131 Bramblings had been ringed on Lundy by the end of 2006, but there are no controls or recoveries involving the island.

Serin *Serinus serinus* [European Serin]

Nationally scarce migrant.

Breeds widely in continental Europe. Partly migratory, with wintering grounds around the Mediterranean basin. 1,560 records for Britain 1958–2003, with an average of 54 per year 2000–2003. Considered by the BBRC until the end of 1982.

The first dated Serin record for Lundy was of a group of four birds watched at close range on 21 April 1943 (F.W. Gade, reported by Davis 1954a). There have since been five authenticated LFS records:[194]

1956 28 Jul to 24 Oct – a female.
1975 3 Nov – one.
1978 3 May – a singing male in Millcombe.
1994 29 & 30 Nov, 1 & 5 Dec – a male in Bull's Paradise.
2005 26 Apr – two, including one adult male, feeding with Linnets on the Upper East Side Path near Quarter Wall.

Serin

252

Greenfinch *Carduelis chloris* [European Greenfinch]

Uncommon spring migrant in small numbers; common autumn migrant; occasional visitor in summer and winter; has bred in three years.

Although Greenfinches have been recorded on Lundy in every month, and have been present on the island in June, July and August in some years, breeding has been confirmed in only three years – and only once since LFS records began in 1947. Listed by Chanter (1871) and Parfitt (1876) as a "summer visitant", Felix Gade recorded single pairs breeding in 1934 and 1938 (reported by Davis 1954a) and a pair that arrived in April 1985 was seen feeding young on 27 June. It seems likely that an adult and two juveniles seen on 29 July 1995 had arrived from the mainland, since prior to this date single birds were seen on only two days in early June.

Spring passage is slight, the first migrants arriving in early March in some years, though most movements occur in late April and early May. Numbers are small, usually fewer than 10, with 20 on 25 March 1978 the only recorded instance of a double-digit count.[195]

In autumn, Greenfinches are regular migrants, usually in small numbers, from late September or early October to late November, with occasional records in early December. In the first 26 years of LFS recording from 1947, a daily total of more than 20 birds was recorded in only one year (about 25 on 10 & 11 Nov 1952). The species was seen more frequently from 1973 onwards, with a marked diurnal passage in the second half of October and early November, peaking towards the end of October. Counts of 100 or more birds have been recorded in six years (to the end of 2006), with the peaks being 210 on 24 October 1973 and 250 on the same day the following year. Since the last three-figure count (200 on 1 October 1990), maximum daily numbers have fluctuated between five (15 October 1993) and 87 (13 November 2002).

There are midwinter records for 19 LFS years, usually involving between one and three birds, the highest number being six on 21 December 1976.

By the end of 2006, 547 Greenfinches had been ringed on Lundy, with six controls and recoveries of these birds – see table (a). In addition, two birds ringed elsewhere have been controlled on the island – see table (b). While three Lundy-ringed birds were subsequently controlled or recovered well to the east on the British mainland, one Norfolk-ringed bird moved in the opposite direction. Ringing studies have shown that most British Greenfinches – especially those in south-west England – spend their entire lives close to the place of hatching, moving less than 20 kilometres. Some, however, particularly females, make seasonal movements, returning to their natal area or previous breeding area in the

(a) Greenfinches ringed on Lundy and controlled or recovered elsewhere

Age/sex	Date ringed on Lundy	Place found	Date controlled or recovered	Speculation about date/place of finding
Full-grown F	27 Oct 1981	High Wycombe, Buckinghamshire	02 Apr 1984	On spring migration
1st-year F	17 Oct 1989	Littlehampton, Sussex	10 Apr 1990	On spring migration
1st-year F	30 Oct 1992	Mullock, near Marloes, Dyfed	13 Dec 1992	In wintering area
1st-year M	28 Oct 1997	Chelworth, Wiltshire	30 Apr 1998	In breeding area
Full-grown M	31 Oct 1997	Holy Vale, St Mary's, Isles of Scilly	30 Mar 1999	On spring migration
1st-year F	25 Oct 1999	Stibb, Bude, Cornwall	04 Nov 1999	On autumn migration

(b) Greenfinches ringed elsewhere and controlled on Lundy

Age/sex	Date ringed	Place ringed	Date controlled on Lundy	Speculation about date/place of ringing
1st-year F	16 Oct 1994	Bardsey Island, Gwynedd	26 Oct 1994	On autumn migration
Juvenile M	20 Jul 1997	Hillborough, Norfolk	30 Oct 1997	Juvenile dispersal

following spring. Such movements are thought to be triggered by high breeding density or food shortages. In addition, variable numbers of Greenfinches from the near continent and Norway winter in Britain (Wernham *et al.* 2002). All of the ringing movements involving Lundy have been within southern Britain and seem most likely to relate to British breeding birds, though continental migrants probably pass through the island from time to time.

Goldfinch

Goldfinch *Carduelis carduelis* [European Goldfinch]

Breeds occasionally; common spring and autumn migrant; irregular in summer and winter.

Goldfinches have been seen on Lundy in every month, especially April, May and October, their tinkling calls often drawing attention to them before they are seen. Millcombe and the well-vegetated east sidelands are their favoured areas, where they feed on the plentiful supply of seeds.

Chanter (1871) and Parfitt (1876) listed Goldfinch as a "summer visitant", Parfitt adding "occasional breeder". Ross & Rousham (1909) reported "one family" in 1908 and Cummings (1909) recorded one pair in 1909. Loyd (1925) stated that in 1922 "a pair successfully reared their brood in an elder-bush in the south-east combe". The only other pre-LFS reference to breeding was a pair reported by F.W. Gade in 1928 (Davis 1954a). Since then Goldfinches have nested or are thought to have nested in at least 10 LFS years: 1959, 1964, 1974, 1989, 1996, 2001, 2002 and 2005 to 2007. The only year in which more than one pair may have bred was 1959 when, in addition to a confirmed successful pair, a second pair was found feeding young in Gannets' Combe – though the inference in the 1959/60 *LFS Annual Report* is that this pair had not necessarily nested on the island.

During migration periods, parties of Goldfinches can be encountered anywhere along the East Side and sometimes in the more sheltered parts of the South End, such as around the Castle. Small movements occur in February and March in some years, but the main spring passage occurs in April and May. Numbers are usually in single figures, sometimes reaching between 10 and 20. Higher counts of between 25 and a peak of 60 birds (on 18 April 1972) have been recorded only seven times, in six different years to the end of 2006.

Odd birds are sometimes encountered during summer in years in which breeding is not proven, and while a few migrants may be seen in September, autumn passage occurs mainly in October and November, peaking in the second half of October. Although more numerous than in spring, autumn Goldfinch counts in excess of 20 birds have occurred in only 15 LFS years; 50 on 22 October 1968 being the autumn record until 70 were counted on 17 October 2002, followed by 54 on 28 October 2003. These figures were dwarfed, however, by unprecedented numbers migrating through the island in October 2005: 50 or more were recorded on 18 days, and over 100 on 10 days, while the two highest counts were 300 on 15 October and 450 on 12 October.

There are occasional records of winter visitors, most involving single birds, the maximum being just 10 on 30 January 1979.

By the end of 2006, 557 Goldfinches had been ringed on Lundy, generating three recoveries, all in Devon and Cornwall. A second-year bird was ringed on 6 May 1992 and found dead at Lee Mill, Plymouth, Devon, on 8 June 1994. Given that the length of time between death and discovery is unknown, it is impossible to determine whether this bird had settled to breed or was still on its northward migration, possibly from France or Iberia, when it died. A first-year male ringed on 26 October 2005 was found dead at St Austell, Cornwall on 18 November the same year, while another first-year male ringed on 14 October 2005 was controlled at Kingsteignton, South Devon on 2 April 2006.

Siskin *Carduelis spinus* [Eurasian Siskin]

Late autumn migrant in greatly varying numbers; very rare in spring; has bred once.

Familiar as late winter and early spring visitors to many garden feeders, Siskins on Lundy are encountered mainly as passage migrants in late autumn. BTO surveys have shown that the breeding range of Siskins in Britain and Ireland has expanded considerably since the 1970s (Baillie *et al.* 2007) and this is reflected in a significant increase in the number of Lundy records since 1972.

The first record for the island was of six birds on 10 December 1929 (F.W. Gade, reported by Davis 1954a). In the first 25 years of LFS recording from 1947 to 1971, Siskins were reported in 14 years. In this period there were spring occurrences in just two years, including the only breeding record: a pair seen between 20 May and 6 August 1952 that bred successfully in Millcombe, raising three young. The only other suggestion of breeding was in 1999 when a pair was present from 29 April to 31 May; both birds were caught and ringed and the female showed a large brood-patch, indicating that breeding may have been attempted.

Since 1972, Siskins have been recorded in every year up to and including 2007. Though still rare in spring, records at this time of year have increased – with sightings in seven of the 10 years 1997–2006. Extreme dates in spring, excluding the years of confirmed and possible breeding, are 15 March (2000) and 30 May (1986). Most sightings involve single birds, with the highest daily count being eight on 5 May 1998.

Autumn Siskin numbers fluctuate considerably from year to year. For example, there were records on only three days in October/November 1995, all of single birds, whereas the following year there were daily records averaging 40 Siskins a day in the second half of October and early November, with a peak of 100 on 19 October. These variations are likely to be closely correlated with availability of tree seeds, the species' main food supply. September sightings were rare until 1984 but occurred in 16 subsequent years to 2006. Peak migration takes place from mid-October to mid-November, with birds present in smaller numbers to the end of November. Spectacular diurnal movements have occurred in some years. The first was in 1959 when, after a gradual build-up of numbers in early October, 200 passed through on 24 October and 250 the next day. Similar movements occurred in 1972 (peaking at 500 birds heading south in parties of up to 50 on 25 October), 1988 (over 300 on 27 October), 1990 (400 on 16 October), 1993 (400 on 10 October), 2002 (500 on 19 October) and 2005 (300 on 16 October). The earliest autumn date is 1 September (1997), but it is difficult to assign a latest date because of the overlap in true autumn migration and the more casual wanderings of winter visitors. In all, there are December records in just eight LFS years, the latest of these being on 20th 1997.

A lone male on 8 January 1989 constitutes the only Siskin record for that month, and none has been seen in February.

A total of 1,136 Siskins had been ringed on Lundy by the end of 2006, with eight controls or recoveries away from the island – see table (a). There are also two controls of birds ringed elsewhere – see table (b). Ringing has shown that birds of continental origin pass through Britain in large but varying numbers in autumn, joining those from northern Britain as they move south. Some stop off to winter in central and southern Britain, while others move on to southern Europe and even North Africa (Wernham *et al.* 2002). The three movements to/from Scandinavia suggest that these birds originated from breeding populations either in Scandinavia or even further north and east, given that none was captured during the nesting season and all were presumably en route to or from their breeding grounds.

(a) Siskins ringed on Lundy and controlled or recovered elsewhere

Age/sex	Date ringed on Lundy	Place found	Date controlled or recovered	Speculation about date/place of finding
1st-year M	21 Sep 1988	Near Midmar, Aberdeenshire	28 Apr 1989	In breeding area or on spring migration
Adult F	19 Oct 1990	Hallstahammar, Västmanland, central **Sweden**	08 Mar 1992	On spring migration
1st-year M	01 Nov 1996	Awirs, Liège, **Belgium**	30 Mar 1997	On spring migration
Adult F	30 Oct 1997	Sandford, Crediton, Mid Devon	27 Dec 1997 & 01 Feb 1998	In wintering area
Adult F	30 Oct 1997	Hono, Västra Götaland, southern **Sweden**	05 Feb 1999	On spring migration
1st-year M	30 Oct 2001	Thorpe St Andrew, Norwich, Norfolk	19 Feb 2004	On spring migration
Adult F	20 Oct 2002	Matlock, Derbyshire	03 Feb 2003	On spring migration
1st-year M	25 Oct 2005	Chestfield, Whitstable, Kent	02 Apr 2006	On spring migration

(b) Siskins ringed elsewhere and controlled on Lundy

Age/sex	Date ringed	Place ringed	Date controlled on Lundy	Speculation about date/place of ringing
2nd-year F	06 Apr 1994	Wash Common, Newbury, Berkshire	29 Oct 1997	On spring migration
1st-year F	30 Oct 1995	Farsund, Vest-Agder, south-west **Norway**	01 Nov 1996	On autumn migration

Linnet *Carduelis cannabina*   [Common Linnet]

Common breeder; irregular spring and autumn migrant, more numerous in autumn; occasional in winter.

The constant twittering song and flight calls of Linnets are some of Lundy's most evocative sounds. Their cheerful presence, whether in pairs of flocks, can be encountered almost anywhere on the island's plateau or sidelands, particularly between April and September.

Chanter (1871) and Parfitt (1876) listed Linnet as "resident all the year", Parfitt adding "and breed there". Loyd (1925) recorded this species as breeding and "very numerous, particularly in the south-eastern part of the island". Wynne-Edwards & Harrisson (1932) reported 38 pairs breeding in 1930, while Perry (1940) recorded only six pairs in 1939.

Assessing the size of the breeding population is fraught with difficulty. Not only is it often hard to separate migrants from breeders, but breeding pairs frequently wander well away from nest sites when collecting nesting material. Consequently it is perhaps the most severely under-recorded of all the island's nesting birds. Between the start of LFS recording in 1947 and 1999, estimates of population size were made in just six years: 1952 (20 pairs), 1953 (20 pairs), 1962 (20–25 pairs), 1972 (at least 40 pairs, many of which raised more than one brood), 1973 (30 pairs) and 1985 (at least 11 pairs). More recently, counts were carried out in 2000 (when three separate surveys were made) and 2004. In May 2000, Davis & Jones (unpublished) located up to 18 pairs, while a month later Parsons (2002) mapped a minimum of 16 territories in roughly the same areas, most on the East Side between Millcombe/St John's Valley and Halfway Wall Bay. However, the observers in both surveys considered these totals to be unrepresentative of the population as a whole. The difficulty in assessing the population accurately is clearly demonstrated by the results obtained by Lock, also in May 2000. Basing counts on singing males and by halving flock sizes, an unlikely figure of 106 pairs was reached, the population concentrated in the southern half of the island and strongly associated with gorse clumps (Lock 2001). The 2004 survey recorded 50 pairs (Lock 2004). In noting the marked reduction since 2000, Lock also highlighted the difficulties in accurately separating passage migrants from apparent breeders.

Linnets

Breeding birds arrive in late March and April and depart in September or October. The main spring migration commences in mid to late March and continues through April and early May. Numbers of migrants are generally small, mixing with resident birds to produce counts of 100 or more in nine years up to and including spring 2007, the highest of these being 200 on 11 & 14 April 1961 and 1 May 1998.[196] Post-breeding flocks build up in July and are augmented by migrants during August, numbers reaching a few hundred in some years (e.g. 350 on 29 August 1994). Given that the Linnet's breeding season extends from April to the end of August, the difficulty of distinguishing between island-breeding birds and passage migrants is encountered in both migration seasons.

The main autumn movements get under way in late August, typically peaking in September and falling away in October, though the highest counts occur in October in some years. Stragglers pass through in November and very few if any Linnets at all are seen in December. Peak autumn numbers vary between 50 and a few hundred, with the maxima to date (up to and including 2006) being: 400 on 5 September 1951 and 22 & 23 September 2002, and an exceptional 2,000 on 24 October 1974 during a large movement of finches.

Small numbers occasionally visit the island in winter, with highs of about 40 during a cold snap on 26 & 27 January 1952 and 35 on 22 January 1973.

A total of 1,487 Linnets had been ringed on Lundy by the end of 2006, with two subsequent controls/recoveries – see table (a). There is also one control on Lundy of a bird ringed elsewhere – see table (b). British and Irish Linnets are partial migrants, some remaining in winter, while others move southwards to western France, central Spain or Morocco (Wernham *et al.* 2002). Since none of the birds controlled or recovered is known to have hatched on Lundy, it is impossible to tell whether Lundy-bred birds remain in Britain or move further afield in autumn and winter.

(a) Linnets ringed on Lundy and controlled or recovered elsewhere

Age/sex	Date ringed on Lundy	Place found	Date controlled or recovered	Speculation about date/place of finding
Adult	16 May 1951	Nr San Sebastian, Basque Country, northern **Spain**	29 Oct 1951	On autumn migration
1st-year	20 Sep 1976	St Agnes, Isles of Scilly	20 Apr 1977	On spring migration

(b) Linnets ringed elsewhere and controlled on Lundy

Age/sex	Date ringed	Place ringed	Date controlled on Lundy	Speculation about date/place of ringing
1st-year	13 Sep 1960	Isles of Scilly	21 Oct 1960	On autumn migration

Twite *Carduelis flavirostris*

Lundy vagrant.

"Mountain Linnet or Twite" was listed by Chanter (1871) and Parfitt (1876) as an "autumn and winter visitant". The first twentieth century record was of a flock of six seen in spring 1937 (F.W. Gade, reported by Davis 1954a). There are 20 LFS records for 13 years but only six occurrences in the last 25 years (to the end of 2006). Most have involved one or two birds but four were seen together on two occasions, and there was a remarkable series of sightings in the autumn and early winter of 1972:

1952	13 Oct – two near Pondsbury.
1953	12 & 13 Feb – one.
1954	5 Jun – a male.
1958	6 May – a female near Quarter Wall Pond.
1972	25 Oct – one.
	28 Oct – four.
	1, 9 & 14 Nov – singles.
	18 Nov – two.
	12 Dec – one.
	14 Dec – two.
1973	26 Oct – two flew south.
	29 Oct – one.
1974	23 Oct – one near Tibbett's.
1981	26 Oct – four.
1990	2 & 3 Sep – one in the village.
	3 Oct – one on the Terrace.
1991	6 Oct – one on the Airfield.
2001	2 Nov – one with Chaffinches on Ackland's Moor and the Airfield.
2002	16 Nov – one flew north along the West Side, calling.
2003	28 Oct – one near the Castle.

It seems likely that Twites occurring on Lundy are from the Scottish and/or Pennines breeding populations of the race *C. f. pipilans* which migrate to winter in coastal areas, mainly in eastern England. Birds of the nominate race *C. f. flavirostris* breeding in western and northern Norway also winter in south-east England (Wernham *et al.* 2002). Twites are thought to be declining nationally and are 'red-listed' (of high conservation concern). This presumably explains the apparent decrease in records from Lundy.

Common Redpoll (Mealy Redpoll) *Carduelis flammea*

Lundy vagrant.

Since 2001 the BOU has recognised three redpoll species as belonging to *The British List*: Common Redpoll (*C. flammea*), Lesser Redpoll (*C. cabaret*) and Arctic Redpoll (*C. hornemanni*). Common and Lesser Redpoll were previously treated as distinct races of a single species. To complicate things further, three races of Common Redpoll are currently recognised by the BOU: *C. f. flammea* (sometimes called 'Mealy Redpoll'), *C. f. rostrata* and *C. f. islandica* (BOURC 2000). The first is a regular passage migrant and winter visitor from continental Europe, particularly to northern and eastern Britain, while *rostrata* and *islandica*, breeding in Greenland and Iceland respectively, are scarce passage migrants (Wernham *et al.* 2002). Some authors recognise only two races, not distinguishing between *rostrata* and *islandica*, but there is general agreement that, with care, individuals of *rostrata* and/or *islandica* can be separated from *flammea* in the field as well as in the hand.

Diamond (2003) noted that: "All redpolls critically examined on Lundy prior to 1980 were found to be of the form *cabaret* (Dymond 1980) and the majority of those examined since have also been of this form, now recognised as a separate species – Lesser Redpoll. However, in recent years the form *rostrata/islandica* of Common Redpoll has been reported on three occasions. The recognition of Lesser and Common Redpolls as separate species means that these records constitute a new species for the Island and most probably for Devon". The three occurrences listed by Diamond are given below.

While there have been no subsequent records to the end of 2006, observers are urged to scrutinise closely any redpoll seen on Lundy so that the species' status can be more fully assessed in future.

1988 30 Sep – one trapped and ringed.[197]

1995 11 to 13 Oct – one trapped in Millcombe, ringed and photographed on 11th, with an additional bird, which appeared similar, observed in the field on 13th.[198]

1997 11 & 12 Oct – one watched at Quarter Wall on 11th, and in the village/Millcombe area and as far as Benjamin's Chair on 12th.

Two Common Redpolls had been ringed on Lundy by the end of 2006, but there are no controls or recoveries involving the island.

Lesser Redpoll *Carduelis cabaret*

Uncommon spring and autumn migrant in variable numbers, but more frequent than formerly; rare in winter; two recent summer records.

Redpolls can be elusive on Lundy. While the trilling flight call is distinctive, and most often to be heard in and around Millcombe, the bird itself, if visible at all, is often little more than a bouncing speck disappearing over the tree tops. When on the ground, the birds feed unobtrusively, often with other finches and are well camouflaged and easily overlooked. The edge of St Helen's Field, where it adjoins the top of Millcombe, seems to be a favoured feeding area, especially when sheltered from the prevailing wind.

Since 2000 the BOU has recognised three distinct redpoll species as belonging to *The British List*: Arctic Redpoll (*C. hornemanni*), Lesser Redpoll (*C. cabaret*) and Common Redpoll (*C. flammea*), the latter two of which were previously treated as races of a single species (BOURC 2000). Lesser Redpoll breeds widely in the UK, including Devon, and of those redpolls studied closely on Lundy the vast majority have been identified as this species (Dymond 1980; Diamond 2003). With the exception of the three known occurrences of Common Redpoll, all Lundy redpolls are therefore treated in this account as Lesser Redpolls.

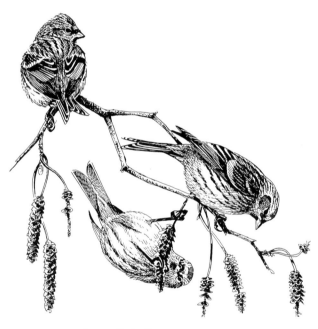

Lesser Redpolls

Boyd (1950) quoted the Heaven Diaries as stating that "many Redpoles" occurred on 30 December 1874 and Dymond (1980) reported F.W. Gade as having seen at least four for a few days from 10 June 1928 and nine on 22 April 1938. From the beginning of regular LFS recording in 1947 until 1970, Lesser Redpolls were very scarce, with autumn records in nine years (maximum seven birds) and spring records in seven years (maximum two). Since 1971 (to the end of 2006), sightings have been almost annual (only 1974, 1983 and 1993 were blank), which is perhaps surprising given that the species' UK breeding population has shown a significant decline over the last 30 years or so (Eaton *et al.* 2006) and is now 'amber-listed' (of medium conservation concern). Perhaps Lundy is reflecting more local increases that buck the national trend; *The New Atlas of Breeding Birds in Britain and Ireland: 1988–1991*

(Gibbons *et al.* 1993) shows a distinct gain in range in West Wales since the time of the first national atlas in 1968–1972 and this might have driven the Lundy increase.

Whatever the explanation, the species is currently a scarce but regular migrant in both spring and autumn, though numbers vary considerably from year to year. Spring records have fallen between 10 March (1958) and 30 June (1996),[199] though most are in late April and May, with the highest count being eight on 9 May 1996. Autumn migrants pass through mainly from September (earliest: 11 & 12 August 2003) to November, exceptionally into December (latest: three on 13 & 15 and one on 16 December 1975), with a peak in October and early November. The highest counts are 13 on 19 October 2002 and 25 on 9 October 1997. Records of more than five in a day remain highly unusual in both spring and autumn.

There are no January or February sightings and, until very recently, there had been no occurrences in July or August either. That changed in 2002 when up to three birds were seen on eight days in July, followed by three, including a juvenile, on 18 August, and one bird from 25 to 27 August. It is tempting to conclude that a pair must have bred, but there is no conclusive proof of this. Single Lesser Redpolls were also recorded on 11 & 12 August 2003 and 29 August 2006.

Forty-two Lesser Redpolls had been ringed on Lundy by the end of 2006, but there are no controls or recoveries of these birds away from the island. A first-year bird ringed at Chobham Common, Surrey, on 13 November 2004 was controlled on Lundy on 25 April 2005, presumably returning to its breeding area.

Two-barred Crossbill *Loxia leucoptera*

British vagrant.

Breeds in eastern Finland, northern Russia and North America. Mainly sedentary but sometimes considerable movements in response to food shortages, Eurasian birds moving south and west. 112 records for Britain 1950–2005.

There is one Lundy record of a single bird:

1972 3 Aug – an immature, first seen flying with two Crossbills (*L. curvirostra*), was present in Millcombe for about 10 minutes. In all, 14 Crossbills arrived on the same day.

Crossbill *Loxia curvirostra*   [Red Crossbill]

Rare summer and autumn migrant, occurring highly irregularly, but in large numbers during 'invasion' years.

Crossbills are well known for undertaking dispersive post-breeding movements in search of good feeding areas. When numbers are high and food resources scarce, these movements can be on a very large scale and over considerable distances and are known as 'irruptions' or 'invasions'. It is during such events that Crossbills are most likely to reach Lundy, which is clearly far from ideal habitat, having no extensive areas of fruiting conifers on which the birds can feed. During invasion years, Crossbills may arrive in the UK from as far afield as Russia and Fennoscandia (Wernham *et al.* 2002).

Chanter (1871) and Parfitt (1876) listed this species as an "occasional visitant", while D'Urban & Mathew (1895) stated: "In November 1869 Crossbills and Snow Buntings mixed together were seen flying across Lundy Island, and some of both were shot." One was seen at Gannets' Combe on 30 August 1927 (T.G. Longstaff, reported by Harrisson 1932); one was killed at the end of August 1930 (F.W. Gade, reported by Harrisson 1932); and Hendy (1933) wrote: "On 4th September [1930] I saw a pair of Crossbills. A hen perched on a dead bush in Millcombe, only a few yards away from me, and there was a cock in resplendent plumage on a tree below. These birds fed voraciously upon dead thistle-heads, which they carried to branches and devoured there." Davis (1954a) also referred to records in 1935 and "1942(?)", most likely sightings by F.W. Gade, but no details were given.

Since LFS recording began in 1947 there have been occurrences in 22 years (to the end of 2006). All records have been within the period 27 May (two females on this date in 1991) to 8 November (10 flying north, 1972), with a marked peak in July and, to a lesser extent, August.

The most significant movements (those involving peak counts of 20 or more birds in a day) were:

1958   Maximum 30 on 11 Jul; first and last dates: 2 & 21 Jul.
1959   Maximum 35 on 30 Jul; first and last dates: 4 Jul & 13 Oct.
1962   Maximum 25 on 12 & 13 Jul; first and last dates: 1 & 31 Jul.
1972   Maximum 25 on 18 to 20 Jul; first and last dates: 26 Jun and 8 Nov.
1997   Maximum 25 on 19 Jul; first and last dates: 22 Jun and 14 Oct.
2002   Maximum 36 on 28 Aug; first and last dates: 10 Aug and 2 Sep.

The 1958 *LFS Annual Report* indicates that on 11 July "there were about four red males in this flock, the majority being immatures", while the report for 1959 states that "the first arrivals were exhausted and easy to catch", and in 1972 "immatures were about twice as numerous as adults".

1997 was also a Crossbill invasion year in the Isles of Scilly, where the first individual was recorded on 23 June "somewhat earlier than normal" (Robinson 2003). This coincides remarkably well with the start of that year's influx to Lundy.

Other years in which Crossbills have reached Lundy (maximum counts in brackets) are: 1949 (three on 13 Aug), 1953 (15 from 28 to 30 Jun), 1956 (10 on 6 Sep), 1960 (one on 13 & 19 Oct), 1963 (seven on 27 Jul), 1966 (11 on 5 & 6 Jul), 1981 (one on 5 Oct), 1984 (one on 8 Sep), 1985 (six on 10 Jul), 1990 (14 on 2 Jul), 1991 (two from 27 May to 12 Jun), 1992 (two on 29 Oct), 1993 (13 on 4 Oct), 2004 (10 on 4 Jul) and 2005 (eight on 20 Jul).

By the end of 2006, 38 Crossbills had been ringed on Lundy, but there are no controls or recoveries involving the island.

Common Rosefinch and Chaffinch (behind)

Common Rosefinch (Scarlet Rosefinch) *Carpodacus erythrinus*

Nationally scarce migrant.

3,338 records for Britain 1958–2003. Numbers have increased dramatically from an average of 10 per year 1958–1969 to 144 per year 2000–2003, and sporadic breeding has occurred in England and Scotland. Nationally, peak spring passage is in late May and peak autumn passage in mid-September. Considered by the BBRC until the end of 1982. Formerly also known as Scarlet Grosbeak.

The first Lundy record (also the first for Devon) was not until 1959 when a female or first-winter bird was trapped and ringed on 10 September, remaining on the island until 13th. There were 10 records (three spring and seven autumn) in the period covered by Dymond (1980) from 1959 up to and including 1978. Since then the number of occurrences has grown markedly, in line with the national trend, with records for all except four years during the period 1979 to 2006 (only 1981, 1993, 2002 and 2006 were blank) and it would now be fair to describe Scarlet Rosefinch (to use its more familiar name) as an uncommon but regular migrant in autumn, primarily in September and October.

Spring occurrences, mainly in late May and June, have also increased but remain irregular, with none since 1999.[200] There have been four singing males in June, while pairs were seen in 1984, 1990 and 1992. In 1984 a male in breeding plumage was in full song from 4 to 13 June and seen together with a female on 11 June.[201] The female was not seen subsequently but the male was seen regularly until 12 July. The pair had been noted flying north up the island and the male was seen to do so regularly, giving rise to thoughts of a possible nesting attempt.[202] In 1990 a singing male present on the Terrace from 1 to 9 June was joined by a female from 4 June (also seen daily until 9th), but neither bird was observed thereafter. In 1992 a pair present from 14 to 27 June got as far as building a nest near Brambles. Whether they laid eggs or not was unclear since observers kept well away to avoid disturbance. However, if laying did occur, the eggs failed to hatch. There have been no further breeding attempts (up to and including 2007).

The earliest and latest dates are 10 May (1984) and 26 October (1988); there is one July record and two for August. The total number of individuals involved is estimated at about 70 (to the end of 2006), the great majority of sightings involving single birds, with no more than two being recorded in a day.

The following is a complete list of records for the 10 years 1997–2006 (2002 and 2006 were blank):

1997 4 Jun – a singing male in Millcombe.
3 Oct – two in Millcombe and St Helen's Copse; one remained until 12 Oct and was trapped and ringed on 8th.
1998 8 Aug – a female or immature male trapped and ringed in St John's Valley.
1999 4 Jun – a singing male in Millcombe.
25 Sep – one in Millcombe.
25 Oct – one in Millcombe.[203]
2000 7 Oct – two in Millcombe.
11 to 13 Oct – one (possibly one of the birds seen on 7th) at Quarry Pond and Quarter Wall Copse.
2001 8 Sep – a female or first-year bird perched on rhododendrons south of the Terrace.
9 to 13 Oct – one, probably a first-year bird, in Millcombe.
26 Oct – a first-year bird in Millcombe, trapped and ringed.
2003 8 & 9 Sep – one in the village area.
18 to 27 Sep – one trapped and ringed on 18th remained in the Millcombe area.
2004 3 Oct – one in Millcombe.
2005 29 Sep – a first-year bird in Millcombe, joined by a second on 2 Oct; both were trapped and ringed (on 3 & 4 Oct) but not seen subsequently.
9 Oct – an unringed bird.

Nineteen Scarlet Rosefinches had been ringed by the end of 2006, but there are no controls or recoveries involving the island.

Bullfinch *Pyrrhula pyrrhula*   [Eurasian Bullfinch]

Rare spring migrant and very rare autumn migrant; recent evidence of possible breeding; one winter record.

Bullfinches have been recorded in 40 LFS years (1947 to 2006), with spring sightings in 32 years and autumn records in 20 years. This species was listed by Chanter (1871) and Parfitt (1876) as an "occasional visitant", while Davis (1954a) reported that a pair was seen by F.W. Gade on 2 May 1931. There were only two further records until 1957, since when occurrences have been rather more regular. Perhaps the paucity of Bullfinches before this date is linked with their historical persecution as pests of fruit trees.

Spring records fall between 7 March (a pair on this date in 1977) and 16 June (a single bird in 1973), with a distinct peak in April. The highest daily counts are five on 7 April 1987 and 31 March 1998, and six on 16 April 1977, but ones and twos are far more typical. In 2003 a female was seen sporadically from 17 April to 11 June, and a male was present on 20 May. In 2004 one was reported on 13 April, a female with a well-developed brood patch was ringed on 15 May and a male was seen on 18 May. Bullfinches are notoriously discreet when breeding and in spite of the absence of additional sightings it appears possible that Bullfinches may have nested in 2004 and perhaps also in 2003.

Autumn occurrences have been less frequent and have involved far fewer birds with never more than two in a day. Extreme dates are 1 September (1957) and 1 December (1987) with a peak at the end of October and the first half of November. Sightings that could be classed as winter records have occurred only once, in 1997, when one was present on 10 December, followed by two on 18th and one on 21st. There are no January or February records.

Twenty-two Bullfinches had been ringed on Lundy by the end of 2006, but there are no controls or recoveries involving the island. British breeding Bullfinches of the race *P. p. pileata* are non-migratory, whereas northern European populations of the race *P. p. pyrrhula* are partially migratory and irruptive (Wernham *et al.* 2002). Newton *et al.* (2006) concluded that the 2004 invasion of northern Bullfinches into parts of western Europe – the largest such movement on record – originated from a wide area of northern Europe into Russia. The Bullfinches recorded on Lundy to date all appear to have been dispersing individuals of the British race, but the occasional occurrence of continental migrants can't be excluded. Careful attention should be paid to the plumage and calls of Bullfinches seen on Lundy in future.

Hawfinch Coccothraustes coccothraustes

Rare autumn migrant and very rare spring migrant.

"Hawfinch or Grosbeak" was listed by Chanter (1871) and Parfitt (1876) as an "occasional visitant". Three barely fledged juveniles were seen in the summer of 1927 by F.W. Gade and there is one other unconfirmed and undated report of breeding from many years ago (Ross & Rousham 1909).

Since LFS recording began in 1947, migrant Hawfinches have been recorded in 22 years (to the end of 2006). There have been sightings in all months except February, though with a significant peak in October (about a dozen records involving around 30 individuals) and a much smaller peak in May (six records). Since 1985 all except two sightings have fallen within these two months. Most records are of single birds, though there have been several instances of two or more together, notably during the remarkable influx of October 1988 when Hawfinches were seen on seven days between 18th and 30th, including a

Hawfinch

maximum of nine on 25th. A slightly smaller influx occurred in October 2005 when birds were present on 10 days (see details overleaf). The highest number seen on any one day in that year was four. The maximum count has not exceeded two in any other month.

Outside the peak months of May and October there have been scattered records, all but one of single birds:

Jan	8th 1979.	**Jul**	3rd, 4th & 6th 1951.
Mar	25th 1983.	**Aug**	22nd to 24th 1949; 18th 1972; 25th 1978.
Apr	7th 1958; 29th 1992.	**Sep**	30th 1949.
Jun	10th, 12th (two) & 13th 1949;	**Nov**	24th 1952; 17th 1953; 3rd & 8th 1978; 4th 2001.
	19th & 28th 1951.	**Dec**	18th 1978.

The following is a complete list of records for the 10 years 1997–2006:

1997 21 May – one.

2000 7 May – one in St John's Valley, Millcombe and around the village.

2001 4 to 28 May – a female seen regularly in Millcombe and around the village, with a male also present in Millcombe on 16th.

4 Nov – one in Millcombe.

2005 10 to 29 Oct – one on 10th, four on 15th, one on 16th, three daily from 17th to 21st, and singles on 22nd and 29th. The measurements of one that was caught and ringed suggested it was of continental origin.

Three Hawfinches had been ringed on Lundy by the end of 2006, but there are no controls or recoveries involving the island.

Wernham *et al.* (2002) stated: "…there are major gaps in our knowledge of Hawfinch movements. It is not known whether birds from any of the British breeding concentrations perform regular seasonal migrations, or how much dispersal may occur between them. While connections with the Continent have been established by ringing, the origins, frequency and scale of continental immigrations are not known, nor whether it is these rather than British birds that occur sporadically in Ireland and on Scilly." This concluding remark clearly applies equally to Lundy.

Yellow-rumped Warbler (Myrtle Warbler) *Dendroica coronata*

British vagrant.

Breeds across much of North America, migrating to wintering grounds from the southern USA to the West Indies. 17 records for Britain 1950–2005.

There is one Lundy record of a single bird in late autumn, only the second for Britain, five years after the first at Newton St Cyres, near Exeter, Devon:

1960 5 to 14 Nov – a first-year bird, found in Millcombe gardens, was mist-netted, ringed and photographed on 8 Nov.

Writing in *British Birds*, LFS warden Bill Workman noted:

"It was first seen at 11.00 a.m. on the 5th in Millcombe gardens. Attention was attracted to it by its bright yellow rump, which was visible in flight. Excellent views were then obtained, at distances down to four yards, as the bird fed on the ground and from an ivy-covered wall where it caught flies in a very flycatcher-like manner" (Workman 1961).

Blackpoll Warbler *Dendroica striata*

British vagrant.

Breeds in north-easternmost USA, Alaska and northern Canada, migrating in late summer to wintering grounds in north-west South America. 36 British records 1950–2005.

There is one Lundy record:

1984 10 to 14 Oct – a first-winter bird found in St Helen's Copse was caught and ringed on the last day of its stay; a photograph appears in the 1984 *LFS Annual Report*.[204]

Common Yellowthroat *Geothlypis trichas*

British vagrant.

Breeds in USA, and southern and western Canada. Winter range extends from southern USA south to Panama and West Indies. 8 records for Britain 1950–2005.

There is one Lundy record of a single bird, which was also the first for Britain:

1954 4 Nov – a first-winter male caught in the Terrace trap was kept overnight and ringed and released the following day.

The LFS warden, Barbara Whitaker, and other observers were unable to identify the bird and a full description, together with specimen feathers from various parts of the body, was sent to W.B. Alexander who identified it from skins in the British Museum (Natural History) (Whitaker 1955d). Whitaker wrote in the 1954 *LFS Annual Report*:

> "When the bird was released on the window-sill of the bird room, it frequently flitted its wings, the movement being accompanied by a monosyllabic 'chat' like note. Later it was released in the catching cage of the trap where it immediately skulked in the bramble and grass near the ground, 'chatting' continuously while anyone was near."

Eastern Towhee (Rufous-sided Towhee) *Pipilo erythrophthalmus*

British vagrant.

Breeds in eastern North America, with northern populations moving south, but staying within the breeding range, in winter. Overshooting of the breeding grounds is regular during spring migration in Canada. 1 record for Britain 1950–2005.

There is one Lundy record of a single bird, which was also the first – and so far only – British and Western Palearctic record; one seen in Lincolnshire between September 1975 and January 1976 was thought likely to have been an escaped cage bird (Sharrock & Grant 1982). At the time of writing (mid-2007) the BOURC is reviewing records of several American vagrants in Category A of the *British List*, including Eastern Towhee.

1966   7 to 11 June – an adult female, trapped and ringed in the Manor Farm Hotel (now Old House) garden.[205]

Writing in *British Birds*, then LFS warden Cliff Waller recalled:

> "During the morning of 7th June 1966 I was informed that an unfamiliar bird had been seen by residents in the garden of the Manor Farm Hotel. Miss J. Mundy and I soon located it in a near-by garden much overgrown with shrubs and weeds and bordered by stone walls. Our first impression was of an enormous warbler, the bird's shape and carriage reminding us of a very large Dartford Warbler, even to carrying its tail in the same half-cocked attitude; its bill, however, was noticeably heavy and finch-like. On the ground it behaved more like a thrush, hopping about on long, strong-looking legs, scratching amongst the dead weeds and rummaging noisily under the bushes. The rufous flanks, contrasting with the white belly were most distinctive, and the red eyes were quite striking even from a range of 20 yards. When disturbed it would fly jerkily away and perch on a fence or wall, landing on one occasion near some Chaffinches against which it appeared half as large again, probably due to the very long tail and heavy-looking head" (Waller 1970).

Lapland Bunting *Calcarius lapponicus*   [Lapland Longspur]

Uncommon but regular autumn migrant; rare spring migrant; very rare in winter.

Lapland Bunting is something of a Lundy speciality, having first been recorded on 10 September 1942 (Alexander & Radford 1942) and then in most years since LFS recording began in 1947, and annually from 1970 to 2006. Experienced birdwatchers listen out for the flight call – a dry rattle followed by a short, clear *tchuu* and absolutely characteristic once learnt – that can be encountered just about anywhere on the island from September to November. If not simply flying straight over, birds are most likely to be flushed singly, or in small parties, from rough grassland, particularly St Helen's Field, South West Field, Ackland's Moor and the Airfield, and further north from the heathland around Pondsbury, the rougher areas of Middle Park and the grassland north of Threequarter Wall. They can occasionally be approached closely, especially in calm conditions, and seem to show a fondness for feeding on seeds in vehicle ruts. Somewhat remarkably, given their preference for remote and open areas, seven have been trapped and ringed over the years, but none has ever been recovered or controlled.

Lapland Bunting

Early and late dates in autumn are 31 August[206] (1977) and 29 November (1956), with most seen between mid-September and the end of October, the same overall pattern as found in the Isles of Scilly (Robinson 2003). Numbers vary considerably from year to year and the great majority of sightings involve from one to three birds, though between four and 10 have been recorded from time to time. The highest numbers seen in a day (all instances of more than 10) are: 12 on 9 & 10 October 1956 (part of a wider influx also noted in the Isles of Scilly; Robinson 2003), 14 on 20 & 22 October 1987, 14 on 15 October 1989, and 14 on 8 & 20 October 1993, while an exceptional influx to Britain in the autumn of 1953 resulted in Lundy counts reaching 17 on 5th, 23 on 10th and 33 on 15 September. Davis (1954a) stated that "probably over 100 individuals" were involved in the 1953 arrivals. After a flurry of high counts in the late 1980s and early 1990s, the number of birds recorded appears to have fallen over the last decade or so, and while sightings have remained annual (to the end of 2006), no more than three have been seen in a day since 1994 when six occurred on 22 October.

Lapland Buntings are one of the most abundant Arctic-breeding passerines, occurring from Norway, across Siberia, to Alaska, northern Canada and parts of Greenland (but not Iceland or Svalbard). In western Europe, the species winters in north-west France, Denmark and around the North Sea (including Britain, mainly along the east coast), though the main wintering areas are in North America and south-east Eurasia. There is "strong evidence" that Lapland Buntings arrive in Britain and Ireland from the west, presumably Canada or Greenland, as well as from Scandinavia (Wernham *et al.* 2002) and it therefore seems likely that the regular autumn migration through Lundy relates to the arrival of birds from arctic Canada and/or Greenland. Wernham *et al.* (2002) also reported that Lapland Buntings vacate Greenland from mid-August to late September, that a small passage is recorded in Iceland from mid-September to mid-October, and that there is regular migration through Scilly between mid-September and mid-November, "probably of birds bound for wintering grounds in Brittany". Again, this tallies well with the pattern observed on Lundy and our own observations suggest that autumn arrivals on the island often coincide with periods of north-westerly winds.

Occurrences on Lundy during return migration in spring are much less regular; indeed, prior to 1981 there was just one record of a single bird flying north on 23 April 1972. Between 1981 and 1990 there was a remarkable sequence of six spring occurrences: a male on 13 & 14 May 1981, a female on 24 April 1982, one on 25 April 1984,[207] a female on 29 May & 1 June 1985, a male on the Airfield on 4 & 5 March 1989, and a female at Halfway Wall on 16 April 1990. Since then, however, there have been no further spring sightings (up to and including 2007).

Finally, there are two winter records of single birds: one, coinciding with very cold weather, from 2 to 16 February 1954 and one on 29 December 1981.

Snow Bunting *Plectrophenax nivalis*

Uncommon but regular autumn migrant in small numbers; uncommon spring migrant; rare in midwinter.

Snow Buntings are at home in the Arctic and, not surprisingly, are most often encountered singly or in small parties on the most rugged parts of the plateau, north of Threequarter Wall. They do turn up elsewhere, though, with recent records from Middle Park, the Airfield, South West Field and South

End, including a fine male that spent nine days around the Castle in May 2004, often perching on the castellations. Snow Buntings on Lundy can often be approached extremely closely, showing little or no fear of people and enabling the details of their surprisingly cryptic plumage to be appreciated.

There are spring records for most years, though only very small numbers are involved, mainly in March and April. Late migrants have been seen in May in 10 years, the latest of these being a female on 20 May 1988, with sightings on 17 May in 1969 and 1991.[208] Generally only ones and twos are involved, but five occurred on 20 March 1961 and six on both 17 March 1986 and 3 March 1987.

Snow Buntings are seen annually in autumn, and while passage has commenced as early as 1 September (when three were seen in 1974), it more often gets under way in late September or early October, continuing well into November, sometimes early December. Small groups of three to 10 birds have been recorded frequently, but higher counts are unusual. The biggest daily count by far was 42 on 9 November 1950 and 32 were present on 11 October the same year. Other high counts have been 14 on 25 September 1982, 20 on 30 October 1967 and 26 November 1977, a flock of 24 that stayed from 7 to 20 November 1957, 27 on 22 October 1987 and 28 on 6 October 1999. In some autumns, Snow Buntings are seen on only one or two days, while in other years they may be recorded virtually daily for a period of several weeks.

Occasional records in early December are probably of late migrants, but there have also been sporadic winter sightings between late December and late February. It is rare for these midwinter occurrences to be of more than one or two birds, so eight on 21 December 1995 was exceptional. Four were seen on both 28 December 1982 and 14 December 1996. The maxima for January and February are two and three birds respectively (two on 27 January 1988 and 4 January 1996; three on 4 February 1973).

There is little information on the status of Snow Bunting before LFS recording began in 1947. Chanter (1871) and Parfitt (1876) listed this species as an "autumn and winter visitant". The Heaven Diaries referred to a flock seen on 4 October 1902 and "first Snow Bunting noticed" on 15 October 1904 (Boyd 1950). According to Loyd (1925), "Robert Hall [the North Lighthouse keeper] reports that they occur regularly on migration". Loyd also referred to a mixed flock of Crossbills and Snow Buntings "which flew over Lundy in November 1869, and from which several specimens of both species were shot", going on to note that "in the *Zoologist* of 1858, p. 6015 we find over the name of Rev. M. A. Mathew the account of a female, shot towards the close of May that year on Lundy, in which well-developed eggs were found". N.V. Allen recorded an adult and an immature during an island census between 13 & 22 October 1944 (1944 *Devon Bird Report*).

Only 10 Snow Buntings had been ringed on Lundy by the end of 2006, but there are no controls or recoveries showing movements of these birds away from the island. A colour-ringed Snow Bunting seen on Lundy on 19 November 1988 had been ringed at Corgarff, Aberdeenshire, between 29 January and 16 March the same year. Most if not all Snow Buntings passing through Lundy probably originate in Iceland, Greenland and perhaps arctic Canada (Wernham *et al.* 2002).

Snow Bunting

Black-faced Bunting *Emberiza spodocephala*

British vagrant.

Breeds in central and eastern Asia, migrating to wintering grounds in south and south-east Asia. 5 British records 1950–2005, all since 1994.

There is one Lundy record of a single bird:

2001   12 Oct – one, probably a first-winter male, seen on several occasions in Millcombe and at the top of St John's Valley was only the third record for Britain. (One occurred a few days later on Fair Isle, Shetland, from 20 to 24 Oct 2001.)

Writing in the 2001 *Devon Bird Report*, Richard Patient described how he and Adrian Cooper initially had brief views of the bird at the top of Millcombe before it dropped out of sight. He continued:

> "I headed back to the top of St John's Valley just as the bunting flew over the stone wall, again landing out of sight, so I waited until the others [three more birders] appeared – luckily more or less simultaneously – a few minutes later. The bunting then hopped into view at the base of a stone wall and all five of us managed some 10 minutes constant viewing of the bird in the open as it worked its way along the wall base before flying off. The bird then showed intermittently until early afternoon with a final sighting at 16:00h. Unfortunately there was no sign of it on 13 October, but a small fall of crests…and probably six different Yellow-browed Warblers seen then perhaps give a clue to its origin" (Patient 2001).

Yellowhammer *Emberiza citrinella*

Rare spring and autumn migrant; very rare winter visitor; formerly more numerous and has bred.

During the years of regular LFS recording since 1947, Yellowhammers have never been especially numerous; the maximum daily counts being just five on 18 April 1953 and six on 23 March 1952, and only one has ever been ringed on the island. However, records were certainly more frequent from the 1950s to the 1970s than in recent decades. During most of that period, except for something of a lull between 1966 and 1971, there were several records per year on a virtually annual basis, typically involving from one to three birds in a day. Most sightings were in spring – particularly March and April – with smaller numbers in autumn and occasional midsummer and winter reports. Two pairs were thought to have nested in 1951 and birds were present during the breeding season in 1952, but there has been no subsequent indication of nesting.

Chanter (1871) listed "Yellow Bunting" as "resident all the year", stating it to be "common", and Parfitt (1876) also listed it as a resident breeding bird. Oldham (1932) recorded one "in the Manor House garden" on 1 September 1907. Loyd (1925) stated that some eight pairs bred in 1922, confined to the south-east corner of the island, and that numbers "had increased very considerably" in 1923.

Not only have Yellowhammers long since disappeared from the island as breeding birds, but they have also become rare in general, making any sighting a significant event in itself nowadays. While there have been occurrences in 17 years from 1980 up to and including 2006, with few exceptions these have all involved single birds, with rarely more than one or two records per year. The majority of sightings continue to be in spring, from late February to early June, with rather fewer between September and November. There have been just two winter records: in December 1981 (single birds on 14th & 26th to 30th) and December 2005, the latter involving three birds on 25th – the highest daily count since three on 28 March 1976 – and one on 27th.

The Yellowhammer's scarcity on Lundy reflects its national status as a 'red-listed' species of high conservation concern, the overall UK population having declined by 54% between 1970 and 2005 (Eaton *et al.* 2006). It would be interesting to investigate whether the cessation of breeding as early as 1952 could be linked to changing land use on Lundy.

Cirl Bunting

Cirl Bunting *Emberiza cirlus*

Lundy vagrant.

Although there has been a recent recovery in South Devon (from 118 pairs in 1989 to over 700 pairs in 2003; RSPB estimates) and a re-establishment project is currently under way in Cornwall, the British breeding population crashed to extinction in most areas during the twentieth century. It is therefore unsurprising that there have been no Lundy records since 1951, when a female was seen on 28 September.[209] Prior to this, there were dated records of single birds on 21 September 1948, 23 September 1949 and 12 April 1950. Dymond (1980) reported that F.W. Gade recorded Cirl Bunting as an occasional winter or spring visitor from 1929 to 1944, with four present in November 1944. Davis (1954a) stated that there were records in 12 years between 1929 and early 1954. There are also published records for May 1900 (Blathwayt 1900) and April 1906 (Joy 1922) but none for the nineteenth century. This species is a migrant in parts of its continental range, and, until such time as there is a more widespread recovery of numbers and range in Britain, it is perhaps just as likely that any future occurrence on Lundy would be of a displaced migrant, rather than a wandering resident.

Ortolan Bunting *Emberiza hortulana*

Nationally scarce migrant.

Scattered breeding distribution across much of continental Europe, wintering in sub-Saharan Africa. 2,163 records for Britain 1968–2003, with an average of 61 per year 2000–2003.

Ortolan Buntings prefer the short grazed grass in the south of the island, being most often encountered between Quarter Wall and the village area. Although not recorded until 1949 (a female on 11 May), Ortolans were seen subsequently in all but six years up to 1992. Since then, however, there is a strong suggestion of a decline, with eight blank years up to and including 2006 and three further years in this period yielding only single records. In total there have been over 80 records involving around 120 individuals.

On Lundy this is a species that is typical of early autumn, occurring mainly between the last few days of August and the end of September, though the extreme autumn dates are 8 August (1971) and 2 November (1982). In fact, the latter is the only November occurrence and there are just a handful of October records. Most sightings are of single birds but small groups of two to six birds have been seen

Ortolan Bunting

(e.g. four on 26 September 1962, six on 12 September 1963, six on 25 September 1965, four on 6 September 1978), although fewer such groups have occurred in recent years. During the 10-year period 1997–2006 inclusive, the only instance of more than two together was of four in September 2003 – one of the best years on record for this species in Britain. There have been eight spring records between 23 April (1989) and 14 June (1985) – two in April, four in May and two in June – but none since May 2000 (see details below).

Nationally, numbers of Ortolan Buntings in autumn showed a marked decline between the mid-1990s and 2001, but recovered strongly in 2002 and 2003 (the last year for which consolidated national data are available at the time of writing). The species' European breeding population underwent a major decline between 1970 and 1990, with a less rapid decline continuing in many countries (BirdLife International 2004).

The following is a complete list of records for the 20 years 1987–2006:

1987 9 May – one.
1989 23 Apr – an immature male, trapped and ringed.
28 Aug – an adult.
3 Sep – a first-year bird at Pondsbury.
10 Sep – a first-year bird around the village.
27 Sep – one at Quarter Wall.
1990 11 May – a male on the East Side.
4 Sep – one in the village.
1991 8 Sep – a first-year bird at Quarry Pond.
29 & 30 Sep – a first-year bird around the village.
1992 18 Sep – one in Millcombe.
1995 8 to 12 Oct – a first-year bird at Quarter Wall and in Millcombe.
1998 26 Sep – a first- year bird near Dead Cow Point.
2000 7 May – one at Quarter Wall.
2002 23 & 24 Sep – one ranging between the village and Quarter Wall Pond.
2003 7 Sep – one, probable first-year bird, in St John's Valley.
13 Sep – four near the helipad in the Tent Field.
21 Sep – a first-year bird around the village.
2005 28 Aug – two by the main track at Quarter Wall.

Six Ortolan Buntings had been ringed on Lundy by the end of 2006, but there are no controls or recoveries involving the island.

Rustic Bunting *Emberiza rustica*

British vagrant.

Breeds in parts of Scandinavia and Russia, wintering mainly in China and Japan. 430 records for Britain 1950–2005. Considered by the BBRC until the end of 2005.

The are five Lundy records, all concentrated in the period 8 to 20 October:

1986   12 to 15 Oct – an immature first seen at North End and subsequently in company with Chaffinches around the Old Light.

1990   9 Oct – a first-year bird caught in Quarter Wall trap was ringed and released and later seen in Millcombe and St John's Valley.

1993   8 Oct – a first-year female caught and ringed in St John's Valley.
20 Oct – an unringed bird in Punchbowl Valley.

1994   12 Oct – one feeding outside the Tavern.

Andrew Jewels' write-up of the 1994 bird in the LFS logbook relates the unusual circumstances:

"Whilst drinking coffee in the Tavern I noticed a bunting hop onto the wall outside. Focusing my binoculars through the window, the bird was identified as a Rustic Bunting by obvious rusty chevrons on its flanks, obvious wing bars, slight crest and bright head pattern, including pale ear covert spot. The bird spent two minutes feeding amongst the grass on top of the wall next to the Gents. Most of the salient features, including the head details were noted, before the bird flew off south, not to be seen again. The bird arrived during a busy period of diurnal migrants in hazy conditions."

Little Bunting *Emberiza pusilla*

Nationally scarce migrant.

Breeds in north-easternmost Europe and north Asia, wintering in south and south-east Asia. 838 records for Britain 1958–2003, with an average of 34 per year 2000–2003. Considered by the BBRC until the end of 1982.

There are 13 Lundy records involving 15 birds, with all but two of the occurrences since 1984, reflecting increased frequency in Britain generally, and all except one in autumn (mainly October):[210]

1951   16 Oct – two adult males, one of which was trapped and ringed and seen again on 19 Oct.

1975   12 & 13 Oct – one in the High Street.

1984   20 to 25 Apr – one.
7 to 12 Oct – a first-winter bird seen on four days in this period, caught and ringed on 9 Oct.[211]
14 Oct – a first-winter bird, caught and ringed.

1985   2 Nov – one by Government House.

1987   25 Oct – one in St Helen's Field.

1990   12 Oct – two; one trapped and ringed in St John's Valley and another seen at the Old Light and Stoneycroft; the second bird stayed until 15 Oct.[212]

1991   14 Oct – one caught and ringed at Quarter Wall.

1994   1 Oct – one flushed from rushes near Quarter Wall, then seen perched on the wall and on the ground by Quarter Wall Pond.[213]
27 Nov – one at Quarter Wall gate.[213]

2001   1 Nov – one seen briefly, feeding with Chaffinches and House Sparrows outside Brambles.

2005   5 Oct – a first-winter bird by the stone crusher in the Tent Field.
8 & 9 Oct – one near the Old Light, presumably the 5 Oct bird.
17 Oct – one by the stone crusher in the Tent Field, thought to be the same bird.

Yellow-breasted Bunting *Emberiza aureola*

British vagrant.

Breeds from north-east Europe eastwards across Russia to Japan, wintering in south and south-east Asia. The European range is restricted to a small and declining population in central Finland. 220 records for Britain 1950–2005.

There are two Lundy records, both of single birds in September:

1982 18 to 26 Sep – one seen on seven days, caught and ringed on 18 Sep.[214]

1989 10 & 11 Sep – a female or immature around the Tavern, tea garden and pig-pen on the first day and (briefly) below Government House early in the morning of 11th.

A record of a bird in the Tent and Lighthouse Fields on 28 September 1984, mentioned in the 1984 and 1985 *LFS Annual Reports*, was rejected by the BBRC.

Reed Bunting

Reed Bunting *Emberiza schoeniclus*   [Common Reed Bunting]

Regular autumn migrant in very small numbers; rare and increasingly irregular spring migrant; not seen in winter for many years; has bred once.

Though both Chanter (1871) and Parfitt (1876) listed this species as an "autumn and winter visitant" under the name "Emberiza schœniculus Black-headed Bunting", the first dated occurrences were not until after the commencement of regular LFS recording, with singles on 15 July (a juvenile) and 28 July 1948. Thereafter, sightings were irregular until 1970, since when there have been records every year (up to and including 2006), with the sole exception of 1995. A pair nested in St John's Valley in 1971 (female seen carrying food on 1 June) but this remains the only breeding record. Midwinter occurrences are similarly exceptional, with singles in January/February 1952, February 1953 and December 1972 the only instances.

Very small numbers pass through the island in spring, from early March to early June, with the majority of records falling in the period late March to late May. Most records are of single birds, the highest number being four on both 12 April 1962 and 3 April 1977.[215] In recent years spring occurrences have become less regular, with sightings on just three days in 1996 (a male on 29 March, one – sex unspecified – on 19 April, a female on 12 June), two in 1998 (a male on 4 & 8 May) and one in 2006 (two on 28 March) being the only examples for the period 1993 to 2006 inclusive.

Autumn migrants have been seen virtually annually since the early 1970s, before which records were more sporadic. Most are seen between late September and mid-November, with a clear peak in the second half of October. The few earlier sightings (three in the second half of July, one in late August and two in early September) are perhaps more likely to relate to post-breeding dispersal rather than true migration. The great majority of records involve single birds, with twos and threes occurring from time to time. The highest one-day counts in autumn have been four on 28 October 1982, 31 October 1985 and 20 October 2006, five on 10 October 1988 and 17 November 1973, and six on 27 October 2003.[216] Reed Bunting is 'red-listed' (of high conservation concern) following a population crash in the 1970s and 1980s, from which the species has only partially recovered (Baillie *et al.* 2007).

Nine Reed Buntings had been ringed on Lundy by the end of 2006, but there are no controls or recoveries involving the island. Almost all individuals from the British breeding population winter within Britain, when they are joined by very small numbers of continental breeding birds, mainly from Scandinavia (Wernham *et al.* 2002). It is therefore likely that most of the Reed Buntings passing through Lundy are of British origin.

Black-headed Bunting *Emberiza melanocephala*

British vagrant.

Breeds in south-eastern Europe and western Asia, migrating south-east to winter in western and central India. 171 records for Britain 1950–2005, mainly in spring, suggestive of birds overshooting their breeding grounds.

There are three Lundy records, all of single birds, including two spring males:

1957 20 & 22 Sep – a female or immature; identification confirmed following comparison of Black-headed and Red-headed Bunting skins in the British Museum.

1993 24 to 27 May & 4 Jun – a male at various locations in the south-east of the island and singing from the top of gorse bushes outside Blue Bung (Old School) on the last date.

1997 15 & 16 Jul – a male feeding on the main track near Pondsbury using the granite marker stones as vantage points.

Corn Bunting *Emberiza calandra*

Lundy vagrant.

Davis (1954a) reported sightings by F.W. Gade on 3 February 1933 (a single bird) and on four days in 1940: 9 April (one), 12 April (four), 9 May (one) and 12 December (one). There have since been 17 LFS records, all of single birds. The predominance of late spring records – 13 have occurred between late April and early June – suggests that these could be mainly continental birds overshooting their breeding grounds, the European population being partly migratory (Wernham *et al.* 2002). Given the collapse in the British population during the second half of the twentieth century – more than 85% decline between the mid-1970s and 2004 (Baillie *et al.* 2007) – and declines elsewhere in Europe, this 'red-listed' species (of high conservation concern) looks set to remain very rare on Lundy.

1951 11 May – one.
        11 & 12 Nov – two.

1954 7 May – one.

1965 29 Apr – one singing in the Brick Field.

1970 17 May – a male in St John's Valley.

1972 20 to 26 Apr – a male.
        18 Nov – one flying south with finches.

1976 29 Jun – one.

1978 19 Apr – one.
        16 May – one.
        3 Jun – one.

1982 2 Nov – one.
1983 12 to 13 May – one.
5 Sep – one.
1984 10 to 17 May – one seen on six days was at the eastern end of Quarter Wall on 13 May and at the western end of Halfway Wall on 16 May.[217]
1999 22 Apr – one feeding in the Tillage Field.
15 May – one at Quarter Wall (considered different to the April bird).[218]

Rose-breasted Grosbeak

Rose-breasted Grosbeak *Pheucticus ludovicianus*

British vagrant.

Breeds in North America, migrating to winter in Mexico and South America. 21 records for Britain 1950–2005.

There are two Lundy records, both in October:

1985 27 Oct – a first-winter male, caught and ringed, was subsequently watched feeding on blackberries in Millcombe.[219]
2001 6 to 9 Oct – a first-winter male feeding on berries and beetles in the walled gardens in Millcombe and on seed outside Brambles in St John's Valley.

Steve Cooper's account in the 2001 *Devon Bird Report* of finding Lundy's second Rose-breasted Grosbeak vividly brings to life the excitement of stumbling on such a rarity:

"Finally 6 October had arrived, and as the annual bout of Lundy sickness had reached fever proportions, the relief of once again walking around the wooded slopes of Millcombe Valley came as the perfect cure. Fellow Cambridgeshire birders Ade Cooper, Richard Patient and myself slowly made our way down to the walled gardens, high with the usual fantasy rarity expectations, where every call and movement was met with a rapid trio of birding reflexes. On approaching the last walled gardens near the pond, Richard and I had drifted ahead, engaged in a conversation on the possibilities for the forthcoming week when, as we moved closer to look over a wall, we were met with an explosion of head stripes and wing bars as a robust passerine shot to the back and alighted in a small elder tree. There, in all its glory, sat a Rose-breasted Grosbeak! Fantasy had turned into reality after only 80 minutes on the Island, and the adrenalin rush caused by the sight of such a familiar American vagrant put us into orbit, especially when the bird moved to the top of the tree to reveal the stunning crimson underwings of a male" (Cooper 2001).

Bobolink *Dolichonyx oryzivorus*

British vagrant.

Breeds in northern USA and southern Canada, migrating to wintering grounds in South America. 26 British records 1950–2005.

There is one Lundy record:

1984   23 to 25 Sep – a first-winter bird was found on the Airfield and seen subsequently in other parts of the plateau, north to Halfway Wall.[220]

Baltimore Oriole (Northern Oriole) *Icterus galbula*

British vagrant.

Breeds in south-eastern Canada and eastern USA, wintering in Mexico and north-west South America. 21 records for Britain 1950–2005.

There are two Lundy records, both in October, involving three individuals, including – in 1958 – the first for Britain:

1958   2 to 9 Oct – a first-year female.[221]

1967   17 Oct – the remains of a partly eaten, freshly dead bird were found during the morning by LFS warden Cliff Waller on his way to check the Terrace Heligoland trap; a second bird was mist-netted on the Terrace in the afternoon (Waller 1967b). The British Museum confirmed identification of the first bird from examination of the remains.[222]

LFS warden Bill Workman wrote of the 1958 occurrence in *British Birds*:

"At 2.30 p.m. on 2nd October 1958 R.H. [Roy] Dennis flushed an unfamiliar bird from an open grass field…where it was keeping company with Meadow Pipits. It was noticeably larger than the pipits and its flight was heavy, but what particularly attracted attention were its black wings with white bars, its bright orange-yellow under-parts and its yellow tail. It landed on the side of a dry stone wall and hung there for a few minutes with its tail fanned and pressed against the stone, before flying down into some bracken and starting to search for food…The bird avoided a mist-net…but was finally caught in the Garden Trap [the Heligoland trap formerly situated between the Old Light and Stoneycroft]…After being photographed and ringed, it was released…in Stoneycroft garden." The bird was trapped again on 7 Oct and found to have increased its weight by approximately 10% in the five days since it was first weighed (Workman 1963).

Baltimore Oriole

Appendix to the Systematic List – additional species

In addition to the 317 species that constitute the Systematic List, a further 36 species are mentioned in published accounts but for varied reasons cannot be accorded full status. These consist of:

○ Unsuccessful introductions and presumed escapes.

○ British vagrants for which published records were either not submitted to the BBRC/BOURC or were rejected.

○ Lundy vagrants published in *LFS Annual Reports* but subsequently omitted from the Lundy list owing to inadequate documentation.

○ Unsubstantiated historical reports.

○ Species seen during the boat crossing but not from the island itself.

Unsuccessful introductions and presumed escapes

Red Grouse *Lagopus lagopus*   [Willow Ptarmigan]

Failed historical introduction to Lundy.

Several introduction attempts were made during the nineteenth and twentieth centuries but all failed. Felix Gade recalled one attempt in the late 1920s:

"Various unsuccessful efforts were made to hatch eggs of those species of birds which Mr. Harman wished to introduce to the island. The first were red grouse eggs from Scotland, and bantam hens were bought to carry out the hatching, but the eggs arrived before the bantams had gone broody, and so the eggs were set under larger hens. There was fair success with the hatching, which was carried out on the short heather in parts of Ackland's Moor, but the big hens were too vigorous for the tiny chicks, sending them flying in their bouts of earth scratching. Apart from that, the chicks had no understanding of the language of domestic poultry and although they were given special feed, and every attention, and the weather was kind, none of them survived" (Gade 1978, pages 71–72).

Davis (1954a) and Dymond (1980) suggested that an adult seen by Martin Coles Harman and others in 1936 could have been a genuine immigrant, but given this species' highly sedentary nature this seems unlikely. At the time, the nearest population was on Exmoor but this has since all but died out.

Grey Partridge *Perdix perdix*

Failed historical introduction to Lundy.

As for Red Grouse, there were several unsuccessful attempts to introduce Grey Partridge to Lundy for shooting purposes during the eighteenth, nineteenth and twentieth centuries. Chanter (1871) stated: "There were about forty brace of partridges in 1791, but all now seem to have disappeared. Sir John Warren stocked it with several sorts of feathered game, and Mr. Heaven has several times renewed the partridges, and also imported grouse; but the rats, the climate, or birds of prey have always destroyed them." Davis (1954a) and Gade (1978) wrote of a dozen pairs of Czechoslovakian birds that were released in 1928 but, in spite of breeding, soon died out. The last attempt took place in 1966, as the 1965-66 *LFS Annual Report* relates: "Five birds, three males and two females, were brought to the Island and released by Mr A. Harman on August 14th, and seem to be doing quite well". The 1967 report, however, states: "At least four of the five birds released last year were seen again in February, but seem to have disappeared since." There have been no further occurrences.

Pheasant *Phasianus colchicus* [Common Pheasant]

Introduced to Lundy; bred 1920s to 1970s; now extinct.

Following several failed attempts, Pheasants were successfully introduced to Lundy during the 1920s and a small breeding population of possibly up to 20 adult birds was established. Loyd (1922) reported that two broods hatched in 1922, and Wynne-Edwards & Harrison (1932) located five pairs in 1930. Perry (1940) listed four breeding pairs in 1939. N.V. Allen counted 16 males and 7 females – the highest recorded total – in October 1944 (1944 *Devon Bird Report*).

No more than 12 were seen at any one time from the commencement of LFS recording in 1947. The *LFS Annual Report* for that year states: "A few birds still exist, mostly among the rhododendron scrub along the east sidings. One hen killed among cut oats, August 28th." Twelve were present in the autumn of 1957, while two different broods had been seen during the summer. Up to seven were counted in 1963 and a further three hens and a cock were released in October of that year. The 1967 *LFS Annual Report* notes: "Although the daily total never exceeded nine, at least seven cocks and five hens were present, four young reached the free-flying stage." Eight were still present before the breeding season in 1972 and two broods were seen, though it was doubted that these survived until winter. Indeed 1972 turned out to be the last throw of the dice for Pheasants on Lundy; from April 1973 only one male remained and was seen from time to time until last reported in the Tillage Field on 8 August 1974. There were no records at all in 1975, so the report of a female in St Helen's Combe[223] on 28 November 1976 was something of a surprise. This remains the last sighting on the island.

Golden Pheasant *Chrysolophus pictus*

Escape from captivity; BOU category E; native to China.

Within the 1959 entry for Pheasant (*Phasianus colchicus*) the 1959/60 *LFS Annual Report* mentions: "A Golden Pheasant which escaped in March may have survived."

Pelican *Pelecanus* sp.

Escape from captivity; BOU categories D & E.

On an unspecified day in May 1953 an escaped pelican was seen perched for a time on top of Great Shutter Rock, eventually flying off in the direction of the North Devon mainland. Described as a "totally white bird" (Gade 1978, p. 361), it was perhaps most likely to have been a Great White Pelican (*Pelecanus onocrotalus*), though other pelican species are also kept in British zoos. No definitely wild pelican has ever been recorded in Britain.

Barbary Dove 'Streptopelia risoria'

Escape from captivity; BOU category E; domestic hybrid.

One was seen on 29 October 1973.

Budgerigar *Melopsittacus undulatus*

Escape from captivity; BOU category E; native to Australia.

A green-plumaged bird stayed from 23 June to 2 July 1973, while another present around the village from 24 July 1990[224] was taken into captivity on 7 September that year.

Ring-necked Parakeet *Psittacula krameri* [Rose-ringed Parakeet]

Escape from captivity; BOU category E; native to Africa and India.

A female or immature was found freshly dead on 3 December 1977. Another bird was seen on 8 May 1979.

Orange-gorgetted Flycatcher *Ficedula strophiata*

Escape from captivity; BOU category E; native to south-east Asia.

One was trapped on 17 November 1973 and another was seen on 11 August 1976.

Red-headed Bunting *Emberiza bruniceps*

All records presumed to relate to escapes from captivity; BOU categories D & E.

This species, which breeds in Central Asia and winters in India, is commonly kept as a cage-bird in Britain and continental Europe and, in the absence of conclusive evidence from ringing, there is reasonable doubt that it has ever occurred in the UK as a genuinely wild vagrant. Red-headed Bunting is therefore not currently included in the official *British List*.

There were at least 25 Lundy records, all of single birds, between 1951 and 1986 (mainly in the 1960s and 1970s), but none since. The majority of these were adult males, lending support to the view that most if not all sightings refer to escaped or released cage-birds (since it might be expected that most genuine vagrants, especially in autumn, would be immatures). However, records of adult males in spring, of which there have been several on Lundy, could possibly be of wild birds overshooting their breeding grounds, as occurs regularly with Black-headed Bunting (*E. melanocephala*).

All records:

1951 14 to 20 Jul – an adult male.

30 Sep to 3 Oct – a female or first-winter bird which frequented the walls and fences around the cultivated fields (Brian White, personal communication).

1952 15 to 21 Aug – an adult male.

2 & 3 Oct – one.

1953 4 Jun – a male.

1956 4 to 10 Sep – a male, probably first-winter, with "rather abraded and broken tail feathers" suggesting it was an escaped cage-bird.

1960 18 to 24 Aug & 1 to 3 Sep – a male.[225]

1961 25 Jul to 27 Aug – a male, regularly seen feeding with Chaffinches on chicken corn near the kitchen garden.

1962 3 May – a male near Benjamin's Chair.

2 Sep – a male.

4 Oct – a male.

1964 28 Apr – one.

Aug – one in the Brick Field late in the month.[226]

1965 4 Jul to 8 Aug – a male at Quarter Wall, then Pondsbury and "eventually residing in the oats".

14 to 18 Sep – a male, possibly different from the one seen in Jul/Aug.

1966 23 Aug – an adult male.

1967 22 Jun – a male, trapped and ringed on 23rd (the first and only Red-headed Bunting ringed on Lundy).

8 Aug – a male.

1969 One "many times during May, July and September" (1969 *LFS Annual Report*); the surviving logbook includes sightings on 12 & 26 May and a male daily from 8 to 14 Sep.

1970 22 Aug – one at Quarry Pond.

1971 29 May to 4 Jun – one in St John's Valley and on the main track north of the High Street.

1972 11 Aug – a male in Millcombe.

1976 One "several times during the summer" (1976 *LFS Annual Report*); the only entries in the original logbook are for a male seen on 5 & 6 Jun.

1977 20 to 23 May – a male seen daily.

1979 22 Apr – a male.

1986 4 Jun – one by the Church.

Canary *Serinus canaria*   [Island Canary]

Escape from captivity; BOU category E; native to North Atlantic islands.

A male was seen from 23 July to 15 August 1972 and one was present in Millcombe from 29 to 31 July 1994.

White-headed Munia *Lonchura maja*

Escape from captivity; BOU category E; native to south-east Asia.

One was seen on the Terrace on 12 July 1978.[227]

Red-billed Quelea *Quelea quelea*

Escape from captivity; BOU category E; native to Africa.

A strange sparrow-like bird that arrived on the island on 30 September 2000 generated considerable speculation about its identity during its five-week stay to 7 November (2000 & 2001 *LFS Annual Report*, p. 33) but was eventually identified as a Red-billed Quelea (Tony Taylor, personal communication).

British vagrants for which published records were either not submitted to the BBRC/BOURC or were rejected

Blue-winged Teal *Anas discors*

British vagrant.

Breeds throughout north and central North America, migrating to winter in Central and South America. 221 records for Britain 1950–2005.

The 1987 *LFS Annual Report* states that a female Blue-winged Teal was present from 13 to 16 September 1987 (probably since 11th) and that a description had been submitted to the BBRC. However, there is no trace of the record's acceptance or rejection by the BBRC. The LFS logbook shows that between 11 & 16 September there were possibly two birds present on Pondsbury, a female Shoveler (*A. clypeata*) and a smaller duck identified by several observers as a female Blue-winged Teal. However, the two birds do not appear to have been seen together and possible confusion surrounding the record may mean that it was not submitted to the BBRC as a definite Blue-winged Teal. (It is interesting to note that the 1987 *Devon Bird Report* shows two Blue-winged Teal present at Upper Tamar Lake, on the North Devon/Cornwall border, from 13 to 26 September; a record that was accepted by the BBRC.)

Harlequin Duck *Histrionicus histrionicus*

British vagrant.

Breeds in Iceland, Greenland, northern North America and eastern Siberia; Icelandic birds mainly sedentary; other populations migrate south in winter. 11 records for Britain 1950–2005.

The 1991 *LFS Annual Report* mentions a tideline corpse thought to be a female or immature of this species; however, the record was not submitted to the BBRC (Tony Taylor, personal communication).

Lesser Kestrel *Falco naumanni*

Britain vagrant.

Breeds in southern and eastern Europe. 7 records for Britain 1950–2005.

The 1989 *LFS Annual Report* lists the sighting of a female in the northern half of the island on 6 May 1989. However, the record was rejected by the BBRC (*British Birds* 83, p. 493, where the date is given as 7 May, though the original logbook shows 6th is correct).

Lesser Yellowlegs *Tringa flavipes*

British vagrant.

Breeds in Alaska and Canada, wintering mainly in West Indies and South America. 252 records for Britain 1950–2005.

One was listed in the 1959/60 *LFS Annual Report* as being at Pondsbury from 26 to 28 October 1959. However, there is no record of the sighting having been submitted to either the Devon Bird Recorder or the BBRC. Unfortunately the original LFS data for 1959 no longer exist, so without substantiating details the species is regretfully excluded from the Systematic List. (A Lesser Yellowlegs was seen on the Torridge Estuary, North Devon, on 30 August the same year.)

Moustached Warbler *Acrocephalus melanopogon*

Formerly included in 'The British List' as a vagrant, but removed in 2006 by the BOU Records Committee following a comprehensive review (BOURC 2006), which found no satisfactory British record.

There is one published record for Lundy (1959/60 *LFS Annual Report*) of a bird watched with Sedge Warblers (*A. schoenobanus*) in Millcombe gardens on 2 May 1959. In the light of the BOURC review, this record has been deleted from the Lundy list.

Collared Flycatcher *Ficedula albicollis*

British vagrant.

Breeds in central and eastern Europe. 24 records for Britain 1950–2005.

The 1990 *LFS Annual Report* lists one seen in St Helen's Combe on 24 October 1990. However, the record was rejected by the BBRC (*British Birds 87*, p. 570).

Pine Grosbeak *Pinicola enucleator*

British vagrant.

Breeds in northern Eurasia and North America. Largely resident; in some years moves south in large numbers in response to food shortages. 8 records for Britain 1950–2005.

A record of a female seen on the Terrace by LFS warden Barbara Whitaker on 7 May 1958 is listed in the 1958 *LFS Annual Report* and was subsequently published in the 1958 *Devon Bird Report* as the "first authentic record for Devon". Moore (1969) wrote in *The Birds of Devon*: "The account of this occurrence…gives only the bare facts and omits even a brief description of the bird and the circumstances under which it was observed". Unfortunately, the original LFS data for 1958 no longer exist, and there is no record of the sighting having been submitted to either the Devon Bird Recorder or the BBRC (then in its formative year). Given the observer's scientific reputation, integrity and skill as a field ornithologist, the record is in all probability wholly reliable, but in the absence of substantiating details this species is regretfully excluded from the Systematic List.

Lundy vagrants published in *LFS Annual Reports* but subsequently omitted from the Lundy list owing to inadequate documentation

Water Pipit *Anthus spinoletta*

Reported on several occasions, but no adequately documented record to date.

This species was only separated from Rock Pipit (*A. petrosus*) by the BOU in 1986, having formerly been treated as a sub-species *A. p. spinoletta*. There was one Lundy record assigned to *A. p. spinoletta* prior to the split; a single bird reported on 14 April 1985, though without any supporting description). There are further entries for Water Pipit in the LFS logbooks for 1987 and 1998. In 1987 there were reports of singles on 30 April & 1 May, 18 July, and 1, 2 & 17 October. None of these sightings was accompanied by a description of any kind and, regretfully, all are discounted, in spite of publication in the 1987 *LFS Annual Report*. The nearest candidate, to date, for acceptance as Lundy's first Water Pipit is a bird seen on 10 May 1998. While a brief description noted the pale rosy flush on the breast, the pale white supercilium, whitish underparts and blue-grey head, the information provided was considered insufficient to rule out the Scandinavian race of Rock Pipit (*A. p. littoralis*), a few individuals of which may resemble Water Pipits (Tony Taylor, personal communication). This is a species that is long overdue for promotion to the full Lundy list and it must only be a matter of time before a cast-iron record is clinched.

Unsubstantiated historical reports

Egyptian Goose *Alopochen aegyptiaca*

Unsubstantiated historical report. Naturalised in Britain and north-west Europe.

Listed by Parfitt (1876) and Chanter (1877) as "reported, but not accurately identified" and therefore regarded by Chanter as doubtful. There are no further details.

Velvet Scoter *Melanitta fusca*

Unsubstantiated historical report; also recorded during boat crossing.

Listed by Parfitt (1876) and Chanter (1877) as "reported, but not accurately identified" and therefore regarded by Chanter as doubtful.

There is one record of three birds seen by former LFS Warden Cliff Waller during the boat crossing on 15 October 1969. This must rank as the species most likely to be promoted to the full-status Lundy list in the near future; it seems extraordinary that none has been seen from the island in more than 60 years of regular recording.

Albatross *Diomedea* sp.

Unsubstantiated historical report.

Two entries in the Heaven Diaries are mentioned by Boyd (1950). One for 13 June 1874 stated: "Albatross skin on beach"; the second, for 23 September 1874, noted: "Except Albatross's head no striking appearance put in to-day." Boyd concluded that in the absence of any mention of albatross in Chanter's 1877 list (which had been reviewed by the Rev. H.G. Heaven) "it must be presumed these records were later rejected by him [Heaven]".

Spotted Eagle *Aquila clanga*   [Greater Spotted Eagle]

Unsubstantiated historical report. Vagrant to Britain from continental breeding grounds; only 12 records for Britain, all prior to 1950.

Mathew (1861), writing in *The Zoologist*, stated: "My friend Mr. Heaven, of Lundy, some three years since shot a specimen of the spotted eagle on the island." D'Urban & Mathew (1895) wrote: "In the winter of 1858, Mr. Spencer Heaven, of Lundy Island, in turning a corner of the cliffs, came suddenly on an Eagle engaged in devouring a rabbit, and having a gun with him fired at it, when the bird in its death-struggles, rolled over the edge of the cliff, and, falling into the sea below, could not be recovered. From some feathers which were picked up it was concluded that this bird was a Spotted Eagle in the same stage of plumage as two very fine examples soon after obtained in Cornwall, which also occurred in the winter [on 4 December 1860 and in November 1861]." Davis (1954a) stated: "In the absence of any details, this cannot be considered a satisfactory record". It appears that this solitary record prompted Chanter (1871) and Parfitt (1876) to list this species as an "occasional visitant".

Golden Eagle *Aquila chrysaetos*

Unsubstantiated historical report.

Chanter (1871) and Parfitt (1876) listed this species as an "occasional visitant" but gave no further details and there are no dated records. Referring to Parfitt's account, D'Urban & Mathew (1895) stated: "The Golden Eagle is included amongst occasional visitors to Lundy Island, but probably in error."

Crane *Grus grus*   [Common Crane]

Unsubstantiated historical report.

"Crane Grus cinerea" is listed by Parfitt (1876) and Chanter (1877) as "reported, but not accurately identified" and therefore regarded by Chanter as doubtful. There are no further details and there is no mention in either D'Urban & Mathew (1895) or Boyd's 1950 analysis of the Heaven Diaries. In the past, 'Crane' was also used commonly to refer to Grey Heron (*Ardea cinerea*). Though "Common Heron Ardea cinerea" is also listed by Chanter and Parfitt, it seems possible that the two species got muddled up at some point; there is certainly no unequivocal evidence that Crane (*Grus grus*) has ever been seen on the island.

Bonaparte's Gull *Larus philadelphia*

Unsubstantiated historical report.

Vagrant to Britain from North America. 125 records for Britain 1950–2005.

Parfitt (1876) and Chanter (1877) included entries for "Masked or Bonaparte's Gull Larus capistratus", recording it as "reported but not accurately identified" and therefore regarded by Chanter as doubtful. There is some confusion about the use of the scientific name *Larus capistratus* which appears also to have been applied historically in some cases to the species we know as Black-headed Gull *Larus ridibundus* (Hoek Ostende 1997). It is therefore possible that Chanter was referring to the latter species (see page 118), itself unusual on Lundy but common on the Devon mainland.

Great Snipe *Gallinago media*

Unsubstantiated historical report.

Vagrant to Britain from northern and eastern European breeding grounds. 148 records for Britain 1950–2005.

Chanter (1871) and Parfitt (1876) listed this species (using the then common name of 'Solitary Snipe') as an "autumn and winter visitant", while D'Urban & Mathew (1895) stated that "one was killed on Lundy". None of these authors provided any further details. One was recorded daily in the LFS logbook from 24 to 29 April 1978 but the record, which was not published in the *LFS Annual Report*, was rejected by the BBRC (*British Birds* 72, page 545).

Great Auk *Pinguinus impennis*

Unsubstantiated historical report.

This large, flightless species became extinct in the mid-nineteenth century due to hunting pressure. The last specimen taken was killed in Iceland in 1844 and the last reliable sighting was off the Newfoundland Banks in 1852 (Halliday 1979; Gaston & Jones 1998). The nearest known breeding site to Lundy was the remote Scottish island of St Kilda, but the species had been exterminated there by 1760. The Calf of Man (Isle of Man) has been listed as a possible breeding site (Nettleship & Birkhead 1985). All British waters lie within the likely limits of the Great Auk's original winter range, as based on archaeological and fossil evidence (Gaston & Jones 1998; Bengston 1984) and it is therefore likely that the species occurred off Lundy from time to time, albeit hundreds or even thousands of years ago.

Great Auks

More intriguingly, there are also tantalising suggestions, discussed in detail by Davis (1954a) and more recently by Tony Langham in the 1994 *LFS Annual Report*, that Great Auks could once have bred on Lundy. However, in the absence of conclusive evidence, it seems unlikely that the truth will ever be known.

One of the earliest historical references to the Great Auk and Lundy was by Moore (1837), who wrote: "Mr. Gosling of Leigham informed me that a specimen of this bird was picked up, dead, near Lundy Island, in the year 1829." Mathew in *The Zoologist* (1866b) quoted extracts from a letter written by the Rev. H.G. Heaven dated 6 September 1865, replying to Mathew's question as to whether the Great Auk had occurred on the island. Heaven stated there was "strong presumptive evidence" that the species had been "seen alive on the island within the last thirty years".

Heaven continued: "In the year 1838 or 1839…one of our men in the egging season brought us an enormous egg, which we took for an abnormal specimen of the guillemot's egg, or, as they are locally named, the 'pick-billed murr.' This, however, the man strenuously denied, saying it was the egg of the 'king and queen murr,' and that is was very rare to get them, as there were only two or three 'king and queen murrs' ever on the island. On being further questioned, he said the birds were not like the 'picked-bills,' but like the 'razor-billed murrs'…that they were much larger than either of them; and he did not think they could fly, as he never saw them on the wing nor high up the cliffs like the other birds, and that they, as he expressed it, 'scuttled' into the water, tumbling among the boulders, the egg being only a little way above high-water. He thought they had deserted the island, as he had not seen them or an egg for fifteen years till the one he brought to us; but that [the people of the island] sometimes saw nothing of them for four or five years together, which he accounted for by supposing the birds had fixed on a spot inaccessible to the eggers from the land, for breeding purposes. The shell of the egg we kept for some years, but unfortunately it at last got broken. It was precisely like the guillemot's egg in shape, nearly, if not quite, twice the size…The man has been dead some years now…an inhabitant of the island some twenty-five or thirty years…He spoke of the birds in such a way that one felt convinced of their existence, and that he himself had seen them, but he evidently knew no other name for them than 'king and queen murrs,' which he said the islanders called them 'because they were so big, and stood up so bold-like'…Nobody, he said, had ever succeeded in catching one…because they were so close to the water, and scuttled into it so fast. The existence of these birds had been traditional on the Island when he came to it, and even the oldest agreed there were never more than two or three couple. He himself never knew of more than one couple at a time."

Chanter related this story in 1871 and later, in his monograph on Lundy (1877), added: "…an egg was found and brought to Mr Heaven in 1838…unfortunately the specimen was not preserved; and naturalists do not consider the claim sufficiently established." Blathwayt (1900) related a similar story with a cautionary tone: "Mr. Heaven told me of a tradition which still exists on the island relating to the former occurrence of a bird which, if not simply mythical, could be none other than the Great Auk. The story is, I think, worth repeating, but must, however, as Mr. Heaven impressed upon me, be taken for what it is worth". The same story was told by Mr Heaven (junior) in 1914 (Hendy 1933).

Dipper *Cinclus cinclus* [White-throated Dipper]

Unsubstantiated, probably erroneous report.

Parfitt (1876) and Chanter (1877) included "Turnstone Cinclus interpres" in their lists of "occasional visitants". Davis (1954a) and Dymond (1980) both incorrectly stated that Dipper was listed as an occasional visitor by Chanter, presumably considering the mention of 'Cinclus' in Chanter's 1877 list as referring to Dipper (*Cinclus cinclus*). In fact, *Cinclus interpres* was a scientific name formerly applied to Turnstone (*Arenaria interpres*), a species which also appears in both of Chanter's lists as "Turnstone Strepsilas interpres". Dipper is not mentioned in relation to Lundy by either D'Urban & Mathew (1895) or Loyd (1925) and it therefore seems certain that a mistaken interpretation was made by Davis and Dymond of a duplication of Turnstone entries in Chanter's 1877 listing.

Lesser Spotted Woodpecker *Dendrocopos minor*

Unsubstantiated historical report.

Listed by Chanter (1877) as an "occasional visitant" but without any supporting information and this species is not mentioned by Parfitt (1876) or in Chanter's original 1871 list. There is no subsequent indication that this highly sedentary bird has occurred on Lundy. Furthermore, Great Spotted Woodpecker is absent from Chanter and Parfitt's listings, but given that this species has since been recorded on the island from time to time, it seems possible that Lesser Spotted Woodpecker was either mistakenly identified or listed in error.

Species seen during the boat crossing but not from the island itself

Cory's Shearwater *Calonectris diomedea*

There are two published records:

1992 31 May – one (1992 *Devon Bird Report*).
2002 28 Aug – two (2002 *Devon Bird Report*).

Pomarine Skua *Stercorarius pomarinus* [Pomarine Jaeger]

There are eight records:[228]

1968 31 Aug – one.
1971 5 Oct – one "about six miles east of Lundy from *Lundy Gannet*" (entry in the LFS logbook).
1972 18 Jun – one.
1978 8 Apr – one.
1990 2 Jun – two.
1994 29 May – a light-phase bird.
2002 4 Sep – one.
2004 8 May – a light-phase bird about five kilometres off the island.

Roseate Tern *Sterna dougallii*

One was seen on 6 June 1976 (1976 *Devon Bird Report*).

Black Guillemot *Cepphus grylle*

One was seen on 30 May 1991 (1991 *Devon Bird Report*).

Checklist of the birds of Lundy

The sequence and nomenclature follow the 7th Edition of *The British List* (BOU 2006). The total number of species in categories A–C of *The British List* recorded on Lundy (excluding Red Grouse, Grey Partridge and Pheasant, which were all unsuccessfully introduced to the island) is **317**. The following seven species, though listed in category A of *The British List* (recorded in the wild in Britain at least once since 1 January 1950), have not occurred on Lundy within this period – the year of the last Lundy record is given in brackets: Smew (1933), Goosander (1934), Bittern (1930), White-tailed Eagle (c.1880), Collared Pratincole (1945), Pallas's Sandgrouse (1888), Roller (1949).

- [ ] **Mute Swan** (*Cygnus olor*)
- [ ] **Bewick's Swan** (*Cygnus columbianus*)
  Tundra Swan
- [ ] **Whooper Swan** (*Cygnus cygnus*)
- [ ] **Bean Goose** (*Anser fabalis*)
- [ ] **Pink-footed Goose** (*Anser brachyrhynchus*)
- [ ] **White-fronted Goose** (*Anser albifrons*)
  Greater White-fronted Goose
- [ ] **Greylag Goose** (*Anser anser*)
- [ ] **Snow Goose** (*Anser caerulescens*)
- [ ] **Canada Goose** (*Branta canadensis*)
- [ ] **Barnacle Goose** (*Branta leucopsis*)
- [ ] **Brent Goose** (*Branta bernicla*) Brant Goose
- [ ] **Ruddy Shelduck** (*Tadorna ferruginea*)
- [ ] **Shelduck** (*Tadorna tadorna*)
  Common Shelduck
- [ ] **Wigeon** (*Anas penelope*) Eurasian Wigeon
- [ ] **Gadwall** (*Anas strepera*)
- [ ] **Teal** (*Anas crecca*) Eurasian Teal
- [ ] **Green-winged Teal** (*Anas carolinensis*)
- [ ] **Mallard** (*Anas platyrhynchos*)
- [ ] **Pintail** (*Anas acuta*) Northern Pintail
- [ ] **Garganey** (*Anas querquedula*)
- [ ] **Shoveler** (*Anas clypeata*) Northern Shoveler
- [ ] **Pochard** (*Aythya ferina*) Common Pochard
- [ ] **Tufted Duck** (*Aythya fuligula*)
- [ ] **Scaup** (*Aythya marila*) Greater Scaup
- [ ] **Eider** (*Somateria mollissima*) Common Eider
- [ ] **Common Scoter** (*Melanitta nigra*)
  Black Scoter
- [ ] **Surf Scoter** (*Melanitta perspicillata*)
- [ ] **Goldeneye** (*Bucephala clangula*)
  Common Goldeneye
- [ ] **Smew** (*Mergellus albellus*)
- [ ] **Red-breasted Merganser** (*Mergus serrator*)
- [ ] **Goosander** (*Mergus merganser*)
  Common Merganser
- [ ] **Ruddy Duck** (*Oxyura jamaicensis*)
- [ ] **Quail** (*Coturnix coturnix*) Common Quail
- [ ] **Red-throated Diver** (*Gavia stellata*)
  Red-throated Loon

- [ ] **Black-throated Diver** (*Gavia arctica*)
  Black-throated Loon
- [ ] **Great Northern Diver** (*Gavia immer*)
  Great Northern Loon
- [ ] **Little Grebe** (*Tachybaptus ruficollis*)
- [ ] **Great Crested Grebe** (*Podiceps cristatus*)
- [ ] **Red-necked Grebe** (*Podiceps grisegena*)
- [ ] **Slavonian Grebe** (*Podiceps auritus*)
  Horned Grebe
- [ ] **Black-necked Grebe** (*Podiceps nigricollis*)
- [ ] **Fulmar** (*Fulmarus glacialis*) Northern Fulmar
- [ ] **Great Shearwater** (*Puffinus gravis*)
- [ ] **Sooty Shearwater** (*Puffinus griseus*)
- [ ] **Manx Shearwater** (*Puffinus puffinus*)
- [ ] **Balearic Shearwater** (*Puffinus mauretanicus*)
- [ ] **Storm Petrel** (*Hydrobates pelagicus*)
  European Storm Petrel
- [ ] **Leach's Petrel** (*Oceanodroma leucorhoa*)
  Leach's Storm Petrel
- [ ] **Gannet** (*Morus bassanus*) Northern Gannet
- [ ] **Cormorant** (*Phalacrocorax carbo*)
  Great Cormorant
- [ ] **Shag** (*Phalacrocorax aristotelis*)
  European Shag
- [ ] **Bittern** (*Botaurus stellaris*) Eurasian Bittern
- [ ] **Little Bittern** (*Ixobrychus minutus*)
- [ ] **Night Heron** (*Nycticorax nycticorax*)
  Black-crowned Night Heron
- [ ] **Little Egret** (*Egretta garzetta*)
- [ ] **Grey Heron** (*Ardea cinerea*)
- [ ] **Purple Heron** (*Ardea purpurea*)
- [ ] **White Stork** (*Ciconia ciconia*)
- [ ] **Glossy Ibis** (*Plegadis falcinellus*)
- [ ] **Spoonbill** (*Platalea leucorodia*)
  Eurasian Spoonbill
- [ ] **Honey Buzzard** (*Pernis apivorus*)
  European Honey-buzzard
- [ ] **Black Kite** (*Milvus migrans*)
- [ ] **Red Kite** (*Milvus milvus*)
- [ ] **White-tailed Eagle** (*Haliaeetus albicilla*)
- [ ] **Marsh Harrier** (*Circus aeruginosus*)
  Western Marsh Harrier

- [ ] **Hen Harrier** (*Circus cyaneus*)
  Northern Harrier
- [ ] **Montagu's Harrier** (*Circus pygargus*)
- [ ] **Goshawk** (*Accipiter gentilis*)
  Northern Goshawk
- [ ] **Sparrowhawk** (*Accipiter nisus*)
  Eurasian Sparrowhawk
- [ ] **Buzzard** (*Buteo buteo*) Common Buzzard
- [ ] **Rough-legged Buzzard** (*Buteo lagopus*)
  Roughleg
- [ ] **Osprey** (*Pandion haliaetus*)
- [ ] **Kestrel** (*Falco tinnunculus*) Common Kestrel
- [ ] **Red-footed Falcon** (*Falco vespertinus*)
- [ ] **Merlin** (*Falco columbarius*)
- [ ] **Hobby** (*Falco subbuteo*) Eurasian Hobby
- [ ] **Gyr Falcon** (*Falco rusticolus*) Gyrfalcon
- [ ] **Peregrine** (*Falco peregrinus*) Peregrine Falcon
- [ ] **Water Rail** (*Rallus aquaticus*)
- [ ] **Spotted Crake** (*Porzana porzana*)
- [ ] **Little Crake** (*Porzana parva*)
- [ ] **Baillon's Crake** (*Porzana pusilla*)
- [ ] **Corncrake** (*Crex crex*) Corn Crake
- [ ] **Moorhen** (*Gallinula chloropus*)
  Common Moorhen
- [ ] **Coot** (*Fulica atra*) Common Coot
- [ ] **Oystercatcher** (*Haematopus ostralegus*)
  Eurasian Oystercatcher
- [ ] **Stone Curlew** (*Burhinus oedicnemus*)
  Eurasian Stone-curlew
- [ ] **Collared Pratincole** (*Glareola pratincola*)
- [ ] **Little Ringed Plover** (*Charadrius dubius*)
- [ ] **Ringed Plover** (*Charadrius hiaticula*)
  Common Ringed Plover
- [ ] **Dotterel** (*Charadrius morinellus*)
  Eurasian Dotterel
- [ ] **Golden Plover** (*Pluvialis apricaria*)
  European Golden Plover
- [ ] **Grey Plover** (*Pluvialis squatarola*)
- [ ] **Lapwing** (*Vanellus vanellus*)
  Northern Lapwing
- [ ] **Knot** (*Calidris canutus*) Red Knot
- [ ] **Sanderling** (*Calidris alba*)
- [ ] **Semipalmated Sandpiper** (*Calidris pusilla*)
- [ ] **Little Stint** (*Calidris minuta*)
- [ ] **Temminck's Stint** (*Calidris temminckii*)
- [ ] **Least Sandpiper** (*Calidris minutilla*)
- [ ] **White-rumped Sandpiper** (*Calidris fuscicollis*)
- [ ] **Baird's Sandpiper** (*Calidris bairdii*)
- [ ] **Pectoral Sandpiper** (*Calidris melanotos*)
- [ ] **Curlew Sandpiper** (*Calidris ferruginea*)
- [ ] **Purple Sandpiper** (*Calidris maritima*)
- [ ] **Dunlin** (*Calidris alpina*)
- [ ] **Buff-breasted Sandpiper**
  (*Tryngites subruficollis*)

- [ ] **Ruff** (*Philomachus pugnax*)
- [ ] **Jack Snipe** (*Lymnocryptes minimus*)
- [ ] **Snipe** (*Gallinago gallinago*) Common Snipe
- [ ] **Woodcock** (*Scolopax rusticola*)
  Eurasian Woodcock
- [ ] **Black-tailed Godwit** (*Limosa limosa*)
- [ ] **Bar-tailed Godwit** (*Limosa lapponica*)
- [ ] **Whimbrel** (*Numenius phaeopus*)
- [ ] **Curlew** (*Numenius arquata*) Eurasian Curlew
- [ ] **Spotted Redshank** (*Tringa erythropus*)
- [ ] **Redshank** (*Tringa totanus*)
  Common Redshank
- [ ] **Greenshank** (*Tringa nebularia*)
  Common Greenshank
- [ ] **Green Sandpiper** (*Tringa ochropus*)
- [ ] **Wood Sandpiper** (*Tringa glareola*)
- [ ] **Common Sandpiper** (*Actitis hypoleucos*)
- [ ] **Turnstone** (*Arenaria interpres*)
  Ruddy Turnstone
- [ ] **Wilson's Phalarope** (*Phalaropus tricolor*)
- [ ] **Red-necked Phalarope** (*Phalaropus lobatus*)
- [ ] **Grey Phalarope** (*Phalaropus fulicarius*)
  Red Phalarope
- [ ] **Arctic Skua** (*Stercorarius parasiticus*)
  Parasitic Jaeger
- [ ] **Long-tailed Skua** (*Stercorarius longicaudus*)
  Long-tailed Jaeger
- [ ] **Great Skua** (*Stercorarius skua*)
- [ ] **Mediterranean Gull** (*Larus melanocephalus*)
- [ ] **Laughing Gull** (*Larus atricilla*)
- [ ] **Little Gull** (*Larus minutus*)
- [ ] **Sabine's Gull** (*Larus sabini*)
- [ ] **Black-headed Gull** (*Larus ridibundus*)
  Common Black-headed Gull
- [ ] **Common Gull** (*Larus canus*) Mew Gull
- [ ] **Lesser Black-backed Gull** (*Larus fuscus*)
- [ ] **Yellow-legged Gull** (*Larus michahellis*)
- [ ] **Herring Gull** (*Larus argentatus*)
- [ ] **Iceland Gull** (*Larus glaucoides*)
- [ ] **Glaucous Gull** (*Larus hyperboreus*)
- [ ] **Great Black-backed Gull** (*Larus marinus*)
- [ ] **Kittiwake** (*Rissa tridactyla*)
  Black-legged Kittiwake
- [ ] **Bridled Tern** (*Onychoprion anaethetus*)
- [ ] **Little Tern** (*Sternula albifrons*)
- [ ] **Black Tern** (*Chlidonias niger*)
- [ ] **Sandwich Tern** (*Sterna sandvicensis*)
- [ ] **Common Tern** (*Sterna hirundo*)
- [ ] **Arctic Tern** (*Sterna paradisaea*)
- [ ] **Guillemot** (*Uria aalge*) Common Murre
- [ ] **Razorbill** (*Alca torda*)
- [ ] **Ancient Murrelet**
  (*Synthliboramphus antiquus*)

☐ **Little Auk** (*Alle alle*)
☐ **Puffin** (*Fratercula arctica*) Atlantic Puffin
☐ **Pallas's Sandgrouse** (*Syrrhaptes paradoxus*)
☐ **Rock Dove / Feral Pigeon** (*Columba livia*)
Common Pigeon
☐ **Stock Dove** (*Columba oenas*)
☐ **Woodpigeon** (*Columba palumbus*)
Common Wood Pigeon
☐ **Collared Dove** (*Streptopelia decaocto*)
Eurasian Collared Dove
☐ **Turtle Dove** (*Streptopelia turtur*)
European Turtle Dove
☐ **Great Spotted Cuckoo** (*Clamator glandarius*)
☐ **Cuckoo** (*Cuculus canorus*) Common Cuckoo
☐ **Black-billed Cuckoo**
(*Coccyzus erythrophthalmus*)
☐ **Yellow-billed Cuckoo** (*Coccyzus americanus*)
☐ **Barn Owl** (*Tyto alba*)
☐ **Little Owl** (*Athene noctua*)
☐ **Tawny Owl** (*Strix aluco*)
☐ **Long-eared Owl** (*Asio otus*)
☐ **Short-eared Owl** (*Asio flammeus*)
☐ **Nightjar** (*Caprimulgus europaeus*)
European Nightjar
☐ **Swift** (*Apus apus*) Common Swift
☐ **Alpine Swift** (*Apus melba*)
☐ **Kingfisher** (*Alcedo atthis*)
Common Kingfisher
☐ **Bee-eater** (*Merops apiaster*) European Bee-eater
☐ **Roller** (*Coracias garrulus*) European Roller
☐ **Hoopoe** (*Upupa epops*) Eurasian Hoopoe
☐ **Wryneck** (*Jynx torquilla*) Eurasian Wryneck
☐ **Great Spotted Woodpecker**
(*Dendrocopos major*)
☐ **Eastern Phoebe** (*Sayornis phoebe*)
☐ **Bimaculated Lark** (*Melanocorypha bimaculata*)
☐ **Short-toed Lark** (*Calandrella brachydactyla*)
Greater Short-toed Lark
☐ **Woodlark** (*Lullula arborea*) Wood Lark
☐ **Skylark** (*Alauda arvensis*) Sky Lark
☐ **Shore Lark** (*Eremophila alpestris*)
Horned Lark
☐ **Sand Martin** (*Riparia riparia*)
☐ **Swallow** (*Hirundo rustica*) Barn Swallow
☐ **House Martin** (*Delichon urbicum*)
Common House Martin
☐ **Red-rumped Swallow** (*Cecropis daurica*)
☐ **Richard's Pipit** (*Anthus richardi*)
☐ **Tawny Pipit** (*Anthus campestris*)
☐ **Olive-backed Pipit** (*Anthus hodgsoni*)
☐ **Tree Pipit** (*Anthus trivialis*)
☐ **Meadow Pipit** (*Anthus pratensis*)
☐ **Red-throated Pipit** (*Anthus cervinus*)

☐ **Rock Pipit** (*Anthus petrosus*)
Eurasian Rock Pipit
☐ **Yellow Wagtail** (*Motacilla flava*)
☐ **Citrine Wagtail** (*Motacilla citreola*)
☐ **Grey Wagtail** (*Motacilla cinerea*)
☐ **Pied / White Wagtail** (*Motacilla alba*)
White Wagtail
☐ **Waxwing** (*Bombycilla garrulus*)
Bohemian Waxwing
☐ **Wren** (*Troglodytes troglodytes*) Winter Wren
☐ **Dunnock** (*Prunella modularis*)
☐ **Alpine Accentor** (*Prunella collaris*)
☐ **Robin** (*Erithacus rubecula*) European Robin
☐ **Thrush Nightingale** (*Luscinia luscinia*)
☐ **Nightingale** (*Luscinia megarhynchos*)
Common Nightingale
☐ **Bluethroat** (*Luscinia svecica*)
☐ **Red-flanked Bluetail** (*Tarsiger cyanurus*)
☐ **Black Redstart** (*Phoenicurus ochruros*)
☐ **Redstart** (*Phoenicurus phoenicurus*)
Common Redstart
☐ **Whinchat** (*Saxicola rubetra*)
☐ **Stonechat** (*Saxicola torquatus*)
Eurasian Stonechat
☐ **Wheatear** (*Oenanthe oenanthe*)
Northern Wheatear
☐ **Black-eared Wheatear** (*Oenanthe hispanica*)
☐ **Desert Wheatear** (*Oenanthe deserti*)
☐ **White's Thrush** (*Zoothera dauma*)
Scaly Thrush
☐ **Swainson's Thrush** (*Catharus ustulatus*)
☐ **Grey-cheeked Thrush** (*Catharus minimus*)
☐ **Veery** (*Catharus fuscescens*)
☐ **Ring Ouzel** (*Turdus torquatus*)
☐ **Blackbird** (*Turdus merula*)
Common Blackbird
☐ **Fieldfare** (*Turdus pilaris*)
☐ **Song Thrush** (*Turdus philomelos*)
☐ **Redwing** (*Turdus iliacus*)
☐ **Mistle Thrush** (*Turdus viscivorus*)
☐ **American Robin** (*Turdus migratorius*)
☐ **Cetti's Warbler** (*Cettia cetti*)
☐ **Grasshopper Warbler** (*Locustella naevia*)
Common Grasshopper Warbler
☐ **Aquatic Warbler** (*Acrocephalus paludicola*)
☐ **Sedge Warbler** (*Acrocephalus schoenobaenus*)
☐ **Marsh Warbler** (*Acrocephalus palustris*)
☐ **Reed Warbler** (*Acrocephalus scirpaceus*)
Eurasian Reed Warbler
☐ **Icterine Warbler** (*Hippolais icterina*)
☐ **Melodious Warbler** (*Hippolais polyglotta*)
☐ **Blackcap** (*Sylvia atricapilla*) Eurasian Blackcap
☐ **Garden Warbler** (*Sylvia borin*)

- ☐ **Barred Warbler** (*Sylvia nisoria*)
- ☐ **Lesser Whitethroat** (*Sylvia curruca*)
- ☐ **Whitethroat** (*Sylvia communis*) Common Whitethroat
- ☐ **Dartford Warbler** (*Sylvia undata*)
- ☐ **Rüppell's Warbler** (*Sylvia rueppelli*)
- ☐ **Subalpine Warbler** (*Sylvia cantillans*)
- ☐ **Sardinian Warbler** (*Sylvia melanocephala*)
- ☐ **Greenish Warbler** (*Phylloscopus trochiloides*)
- ☐ **Arctic Warbler** (*Phylloscopus borealis*)
- ☐ **Pallas's Warbler** (*Phylloscopus proregulus*) Pallas's Leaf Warbler
- ☐ **Yellow-browed Warbler** (*Phylloscopus inornatus*)
- ☐ **Radde's Warbler** (*Phylloscopus schwarzi*)
- ☐ **Western Bonelli's Warbler** (*Phylloscopus bonelli*)
- ☐ **Eastern Bonelli's Warbler** (*Phylloscopus orientalis*)
- ☐ **Wood Warbler** (*Phylloscopus sibilatrix*)
- ☐ **Chiffchaff** (*Phylloscopus collybita*)
- ☐ **Willow Warbler** (*Phylloscopus trochilus*)
- ☐ **Goldcrest** (*Regulus regulus*)
- ☐ **Firecrest** (*Regulus ignicapilla*)
- ☐ **Spotted Flycatcher** (*Muscicapa striata*)
- ☐ **Red-breasted Flycatcher** (*Ficedula parva*)
- ☐ **Pied Flycatcher** (*Ficedula hypoleuca*) Eurasian Pied Flycatcher
- ☐ **Long-tailed Tit** (*Aegithalos caudatus*) Long-tailed Bushtit
- ☐ **Blue Tit** (*Cyanistes caeruleus*)
- ☐ **Great Tit** (*Parus major*)
- ☐ **Coal Tit** (*Periparus ater*)
- ☐ **Willow Tit** (*Poecile montanus*)
- ☐ **Marsh Tit** (*Poecile palustris*)
- ☐ **Treecreeper** (*Certhia familiaris*) Eurasian Treecreeper
- ☐ **Golden Oriole** (*Oriolus oriolus*) Eurasian Golden Oriole
- ☐ **Isabelline Shrike** (*Lanius isabellinus*)
- ☐ **Red-backed Shrike** (*Lanius collurio*)
- ☐ **Lesser Grey Shrike** (*Lanius minor*)
- ☐ **Great Grey Shrike** (*Lanius excubitor*)
- ☐ **Woodchat Shrike** (*Lanius senator*)
- ☐ **Jay** (*Garrulus glandarius*) Eurasian Jay
- ☐ **Magpie** (*Pica pica*) Eurasian Magpie
- ☐ **Chough** (*Pyrrhocorax pyrrhocorax*) Red-billed Chough
- ☐ **Jackdaw** (*Corvus monedula*) Western Jackdaw
- ☐ **Rook** (*Corvus frugilegus*)
- ☐ **Carrion Crow** (*Corvus corone*)
- ☐ **Hooded Crow** (*Corvus cornix*)
- ☐ **Raven** (*Corvus corax*) Northern Raven
- ☐ **Starling** (*Sturnus vulgaris*) Common Starling
- ☐ **Rose-coloured Starling** (*Sturnus roseus*) Rosy Starling
- ☐ **House Sparrow** (*Passer domesticus*)
- ☐ **Spanish Sparrow** (*Passer hispaniolensis*)
- ☐ **Tree Sparrow** (*Passer montanus*) Eurasian Tree Sparrow
- ☐ **Red-eyed Vireo** (*Vireo olivaceus*)
- ☐ **Chaffinch** (*Fringilla coelebs*)
- ☐ **Brambling** (*Fringilla montifringilla*)
- ☐ **Serin** (*Serinus serinus*) European Serin
- ☐ **Greenfinch** (*Carduelis chloris*) European Greenfinch
- ☐ **Goldfinch** (*Carduelis carduelis*) European Goldfinch
- ☐ **Siskin** (*Carduelis spinus*) Eurasian Siskin
- ☐ **Linnet** (*Carduelis cannabina*) Common Linnet
- ☐ **Twite** (*Carduelis flavirostris*)
- ☐ **Common Redpoll** (*Carduelis flammea*)
- ☐ **Lesser Redpoll** (*Carduelis cabaret*)
- ☐ **Two-barred Crossbill** (*Loxia leucoptera*)
- ☐ **Crossbill** (*Loxia curvirostra*) Red Crossbill
- ☐ **Common Rosefinch** (Scarlet Rosefinch) (*Carpodacus erythrinus*)
- ☐ **Bullfinch** (*Pyrrhula pyrrhula*) Eurasian Bullfinch
- ☐ **Hawfinch** (*Coccothraustes coccothraustes*)
- ☐ **Yellow-rumped Warbler** (*Dendroica coronata*)
- ☐ **Blackpoll Warbler** (*Dendroica striata*)
- ☐ **Common Yellowthroat** (*Geothlypis trichas*)
- ☐ **Eastern Towhee** (*Pipilo erythrophthalmus*)
- ☐ **Lapland Bunting** (*Calcarius lapponicus*) Lapland Longspur
- ☐ **Snow Bunting** (*Plectrophenax nivalis*)
- ☐ **Black-faced Bunting** (*Emberiza spodocephala*)
- ☐ **Yellowhammer** (*Emberiza citrinella*)
- ☐ **Cirl Bunting** (*Emberiza cirlus*)
- ☐ **Ortolan Bunting** (*Emberiza hortulana*)
- ☐ **Rustic Bunting** (*Emberiza rustica*)
- ☐ **Little Bunting** (*Emberiza pusilla*)
- ☐ **Yellow-breasted Bunting** (*Emberiza aureola*)
- ☐ **Reed Bunting** (*Emberiza schoeniclus*) Common Reed Bunting
- ☐ **Black-headed Bunting** (*Emberiza melanocephala*)
- ☐ **Corn Bunting** (*Emberiza calandra*)
- ☐ **Rose-breasted Grosbeak** (*Pheucticus ludovicianus*)
- ☐ **Bobolink** (*Dolichonyx oryzivorus*)
- ☐ **Baltimore Oriole** (*Icterus galbula*)

Lundy ringing totals 1947–2006

Greylag Goose	1	Stock Dove	1
Mallard	40	Woodpigeon	14
Quail	1	Collared Dove	21
Little Grebe	1	Turtle Dove	12
Fulmar	147	Cuckoo	42
Manx Shearwater	1,162	Long-eared Owl	3
Storm Petrel	232	Short-eared Owl	2
Cormorant	46	Nightjar	2
Shag	1,187	Swift	6
Sparrowhawk	15	Hoopoe	1
Buzzard	7	Wryneck	19
Kestrel	24	Great Spotted Woodpecker	4
Merlin	3	Short-toed Lark	1
Peregrine	10	Skylark	608
Water Rail	41	Sand Martin	141
Spotted Crake	1	Swallow	6,155
Corncrake	5	House Martin	309
Moorhen	1	Richard's Pipit	1
Oystercatcher	37	Olive-backed Pipit	1
Ringed Plover	3	Tree Pipit	65
Dotterel	6	Meadow Pipit	3,215
Golden Plover	3	Red-throated Pipit	1
Lapwing	211	Rock Pipit	16
Knot	3	Yellow Wagtail	4
Semipalmated Sandpiper	1	Citrine Wagtail	1
Little Stint	6	Grey Wagtail	63
Least Sandpiper	2	Pied Wagtail	170
Pectoral Sandpiper	6	Wren	978
Curlew Sandpiper	2	Dunnock	868
Dunlin	82	Robin	1,687
Buff-breasted Sandpiper	2	Thrush Nightingale	1
Jack Snipe	11	Nightingale	8
Snipe	30	Bluethroat	3
Woodcock	10	Red-flanked Bluetail	1
Bar-tailed Godwit	1	Black Redstart	35
Whimbrel	21	Redstart	348
Curlew	32	Whinchat	111
Greenshank	2	Stonechat	194
Green Sandpiper	1	Wheatear	429
Wood Sandpiper	1	Desert Wheatear	1
Common Sandpiper	1	Swainson's Thrush	2
Turnstone	3	Grey-cheeked Thrush	1
Lesser Black-backed Gull	429	Veery	2
Herring Gull	2,930	Ring Ouzel	35
Great Black-backed Gull	131	Blackbird	4,008
Kittiwake	2,535	Fieldfare	26
Guillemot	2,701	Song Thrush	857
Razorbill	1,237	Redwing	823
Puffin	10	Mistle Thrush	4

Lundy ringing totals 1947–2006, continued

American Robin	1	Golden Oriole	5
Cetti's Warbler	2	Red-backed Shrike	10
Grasshopper Warbler	354	Great Grey Shrike	1
Aquatic Warbler	1	Woodchat Shrike	11
Sedge Warbler	2,117	Jackdaw	2
Marsh Warbler	3	Carrion Crow	20
Reed Warbler	94	Raven	47
Icterine Warbler	17	Starling	1,192
Melodious Warbler	30	House Sparrow	547
Blackcap	4,140	Tree Sparrow	5
Garden Warbler	759	Red-eyed Vireo	6
Barred Warbler	10	Chaffinch	6,885
Lesser Whitethroat	92	Brambling	131
Whitethroat	2,977	Greenfinch	547
Dartford Warbler	1	Goldfinch	557
Rüppell's Warbler	1	Siskin	1,136
Subalpine Warbler	6	Linnet	1,487
Sardinian Warbler	1	Common Redpoll	2
Greenish Warbler	2	Lesser Redpoll	42
Arctic Warbler	2	Crossbill	38
Pallas's Warbler	2	Common Rosefinch	19
Yellow-browed Warbler	48	Bullfinch	22
Radde's Warbler	1	Hawfinch	4
Western Bonelli's Warbler	2	Yellow-rumped Warbler	1
Wood Warbler	46	Blackpoll Warbler	1
Chiffchaff	3,979	Common Yellowthroat	1
Willow Warbler	12,814	Eastern Towhee	1
Goldcrest	8,353	Lapland Bunting	7
Firecrest	202	Snow Bunting	10
Spotted Flycatcher	1,240	Yellowhammer	1
Red-breasted Flycatcher	21	Ortolan Bunting	6
Pied Flycatcher	730	Rustic Bunting	2
Long-tailed Tit	13	Little Bunting	5
Blue Tit	122	Yellow-breasted Bunting	1
Great Tit	35	Reed Bunting	9
Coal Tit	64	Rose-breasted Grosbeak	1
Treecreeper	21	Baltimore Oriole	2
		Total – 172 species	**85,741**

(Totals include birds ringed as nestlings)

Scientific names of plants and animals referred to in the text

Lichens, ferns and flowering plants

Balm-leaved Figwort	*Scrophularia scorodonia*
Blackthorn	*Prunus spinosa*
Bog Asphodel	*Narthecium ossifragum*
Bracken	*Pteridium aquilinum*
Golden Hair Lichen	*Teloschistes flavicans*
gorse	*Ulex* sp.
Heath Spotted-orchid	*Dactylorhiza maculata*
Heather	*Calluna vulgaris*
Kidney Vetch	*Anthyllis vulneraria*
Lundy Cabbage	*Coincya wrightii*
Rhododendron	*Rhododendron ponticum*
Round-leaved Sundew	*Drosera rotundifolia*
Rowan/Mountain Ash	*Sorbus aucuparia*
Royal Fern	*Osmunda regalis*
Small Adder's-tongue Fern	*Ophioglossum azoricum*
Sycamore	*Acer pseudoplatanus*
Thrift	*Armeria maritima*
willow	*Salix* sp.

Invertebrates

Bronze Lundy Cabbage Flea Beetle	*Psylliodes luridipennis*
Dor Beetle	*Geotrupes stercorarius*
Hummingbird Hawk-moth	*Macroglossum stellatarum*
Painted Lady	*Vanessa cardui*
Red Admiral	*Vanessa atalanta*

Fishes

Basking Shark	*Cetorhinus maximus*
sandeel	*Ammodytes* sp.
Sprat	*Sprattus sprattus*
Sunfish	*Mola mola*

Mammals

Atlantic Grey Seal	*Halichoerus grypus*
Brown Hare	*Lepus europaeus*
Common Seal	*Phoca vitulina*
Fallow Deer	*Dama dama*
Guinea Pig	*Cavia* sp.
Japanese Sika Deer	*Cervus nippon*
Long-eared Bat	*Plecotus austriacus*
Lundy Pony	*Equus caballus*
Pipistrelle Bat	*Pipistrellus pipistrellus*
Pygmy Shrew	*Sorex minutus*
Rabbit	*Oryctolagus cuniculus*
Red Deer	*Cervus elaphus*
Red Squirrel	*Sciurus vulgaris*
Rock Wallaby	*Petrogale* sp.
Roe Deer	*Capreolus capreolus*
Soay Sheep	*Ovis aries*

Acronyms used in the text

BBRC	*British Birds* Rarities Committee
BOU	British Ornithologists' Union
BOURC	British Ornithologists' Union Records Committee
BTO	British Trust for Ornithology
DBR	*Devon Bird Report*
DBRC	Devon Birds Records Committee
DBWPS	Devon Bird Watching & Preservation Society
LFS	Lundy Field Society
RSPB	Royal Society for the Protection of Birds

Endnotes

The following notes are intended to assist anyone undertaking detailed work on Lundy's birds in future. They summarise the errors and discrepancies we have come across and our conclusions or judgements where relevant. A general finding is that the bird records in the *LFS Annual Reports* for 1977 to 1984 contain many inaccuracies and omissions and should not be relied on.

Whooper Swan

1   The 1981 *LFS Annual Report* incorrectly gives one bird; the LFS logbook records three.

White-fronted Goose

2   These records are reported by Dymond (1980) but are not included in the *LFS Annual Reports* for the years in question. They were presumably derived at a later date from another source, most likely the observations of F.W. Gade.

3   The 1980 *LFS Annual Report* incorrectly states the dates as 19 Nov to the end of the year. The original logbook shows that the birds were first seen on 16 Nov, remaining to 29 Nov only.

4   The 2003 *LFS Annual Report* and 2003 *Devon Bird Report* incorrectly state the dates as 24 & 25 Oct, whereas reference to the original logbook shows that 27 & 28 Oct are correct.

Greylag Goose

5   The 1976 *LFS Annual Report* and 1976 *Devon Bird Report* state that two birds were present until 25 Feb; the original logbook shows that 26 Feb is the correct date.

6   The 1979 *LFS Annual Report* and 1979 *Devon Bird Report* give the date as 3 Feb; the original logbook shows that a single bird was seen on 31 Jan and 5 Feb.

7   The 1979 *LFS Annual Report* and 1979 *Devon Bird Report* give the date as 12 to 31 May; the original logbook shows that 17 May to 2 Jun are the correct dates.

Brent Goose

8   The 1988 *LFS Annual Report* notes that this record was rejected due to the lack of a description in the logbook. On 19 Oct the bird was seen by T. Jones and A. Vickery; the authors have provided confirming details to LFS.

9   This record appears in the 1999 *Devon Bird Report* but not in either the LFS logbook or *LFS Annual Report* for that year.

Shelduck

10   Though clearly entered in the original logbook, this record was excluded, presumably in error, from the 2001 *LFS Annual Report*.

Shoveler

11   This record appears correctly in the 1978 *LFS Annual Report*, but the 1979 report erroneously duplicates the details, stating incorrectly that one was seen on 7 Apr 1979.

Pochard

12   First date incorrectly given as 18 Sep in 1982 *LFS Annual Report*; the LFS logbook shows 19th.

Tufted Duck

13   The entry in the original logbook reads "black and white waterbird, Tufted Duck?". The record was published in the 1970 *LFS Annual Report* and we have presumed that identification was correct.

14   The 1999 *Devon Bird Report* incorrectly gives the dates as 2 to 14 May; the original logbook shows that 12 to 14 May is correct.

15   The 2002 *LFS Annual Report* and 2002 *Devon Bird Report* incorrectly give the dates as 4 to 7 July ; the original logbook shows that 3 to 7 July is correct.

Eider

16   The 1979 *LFS Annual Report* incorrectly states that two females were seen on 6 Mar and two males on 20 Apr that year; the original LFS logbook shows that no Eiders were recorded on 6 Mar 1979 (the valid 6 Mar 1978 record had clearly been duplicated in error), while the two males were seen on 29 Apr 1979, not on 20 Apr 1979.

Ruddy Duck

17 The 1975 *LFS Annual Report* gives 4 Oct as the last date when four were seen together, while Dymond (1980) gave 1 Oct; the original LFS logbook shows four on 5 Oct.

Quail

18 Although the 1953 *LFS Annual Report* gives this as the first record since 1948, Quail was not in fact recorded on the island in 1948 (Hugh Boyd, personal communication).

19 The 1996 *LFS Annual Report* gives the date as 15 Jun; the original logbook shows that 17th is correct.

Slavonian Grebe

20 The 1984 *LFS Annual Report* includes a record of one seen on 19 Feb 1984 but there is no trace of such a sighting in the original logbook and we have assumed that the 19 Feb 1985 record was transcribed in error.

Black-necked Grebe

21 Up to four Slavonian Grebes were present in April 1947 and we presume that there was insufficient information available to rule out mistaken identification.

Great Shearwater

22 This record was published in the 1966 *Devon Bird Report* but did not appear in the 1965-66 *LFS Annual Report*.

23 The 1980 *Devon Bird Report* incorrectly gives the date as 7 June; the original logbook shows 6 Jul is correct.

Sooty Shearwater

24 These records appear in the 1970, 1972 and 2002 *Devon Bird Reports*, but are not included in the *LFS Annual Reports* for those years.

Storm Petrel

25 This record appears in the 2000 *Devon Bird Report* but not in the *LFS Annual Report* for that year. The *Devon Bird Report* entry implies that the bird was seen from the island but the original logbook shows that it was recorded on the crossing about 30 minutes out from the island.

Leach's Petrel

26 This record is also included in the 1971 *Devon Bird Report*, with the *LFS Annual Report* given as the source. However, the *Devon Bird Report* does not mention the element of doubt surrounding the birds' identification – a point that is clear from the LFS report.

Little Egret

27 The 1995 *Devon Bird Report* incorrectly states that this was the fourth record for Lundy; it was the fifth.

28 The 2001 *LFS Annual Report* states that three were present on the first date, but the original logbook shows only two.

29 This record appears in the original logbook and in the 2002 *Devon Bird Report* but is not included in the *LFS Annual Report* for that year.

Grey Heron

30 The 1975 *LFS Annual Report* and Dymond (1980) give the date as 16 July 1975, but the original logbook shows that 25th is correct.

Purple Heron

31 There is a good description of this bird in the 1987 LFS logbook and the record was published in the 1987 *LFS Annual Report*; however, it does not appear in the *Devon Bird Report* for 1987 or 1988.

Honey Buzzard

32 The 1983 *LFS Annual Report* states that two were seen on this date but the original LFS logbook entry shows clearly that only one bird was involved.

Black Kite

33 A sighting of a Black Kite flying north over the campsite being mobbed by gulls on 27 Apr 1997 is included in the 1997 *LFS Annual Report* with a note that the record had been submitted to the BBRC. It is also listed in the 1997 *Devon Bird Report* as "requiring additional details". However, it appears that these details were not submitted to either the BBRC or the Devon Birds Records Committee and it is therefore discounted here.

34 The 2001 *LFS Annual Report* incorrectly gives the date as 25 May, whereas the LFS logbook shows 24th. While the record was initially not accepted by the BBRC, it was later accepted upon review.

Marsh Harrier

35 This record appears in the 1997 *Devon Bird Report* but not in the *LFS Annual Report* for that year.

Hen Harrier

36 The 1979 *LFS Annual Report* states that one was seen on 6 Aug 1979; however, there is no trace of this sighting in the LFS logbook and given that the *Annual Report* contains a number of significant errors relating to other species, we have reluctantly decided not to include this record as the earliest autumn occurrence of Hen Harrier.

Osprey

37 The 1978 *LFS Annual Report* incorrectly gives 1 Sep.

38 This record was published in the 1992 *Devon Bird Report* but does not appear in either the original LFS logbook or the *LFS Annual Report* for that year.

39 The 1997 *LFS Annual Report* and 1997 *Devon Bird Report* incorrectly give the date as 29 September; the original logbook shows that 23 Sep is correct.

Red-footed Falcon

40 A record in the 1990 *LFS Annual Report* of an immature female on 10 May 1990 appears not to have been submitted to the BBRC and is therefore discounted here.

41 The BBRC shows 1 Jun only, while the 1977 *Devon Bird Report* erroneously states 1 & 2 Feb; the original logbook shows that 1 & 2 Jun is correct.

Merlin

42 The 1980 *LFS Annual Report* wrongly gives the date as 6 June; the original logbook shows that 6 July is correct.

Gyr Falcon

43 1986 *LFS Annual Report* gives the second date only.

Coot

44 This record appears in the 1991 *Devon Bird Report* but not in the *LFS Annual Report* for that year.

Ringed Plover

45 The 1989 *LFS Annual Report* states that up to seven were seen at Pondsbury from 7 to 19 Sep; the original logbook shows that the maximum of seven occurred only on 10 & 11 Sep.

Dotterel

46 The 1990 *Devon Bird Report* incorrectly gives the date as 7 May; the original logbook shows that 6th is correct.

Lapwing

47 This record appears in the 1991 *Devon Bird Report* but not in the *LFS Annual Report* for that year.

Semipalmated Sandpiper

48 The 1981 *Devon Bird Report* (in which the 1980 record was listed, having being accepted by the BBRC) erroneously gives the date as 7 September. The original logbook and the BBRC both show that 5 & 6 Sep are correct. This record did not appear at all in the 1980 *LFS Annual Report* (which stated only that "a small wader that appeared on 5th September was believed to be a Pectoral Sandpiper". Clarification was given in the 1983 *LFS Annual Report*.

Least Sandpiper

49 The 1965-66 *LFS Annual Report* gives 14 Sep only but the BBRC report shows both dates; since the original LFS data no longer exist, the BBRC record is presumed correct.

50 The 1957 *Devon Bird Report* erroneously gives the dates as 24 to 26 August.

Pectoral Sandpiper

51 The 1970 *Devon Bird Report* gives 17 Sep, the date of ringing, only; the original logbook and the 1970 *LFS Annual Report* make clear that birds were present as described.

52 The 1978 *LFS Annual Report* and 1978 *Devon Bird Report* (the latter quoting the LFS report) both refer to a Pectoral Sandpiper seen on 28 March that year. However, there is no trace in the island logbook – though two Purple Sandpipers were seen on that date – and the record was not mentioned by Dymond (1980). We believe that an error was made in the 1978 *LFS Annual Report* and have therefore excluded the record here.

53 Neither record is shown in the 1982 or subsequent *Devon Bird Reports*.

54 Not shown in the 1985 or subsequent *Devon Bird Reports*.

55   Not shown in the 1985 or subsequent *Devon Bird Reports*.

56   The 2004 *LFS Annual Report* gives 21 & 22 Sep only; the original LFS logbook records 23rd as the last date.

Curlew Sandpiper

57   This record appears in the 1995 *Devon Bird Report* but not in the *LFS Annual Report* for that year.

Dunlin

58   Dymond (1980) assigned this record to 6 & 7 May 1973, but it appears as 6 & 7 May 1972 in the 1972 *LFS Annual Report* and there is no mention of these dates in the 1973 *LFS Annual Report*. 1972 has therefore been applied here.

Buff-breasted Sandpiper

59   Record not included in the BBRC database.

60   The 1965-66 *LFS Annual Report* indicates that the bird stayed until "a few days later", while the BBRC and 1965 *Devon Bird Report* state 27 & 28 Sep, which are used here. The original LFS data for 1965 no longer exist.

Black-tailed Godwit

61   The 2003 *Devon Bird Report* includes an erroneous sighting of six on 17 December 2003, arising from an error made in entering a record of six Woodcock in the LFS logbook, published correctly in the 2003 *LFS Annual Report*.

Whimbrel

62   The *LFS Annual Report* for 1992 gives the second date as 7 Mar, but the original logbook shows that 12th is correct.

Green Sandpiper

63   This record appears in the 1997 *Devon Bird Report* but not the *LFS Annual Report* for that year.

Grey Phalarope

64   This record appears in the 2000 *Devon Bird Report* but not in the *LFS Annual Report* for that year; while original details are lacking, the then editor of the *DBR* believes that the bird was seen off the Landing Bay/Rat Island (Mike Langman, personal communication).

65   This record appears in the 1994 *Devon Bird Repor*, but not in the *LFS Annual Report* for that year.

Arctic Skua

66   This record appears in the 1970 *Devon Bird Report* but not in the *LFS Annual Report* for that year.

Great Skua

67   Some of the boat-crossing records appear in the relevant *Devon Bird Report* but not in the corresponding *LFS Annual Report*. All sources have been taken into account here.

Mediterranean Gull

68   The *LFS Annual Report* for the year erroneously states third-year; recorded in the LFS logbook as second-year.

Laughing Gull

69   The original LFS logbook, the 2005 *LFS Annual Report* and the BBRC report for 2005 all give the dates stated here. However, the 2005 *Devon Bird Report* states that the first-winter bird was present from 6 to 14 Nov (i.e. three days prior to the final entry in the LFS logbook) and the adult from 6 to 13 Nov (i.e. two days after it had been found dead according to the logbook). We believe that data-entry errors were made in compiling the *Devon Bird Report* as there appear to be no additional information sources to those used by LFS and the BBRC.

Sabine's Gull

70   This record appears in the 2002 *Devon Bird Report* but is not included in the *LFS Annual Report* for that year.

Iceland Gull

71   While 18 May is the last-mentioned date in the LFS logbook and 2004 *LFS Annual Report*, the 2004 *Devon Bird Report* includes an additional sighting showing that the bird was still present on 20 May.

Black Tern

72   These records appear in the 1970, 1973, 2000 & 2001 *Devon Bird Reports* but not in the *LFS Annual Reports* for those years.

Arctic Tern

73 These records were included in the 1976 and 1981 *Devon Bird Reports* but not the *LFS Annual Reports* for those years.

Ancient Murrelet

74 The BBRC database gives 26 Jun as the last date, while the 1990 *Devon Bird Report* states "to at least 27th June".

75 The earliest 1991 date is stated as 4 April in Waldon (1994); the original logbook and BBRC annual report show that 14 Apr is correct.

Woodpigeon

76 The 1991 *Devon Bird Report* gives 21 October but the LFS logbook and 1991 *LFS Annual Report* show that 21 November is correct.

Collared Dove

77 Although Gade (1978, p. 425) gives the date as 18 May 1961, the 1961 *LFS Annual Report* states: "One was seen on 28th May by W.L. Roseveare and F.W. Gade…There is some evidence that two birds were present for about a week prior to and after this date."

Turtle Dove

78 The 1983 *LFS Annual Report* erroneously states that a Turtle Dove was seen on 25 March 1983, which would be by far the earliest date on record; reference to the original logbook shows that this record relates to Collared Dove.

Great Spotted Cuckoo

79 The BBRC database and the 1990 *Devon Bird Report* incorrectly give the date as 24 Feb; the original logbook shows that 23 February is correct.

Cuckoo

80 Date given as 10 March 1940 in Gade 1978, p. 232.

Black-billed Cuckoo

81 The 1967 *Devon Bird Report* incorrectly gives the date as 17 October.

Yellow-billed Cuckoo

82 This record was accepted by the BBRC but was not published in the 1986 *Devon Bird Report* (or in subsequent *DBRs*).

Tawny Owl

83 The 1978 *LFS Annual Report* records three Tawny Owls on 30 Oct 1978; however, the island logbook shows these to have been Short-eared Owls.

Long-eared Owl

84 A record in the 1975 *LFS Annual Report* of a Long-eared Owl on 11 Oct does not appear in the LFS logbook and so has been discounted here.

85 This sighting was included in the list of "Records rejected because they were undocumented or descriptions inconclusive" in the 2000 *LFS Annual Report*; however, the record was submitted directly to the Devon Bird Recorder and was accepted for publication in the 2000 *Devon Bird Report*.

86 This record was included in the 2002 *Devon Bird Report* but does not appear in the *LFS Annual Report* for that year.

Hoopoe

87 Combined information from the 1967 *LFS Annual Report* and 1967 *Devon Bird Report*; the former records two from 25 to 28 Aug, while the latter includes an additional record of two on 30 Aug.

88 This record appears in the 1997 LFS logbook and 1997 *LFS Annual Report* but not in the *Devon Bird Report* for that year.

89 The 2004 *LFS Annual Report* incorrectly gives 29 Aug.

Great Spotted Woodpecker

90 The BOURC recognises *D. m. major* as a scarce migrant in Britain, but not *D. m. pinetorum* (breeding in central and eastern Europe).

91 The 1975 *LFS Annual Report* gives the last date as 25 Apr, whereas the LFS logbook shows that 29 Apr is correct.

92 The 2004 *Devon Bird Report* incorrectly states the last date as 29 Oct.

93 This record was accidentally excluded from the 2005 *LFS Annual Report* but appears in the 2005 *Devon Bird Report*; ringing details confirmed by Tony Taylor (personal communication).

Short-toed Lark

94 A record of one on Lundy on 22 October 1995, listed as 'pending' in the 1995 *Devon Bird Report*, was eventually rejected.

95 The 1981 *LFS Annual Report* wrongly gives the date as 25 May.

96 The BBRC report and 1984 *Devon Bird Report* give 29 & 30 Sep only, but the original logbook shows that the bird remained until 2 Oct.

97 The BBRC report and the 1984 *Devon Bird Report* give 1 Jun as the last date, while the original logbook shows the bird was present until 3 Jun.

98 The LFS logbook lists two birds on 14 Oct but without any supporting details; only one bird was accepted by the BBRC.

99 The 1988 *Devon Bird Report* incorrectly gives the dates as 25 & 26 May only; the BBRC report and the original logbook show that the bird remained until 27th.

100 The BBRC gives 2 & 3 May only.

Woodlark

101 The 1978 *LFS Annual Report* gives one on 18 Mar; however, the LFS logbook shows this to be a transcription error of "Woodcock".

102 The 1980 *LFS Annual Report* shows 22 Aug only.

Skylark

103 While the 1971 *LFS Annual Report* shows 350 birds, the entry in the original LFS logbook is unclear but appears to be "330+".

Shore Lark

104 Given in error as 24 Apr 1944 in Palmer 1946.

Sand Martin

105 The 1976 *LFS Annual Report* gives the first arrival date for the year as 1 Mar – which would be the earliest on record – but the original LFS logbook shows the first date in 1976 to be 17 Mar.

106 The 2000 *LFS Annual Report* shows counts of 1,000 on 28 & 29 Apr; however, the LFS logbook clearly shows entries of "100+" for these days.

107 The 2002 *LFS Annual Report* includes an entry, taken from the LFS logbook, of 1,000 Sand Martins on 4 Oct 2002; this record is also published in the 2002 *Devon Bird Report*. Given that there is no supporting narrative in the logbook for this exceptionally high number of Sand Martins on an unusually late date, we consider the entry doubtful and it is therefore discounted here.

Red-rumped Swallow

108 A record of a Red-rumped Swallow in the 1980 *LFS Annual Report* for 14 & 15 October was rejected by the BBRC. Another shown in the 1984 *LFS Annual Report* for 11 September that year appears not to have been submitted to the BBRC and has therefore been discounted here.

109 The 1952 *Devon Bird Report* gives the date as 7 Mar but references the 1952 *LFS Annual Report*; we have assumed that the *DBR* date was a transcription error.

Richard's Pipit

110 The 1966 *Devon Bird Report* incorrectly states that three were seen on 18 September 1966.

111 The 1975 *Devon Bird Report* states "Lundy, 20 Sept. to 17 Oct., singles (Lundy Field Society Report, 1975)". Given that the 1975 *LFS Annual Report* gives the dates listed here, it is assumed the mention of 17 Oct and exclusion of the November record were errors made in compiling the *DBR*.

112 The 2002 *LFS Annual Report* gives 22 to 24 Sep, while the 2002 *Devon Bird Report* gives 22 & 23 Sep only; the original LFS logbook shows that 22 <u>and</u> 24 Sep are the correct dates.

113 The 2004 *Devon Bird Report* treats the 12 & 14 Oct records as one bird.

Tawny Pipit

114 A record of a single bird on 30 Sep & 1 Oct 1985 appears in the 1985 *LFS Annual Report* but it appears not to have been submitted to the Devon Birds Records Committee and is therefore discounted here.

Yellow Wagtail

115 These records are included in the 1988 *LFS Annual Report* but were not given in the 1988 or any subsequent *Devon Bird Report*; however, the descriptions, by experienced observers, in the LFS logbook provide convincing evidence that the records are valid.

Rock Pipit

116 The 2005 *LFS Annual Report* incorrectly gives 15 Oct, whereas the LFS logbook confirms 16th.

Yellow Wagtail

117 The 1996 *LFS Annual Report* and the 1996 *Devon Bird Report* give one bird, while the original logbook indicates two.

118 The 1983 *LFS Annual Report* states 24 to 29 Oct, whereas the original logbook shows 31st as the last day.

119 The 30 Aug 2005 record of an east European or Asian race Yellow Wagtail was submitted by the observers to the BBRC and recorded as such in the 2005 *LFS Annual Report*; however, no entry was made in the LFS logbook.

Grey Wagtail

120 The 1986 *LFS Annual Report* states that 17 were recorded on 14 Oct 1986 but the original logbook shows that this was the count for Pied Wagtail and that only two Grey Wagtails occurred on this date.

Pied / White Wagtail

121 The 1981 *LFS Annual Report* incorrectly states 37; the original LFS logbook shows 35.

Waxwing

122 The date published in the 2005 *Devon Bird Report* is incorrectly given as 31 Jan.

Nightingale

123 A record in the 1979 *LFS Annual Report* of one on 24 Oct 1979 is an error; the LFS logbook shows the date to have been 17 Sep.

Bluethroat

124 The record does not appear in the systematic list in the 1963-64 *LFS Annual Report* but is included in the ringing report.

125 The 1993 *Devon Bird Report* gives the date as 28 May; the original LFS logbook makes clear that 27th is correct (as published in the 1993 *LFS Annual Report*).

126 The 2004 *Devon Bird Report* states: "In the field, females are very difficult to identify to a race; statistically, this bird was most likely to be part of the nominate subspecies *svecica*, and was accepted as such by DBRC."

Black Redstart

127 A record in the 1984 *LFS Annual Report* of 12 on 4 Nov 1984 is a misinterpretation of the entry in the LFS logbook, which shows two birds only.

Redstart

128 The 2004 *Devon Bird Report* gives 20 for 1 & 2 May, but this record does not appear in the LFS logbook and may have been sent direct to the Devon Bird Recorder.

129 The 2002 *LFS Annual Report* gives the last date as 19 Nov; the original logbook shows that 16th is correct. In addition, the report gives two "very late" birds on 15 Nov; the original observer has confirmed these were in fact Black Redstarts which had been incorrectly entered in the logbook as Common Redstarts.

Whinchat

130 Confusion between Whinchat and Stonechat may well be responsible for several exceptional early spring and late autumn reports of Whinchat. In particular, the 2002 *LFS Annual Report* mentions an unusual series of early records involving 14 reports between 6 Mar and 3 Apr, peaking at 11 birds on 1 Apr; and the LFS logbook for 2005 gives six birds on 9 Nov 2005. Without substantiating details, all of these reports should be treated with some caution.

Black-eared Wheatear

131 This record does not appear in the 1974 or subsequent *LFS Annual Reports* and was presumably omitted accidentally.

Desert Wheatear

132 The 2003 *Devon Bird Report* incorrectly states the bird to have been a first-year female.

Swainson's Thrush

133 The 1995 *LFS Annual Report* incorrectly states 19 Oct (the LFS logbook indicates 9th), while the 1995 *Devon Bird Report* gives the record as the first for Lundy; it was the third.

Grey-cheeked Thrush

134 The 1985 *LFS Annual Report* and the original LFS logbook both record the bird as present (and ringed) on 11 Oct only; however, both the 1985 *Devon Bird Report* and the 1985 BBRC report give the bird as also being present on 12 Oct.

Ring Ouzel

135 Dymond (1980) stated that the record count of 23 occurred on 16 April 1966. The original logbook for that year no longer exists, but the 1965-66 *LFS Annual Report* states that 23 were present on 7 April. The latter date has been used here.

Fieldfare

136 The 1981 *LFS Annual Report* states that 1,600 birds were present on 4 Nov 1981, whereas the original LFS logbook shows 1,500; the same *LFS Annual Report* gives a high of 200 birds for Dec, whereas the logbook shows peaks of 300 to 500 on three days.

137 The 1986 *LFS Annual Report* states a figure of 1,000 but the original logbook shows 1,170 to be correct.

Song Thrush

138 These numbers are taken from the 1973 *LFS Annual Report*, whereas Dymond (1980) gave the sequence as 500 on 3 Oct, 500 on 24 Oct and 600 on 25 Oct; regrettably, the original logbook for this year no longer exists.

Redwing

139 The 1976 *LFS Annual Report* states that 600 were seen on 22 Mar 1976; the original logbook shows that 1,600 is the correct figure.

Mistle Thrush

140 Mistle Thrush is not included in the 1995 *LFS Annual Report* but according to the LFS logbook one was seen on the East Side on 18 Aug.

Aquatic Warbler

141 The BBRC incorrectly gives the bird as present also on 11 Oct.

Sedge Warbler

142 Davis (1954a) incorrectly stated that the earliest autumn record was 20 July 1953; the 1952 *LFS Annual Report* shows that 1952 is the correct year.

Icterine Warbler

143 The 1949 *Devon Bird Report* gives the date as 8 August but cites the 1949 *LFS Annual Report* and is evidently an error in transcription.

144 A record of two Icterine Warblers on the unusual date of 26 July 1974 was published in the 1974 *LFS Annual Report* but has been discounted due to a lack of substantiating detail. It was not included in the 1974 *Devon Bird Report*.

Melodious Warbler

145 A record in the 1975 *LFS Annual Report* of a Melodious Warbler "in the Graveyard area" on 8 Jun 1975 was later retracted by the observers.

146 The 2003 *LFS Annual Report* incorrectly gives the dates as 15 & 16 Aug, whereas the LFS logbook shows 14th & 15th; the 2003 *Devon Bird Report* incorrectly gives the last date as 16 Aug.

147 The 1966 *Devon Bird Report* mentions just one on 24 September, but the 1965-66 *LFS Annual Report* states that singles were recorded from 18 to 27 August, with two on 22nd.

Blackcap

148 The BTO data file gives the date of finding as 28 May 1990, whereas the 1990 *LFS Annual Report* gives 29 May 1990; the BTO date is used here. In addition, Laufen, the place of finding, has since been transferred from the Swiss canton of Berne to the canton of Basel.

Garden Warbler

149 The 2003 *Devon Bird Report* states that one was seen on 27 & 29 November 2003; the 2003 LFS logbook and *LFS Annual Report* show clearly that these sightings refer to 27 & 29 October.

Barred Warbler

150 These are the facts given in the 1967 *LFS Annual Report*, though the 1967 *Devon Bird Report* states "at least four, of which three were trapped between 18 Sept. and 22 Oct." Given that the *Devon Bird Report* quotes the source as the *LFS Annual Report*, the latter is presumed correct.

151 The 2002 *Devon Bird Report* incorrectly attributes the 13 October 2001 record to 13 October 2002.

152 The 2005 *LFS Annual Report* and 2005 *Devon Bird Report* incorrectly state that 29 September was the last date; the original logbook shows that the bird was still present on 1 October.

Dartford Warbler

153 The 2005 *Devon Bird Report* incorrectly states that this was the third record for Lundy; it was the sixth.

Subalpine Warbler

154 This record appears in the 1990 *Devon Bird Report*.

155 The 2001 *Devon Bird Report* incorrectly states a female; the 1997 LFS logbook and the BBRC report confirm a male.

Sardinian Warbler

156 The 1955 *LFS Annual Report* incorrectly gives this as the "second authenticated record for Britain".

Greenish Warbler

157 The BBRC report incorrectly gives the dates as 2 to 9 Nov, while the 1958 *Devon Bird Report* simply states "November".

158 The BBRC report incorrectly gives the dates as 13 & 14 Jul; the LFS logbook shows the dates used here.

Arctic Warbler

159 The 1959 *Devon Bird Report* gives the dates as 6 & 7 Sep, but at this stage the record was still subject to BBRC acceptance. Both the 1959/60 *LFS Annual Report* and the 1959 BBRC report (as well as Dymond 1980) refer only to 6 Sep, which is therefore the date used here; the original LFS data for 1959 no longer exist.

Yellow-browed Warbler

160 This record appears in the original LFS logbook and in the 1999 *Devon Bird Report* but was accidentally omitted from the 1999 *LFS Annual Report*.

161 The five birds ringed on 22 & 23 October do not appear in the Lundy summary given in the 2005 *Devon Bird Report*.

Wood Warbler

162 The 2002 *Devon Bird Report* erroneously states that one on seen on Lundy on 25 September 2002 was the latest ever recorded in Devon.

Chiffchaff

163 The 1977 *LFS Annual Report* states "perhaps 350" Chiffchaffs on 10 Apr 1977 but the original logbook shows 300 Willow Warblers and 50 Chiffchaffs.

164 The 1970 *LFS Annual Report* states "about 350 Chiffchaffs and some Willow Warblers passed through"; the original logbook shows 350 unidentified Willow Warblers or Chiffchaffs.

Willow Warbler

165 The 1997 *Devon Bird Report* incorrectly states that the previous highest autumn count on Lundy was 350.

166 Shown in the 1977 *LFS Annual Report* as ring number 993086 ringed on 19 Apr 1977, whereas the BTO datafile shows ring number as 993806 and ringing date as 16 Apr 1977.

Red-breasted Flycatcher

167 The sighting on 28 October is included in the 2002 *Devon Bird Report* but does not appear in the LFS logbook or *LFS Annual Report* for that year.

Great Tit

168 The 1996 *Devon Bird Report* incorrectly gives the last date as 8 Jun.

Coal Tit

169 This record was published in the 1997 *Devon Bird Report* but does not appear in the *LFS Annual Report* for that year.

Woodchat Shrike

170 The 1989 *LFS Annual Report* states that the record was submitted to the BBRC, but there is no record of either its acceptance or rejection.

171 The 1991 *LFS Annual Report* and 1991 *Devon Bird Report* give 27 Jun only; the original logbook shows the bird was still present on 28th.

172 The 2002 *LFS Annual Report* and 2002 *Devon Bird Report* state that the bird was also reported on 25 Aug, but there is no evidence for this in the LFS logbook; the BBRC database shows 19th only.

Magpie

173 The 1996 *Devon Bird Report* incorrectly refers to the 1996 records as the first since 1994; 1991 was the last year prior to 1996 in which Magpie was recorded.

Rook

174 The 1977 *LFS Annual Report* states that 30 were seen on 30 Mar, whereas the logbook shows that 25 occurred on this date and the spring maximum of 30 was reached on 3 Apr.

175 The 1976 *LFS Annual Report* gives the peak autumn count as 35 on 30 Oct, whereas the original logbook shows that 42 were seen on 29 Oct.

Hooded Crow

176 This record appears in the 1995 *Devon Bird Report* but not in the *LFS Annual Report* for that year.

Rose-coloured Starling

177 A record of Rose-coloured Starling on 2 Jul 1987 published in the *LFS Annual Report* for that year appears not to have been submitted to the BBRC and has therefore been discounted.

178 The BBRC erroneously states that the bird stayed "to at least 30th September" and this date is repeated in the 1983 *Devon Bird Report*.

179 The 1999 *Devon Bird Report* gives the dates as 22 Sep to 3 Oct; the original logbook shows that the last date was 4 Oct, as stated in the 1999 *LFS Annual Report*.

180 The 2000/2001 *LFS Annual Report* and the 2000 *Devon Bird Report* both state 3 to 10 Aug, whereas the original logbook and the BBRC both show that 12th was the last date.

181 The 2002 *Devon Bird Report* gives one adult from 1 to 27 Jun but makes no mention of the second bird.

House Sparrow

182 Excludes House Sparrows ringed by University of Leicester and University of Sheffield researchers.

Spanish Sparrow

183 The BBRC report for 1966 and the *Devon Bird Report* for the same year give the date as 9 Jun only. However, the 1965-66 *LFS Annual Report*, Dymond (1980), Waller (1981) and Sharrock & Grant (1982) all clearly state that the bird was still present on 12 June. The original LFS data for 1966 no longer exist.

Tree Sparrow

184 The 1958 *Devon Bird Report* gives the dates as "1 to 12 June" and refers to the 1958 *LFS Annual Report* as the source for this information. However, the *LFS Annual Report* states "a flock of twelve appeared on June 2nd and stayed until 10th"; we have therefore used the latter dates here. There is no surviving logbook for that year.

185 The 1977 *LFS Annual Report* gives 2 & 3 Jan but the original logbook shows 3rd only.

186 The 1991 *Devon Bird Report* gives 27 May to 1 Jun; the 1991 *LFS Annual Report* and original logbook show that 10 Jun is correct.

187 The 1978 *LFS Annual Report* gives nine from 30 May to 3 Jun only; the original logbook shows the details given here are correct.

188 The 1995 *LFS Annual Report* gives 4 Aug; the original logbook shows 5th is correct.

Red-eyed Vireo

189 The BBRC report for 2000 incorrectly states the dates as 8 to 12 Oct only.

190 The 2005 *Devon Bird Report* and the BBRC report for 2005 gives 29 & 30 Sep only.

Brambling

191 The 1977 *LFS Annual Report* states that 140 were seen on 27 Oct that year, but the original logbook shows that the maximum count on any day from 20 to 31 Oct was 30 on 26th.

192 The 1991 *LFS Annual Report* states 56 on 22 Oct; the original logbook confirms 23rd is correct.

193 The 1976 *LFS Annual Report* incorrectly states that the singing male occurred on 6 May; the original logbook makes it clear that 2 May is correct.

Serin

194 The 1959/60 and 1982 *LFS Annual Reports* list Serin sightings on 23 Apr 1959 (a first-year male) and 31 Oct & 2 Nov 1982. As neither record appears to have been submitted to the BBRC (there is no trace of their acceptance or rejection), they are omitted from our listing.

Greenfinch

195 The 1979 *LFS Annual Report* incorrectly gives 20 on 25 Mar 1979, inadvertently duplicating the information for 1978.

Linnet

196 Although a report of 250 birds seen "later in April" is given in the 1977 *LFS Annual Report*, the only high count contained in the original logbook is 150 on 16 Apr, so it appears a transcription error was made.

Common Redpoll

197 The 1988 *LFS Annual Report* states that "there were two 29th September to 3rd October, considered to be of the Greenland race *C. f. rostrata*". These dates are quoted by Diamond (2003) but reference to the original logbook shows that while two redpolls were present on 29th, one on 30th and 1st, and two again on 2nd and 3rd, only the 30 Sep bird, which was trapped and ringed on that date, was explicitly identified as *rostrata*.

198 Diamond (2003) listed one *rostrata* trapped on 11 Oct remaining to 12th, with a second seen on 12th, while the 1995 *LFS Annual Report* and 1995 *Devon Bird Report* indicate that one present from 10 to 13 Oct was trapped and ringed, with two seen on 13th. Reference to the original logbook confirms that one *rostrata* trapped and ringed on 11 Oct was present until 13th when it was joined in the field by a second bird that appeared the same and was considered "probably" also to be *rostrata*. A single redpoll was recorded on 10 Oct but was not specifically assigned as either Common Redpoll or Lesser Redpoll.

Lesser Redpoll

199 The latest spring date of 30 Jun does not appear in the 1996 *LFS Annual Report* but is given in both the original LFS logbook and the 1996 *Devon Bird Report*.

Common (Scarlet) Rosefinch

200 Dymond (1980) referred to a bird that was seen on 19 & 20 May and 21 Jun 1975. The latter date is an error and should be 1 Jun, as shown by the original LFS logbook and *LFS Annual Report*.

201 The original logbook shows that the male was last heard singing on 13 Jun and the pair was seen together on 11 Jun, though the 1984 *Devon Bird Report* gives 12 Jun for both events.

202 Subsequent sightings of the male are not mentioned in the original logbook or 1984 *LFS Annual Report* (presumably to avoid attracting attention and possible disturbance) but are included in the 1984 *Devon Bird Report*.

203 Reports on 1, 3 & 7 Oct were rejected owing to the absence of supporting descriptions.

Blackpoll Warbler

204 The 1984 *Devon Bird Report* incorrectly gives the date as 10 Oct only. The BBRC report and the original logbook show that the details given here are correct.

Eastern Towhee

205 The BBRC report for 1966, the 1966 *Devon Bird Report*, Waller (1970) and Sharrock & Grant (1982) all refer to 7 June only, though none states when the bird was last seen. However, the 1965-66 *LFS Annual Report* clearly states that "A female trapped on June 7th remained until June 11th" and these are the dates quoted by Dymond (1980). Unfortunately, the original LFS data for 1966 no longer exist.

Lapland Bunting

206 The 1980 *LFS Annual Report* states incorrectly that one was seen on 3 August 1980; the original logbook makes clear that none was seen until 2 September that year.

207 The 1984 *LFS Annual Report* states that one was seen on 11 May; the original logbook shows that while a Corn Bunting was seen on this date, there is no indication of a Snow Bunting being present.

Snow Bunting

208 The 2004 *Devon Bird Report* incorrectly states that a male present from 5 to 13 May 2004 "became the latest spring sighting for the county"; there are four Lundy records for later in May. In addition, the 1986 *LFS Annual Report* gives one on 17 May; the original logbook shows 16th was the latest date that year.

Cirl Bunting

209 Although the entry in the 1951 *LFS Annual Report* infers that identification was confirmed, the notes kept by the visiting observers, Brian White and Jeremy James, state: "…a female Cirl Bunting was seen though this is not definite" (Brian White, personal communication).

Little Bunting

210 The 1985 *LFS Annual Report* refers to a bird present from 19 to 23 Oct 1985 but emphasises that no description was submitted; the record is therefore discounted here. The 1986 *LFS Annual Report* includes a record of a bird on 19 Sep 1986 but this was rejected by the BBRC and is therefore also omitted.

211 The *Devon Bird Report* incorrectly gives 13 Oct as the last date; the original logbook shows that the bird was last seen on 12 Oct.

212 The BBRC gives the last date as 14 Oct; the original LFS logbook shows 15 Oct.

213 The 1994 *Devon Bird Report* incorrectly gives these records as "only the second and third for Lundy".

Yellow-breasted Bunting

214 The BBRC and the 1982 *Devon Bird Report* show 25 Sep as the last date; the original logbook confirms that 26 Sep is correct.

Yellowhammer

215 The count of four on 3 April 1977 is included in the *LFS Annual Report* for that year but there is no corresponding entry in the original logbook and it is possible that a transcription error was made; many such errors occurred in the late 1970s and early 1980s.

216 The 2004 *Devon Bird Report* refers to six seen on 27 Oct 2004, but it seems probable that this was a duplication of the 27 Oct 2003 record since the original 2004 logbook and the 2004 *LFS Annual Report* show that only a single Reed Bunting was seen on 27 Oct.

Corn Bunting

217 The 1984 *LFS Annual Report* gives the last date as 16 May, whereas the LFS logbook book shows 17 May.

218 Reports of single Corn Buntings on 28 Apr and 15 Sep 1999 were rejected owing to the absence of supporting descriptions.

Rose-breasted Grosbeak

219 The original logbook states first-winter female but the 1985 *Devon Bird Report* and the BBRC report confirm that the record was accepted as a first-winter male.

Bobolink

220 The 1984 *LFS Annual Report* incorrectly gives 26 Sep as the last date; the BBRC report and the original logbook confirm 25 Sep as the last sighting.

Baltimore Oriole

221 The 1958 *Devon Bird Report* gives the dates as 2 to 10 Oct, whereas Bill Workman's detailed account in *British Birds* states clearly "last seen on 9th October".

222 This record was excluded, presumably in error, from the 1967 *Devon Bird Report*.

Pheasant

223 The 1976 *LFS Annual Report* gives the location as "St Helen's Church"; the original logbook makes clear that St Helen's Combe is correct.

Budgerigar

224 The 1990 *LFS Annual Report* gives 27 Jul as the first date; the original logbook shows 24th is correct.

Red-headed Bunting

225 This record appears in the 1960 *Devon Bird Report* but was apparently excluded in error from the 1959/60 *LFS Annual Report*; the original LFS data for 1960 no longer exist.

226 This record was omitted from the 1964 *Devon Bird Report*.

White-headed Munia

227 The name of this species is incorrectly given in the 1978 *LFS Annual Report* as "White-headed Minerva".

Pomarine Skua

228 The records for 1968, 1990, 1994 and 2002 are published in the relevant *Devon Bird Reports* but are not included in the *LFS Annual Reports* for those years.

Bibliography

Alexander, W.B. & Radford, M.C. 1942. Scarce birds at Lundy. *British Birds* 36: 140.

Alexander, W.B., Southern, H.N., Tucker, W.B. & Watson, J.S. 1945. Observations on the breeding birds of Lundy in 1942. *British Birds* 38: 182–191.

Appleton, D., Booker, H., Bullock, D.J., Cordrey, L. & Sampson, B. 2003. Interim Report on the Sea Bird Recovery Project: Lundy. *LFS Annual Report* 53: 57–61.

Baker, H., Stroud, D.A., Aebischer, N.J., Cranswick, P.A., Gregory, R.D., McSorley, C.A., Noble, D.G. & Rehfisch, M.M. Population estimates of birds in Great Britain and the United Kingdom. *British Birds* 99: 25–44.

Baillie, S.R., Marchant, J.H., Crick, H.Q.P., Noble, D.G., Balmer, D.E., Coombes, R.H., Downie, I.S., Freeman, S.N., Joys, A.C., Leech, D.I., Raven, M.J., Robinson, R.A. & Thewlis, R.M. 2006. *Breeding Birds in the Wider Countryside: their conservation status 2005.* BTO Research Report No. 435. BTO, Thetford.

Baillie, S.R., Marchant, J.H., Crick, H.Q.P., Noble, D.G., Balmer, D.E., Barimore, C., Coombes, R.H., Downie, I.S., Freeman, S.N., Joys, A.C., Leech, D.I., Raven, M.J., Robinson, R.A. & Thewlis, R.M. 2007. *Breeding Birds in the Wider Countryside: their conservation status 2006.* BTO Research Report No. 470. BTO, Thetford.

Fraser, P.A., Rogers, M.J. & the Rarities Committee. 2007. Report on rare birds in Great Britain in 2005, Part 2: passerines. *British Birds* 100: 72–104.

Beer, A.J. & Daniels, D. 1996. Observations of the Bow-and-Moan Display Performed by the Kittiwake Gull (*Rissa tridactyla*) on Lundy. *LFS Annual Report* 47: 43–49.

Bengtson, S-A. 1984. Breeding ecology and extinction of the Great Auk (*Pinguinus impennis*): anecdotal evidence and conjectures. *Auk* 101(1): 1–12.

BirdLife International. 2004. *Birds in Europe: population estimates, trends and conservation status.* BirdLife Conservation Series No. 12. BirdLife International, Cambridge.

Blathwayt, F.L. 1900. A visit to Lundy. *The Zoologist* 4(4): 375–380.

Boyd, H.J. 1950. Some notes on the birds of Lundy. *LFS Annual Report* 4: 22–27.

Boyd, H.J. 1956. Gulls on Lundy, 1947–56. *LFS Annual Report* 10: 26–32.

British Ornithologists' Union. 2006. The British List: A Checklist of Birds of Britain (7th Edition). *Ibis* 148: 526–563. Compiled by S.P. Dudley, M. Gee, C. Kehoe, T.M. Melling and the BOURC.

British Ornithologists' Union Records Committee. 1997. 24th Report (October 1997). *Ibis* 140: 182–184.

British Ornithologists' Union Records Committee. 1999. 26th Report (October 1999). *Ibis* 142: 177–179.

British Ornithologists' Union Records Committee. 2000. 27th Report (October 2000). *Ibis* 143: 171–175.

British Ornithologists' Union Records Committee. 2006. 33rd Report (April 2006). *Ibis* 148: 594.

BTO Web. 2006. BirdFacts. http://blx.1bto.org/birdfacts.

Burfield, I.J. & Brooke, M. de L. 2005. The decline of the Ring Ouzel *Turdus torquatus* in Britain: evidence from bird observatory data. *Ringing & Migration* 22: 199–204.

Campey, R.J. 1990. Ancient Murrelet: a new bird for Lundy and the Western Palearctic. *LFS Annual Report* 41: 25.

Cash, J.A. 1948. A bird watcher on Lundy. *Country Life*, 9 April 1948, pp. 730–731.

Castle, R. 2005. Red-flanked Bluetail on Lundy – a first for Devon. *Devon Bird Report* 78: 179–180.

Chanter, J.R. 1871. A History of Lundy Island – Birds: pp. 600–605. *Trans. Devon Assoc.* Vol. 4(2). August 1871, Bideford.

Chanter, J.R. 1877. *Lundy Island: A Monograph.* London: Cassell, Petter & Galpin. Reprinted 1997, Westwell Publishing, Appledore, North Devon.

Cole L. & Reach I. 1999. Puffin numbers on Lundy during summer 1999. *LFS Annual Report* 50: 35–40.

Collier, M.P., Banks, A.N., Austin, G.E., Girling, T., Hearn, R.D. & Musgrove, A.J. 2005. *The Wetland Bird Survey 2003/04: Wildfowl and Wader Counts.* BTO/WWT/RSPB/JNCC, Thetford.

Cooper, S. 2001. Rose-breasted Grosbeak on Lundy. *Devon Bird Report* 74: 225–226.

Crespi, Dr. 1888. Lundy Island. *Science Gossip*, July 1888.

Cummings, B.F. 1909. Notes on the fauna of Lundy Island. *The Zoologist* 1909: 442–446.

Daniels, D., Heath, J., Hannah, R.P. & Hodgeton, S.A. 1995. Frequency and function of Head-Tossing display in the Kittiwake. *LFS Annual Report* 46: 29–38.

Davenport, H.S. 1897. A Visit to Lundy Island. *The Field*, November 6 1897.

Davies, M. 1981. Lundy Seabird Monitoring Sites. *LFS Annual Report* 32: 21–27.

Davis, H.H. 1934. Rose-coloured Starling at Lundy. *British Birds* 28: 49.

Davis, P. 1952. Lundy Bird Observatory, 1951. *British Birds* 45: 297–298.

Davis, P. 1953a. American Robin on Lundy. *British Birds* 46: 364–368.

Davis, P. 1953b. American Robin on Lundy. *Fair Isle Bird Observatory Bulletin* 1(9): 13.

Davis, P. 1953c. Red-rumped Swallow on Lundy. *British Birds* 46: 264–265.

Davis, P. 1953d. White's Thrush on Lundy. *British Birds* 46: 455.

Davis, P. 1953e. Woodchat Shrikes in London (Surrey), Great Saltee (Co. Wexford), Lundy and Orkney. *British Birds* 46: 305–306.

Davis, P. 1954a. *A list of the birds of Lundy*. Lundy Field Society, Exeter.

Davis, P. 1954b. Late Autumn Migration to Ireland through Lundy. *Fair Isle Bird Observatory Bulletin* 2(3): 114–115.

Davis, P. 1954c. The Effects of the Severe Weather of January and February 1954 on Lundy. *Fair Isle Bird Observatory Bulletin* 2(3): 113.

Defra. 2006. *Protecting the White-headed Duck*. Bristol: Defra. http://www.defra.gov.uk/wildlife-countryside/non-native/pdf/ruddy-duck.pdf

Diamond, J.R. 2003. 'Northwestern' Redpolls – *Carduelis flammea/islandica* on Lundy. *Devon Birds* 56(2): 26–28.

Duncan, R.A. 1989. Tree Pipit with Tawny Pipit measurements. *British Birds* 82: 221–223.

D'Urban, W.S.M. & Mathew, M.A. 1895. *The Birds of Devon*. London: R.H. Porter. (First published 1892; revised edition 1895.)

Dymond, J.N. 1972. Lundy Bird Observatory. *BTO News* 55 (December): 7–8.

Dymond, J.N. 1980. *The Birds of Lundy*. Devon Bird Watching and Presevation Society, Exeter.

Eaton, M.A., Ausden, M., Burton, N., Grice, P.V., Hearn, R.D., Hewson, C.M., Hilton, G.M., Noble, D.G., Ratcliffe, N. & Rehfisch, M.M. 2006. *The state of the UK's birds 2005*. RSPB, BTO, WWT, CCW, EN, EHS & SNH, Sandy, Bedfordshire.

Forrester, R. & Andrews, I. (Eds) 2007. *The Birds of Scotland*. SOC, Aberlady.

Fraser, P. & Rogers, M.J. 2006. Report on scarce birds in Britain in 2003. *British Birds* 99: 74–91.

Gade, F.W. 1945. Ruddy sheld-ducks at Lundy and in Angus. *British Birds* 38: 178.

Gade, F.W. 1946. Pratincole on Lundy. *British Birds* 39: 93.

Gade, F.W. 1978. *My Life on Lundy*. Published privately by Myrtle Langham, Reigate.

Gaston, A.J. & Jones, I.L. 1998. *The Auks Alcidae*, pp. 121–125. Bird Families of the World. Oxford University Press.

Gibbons, D.W., Reid, J.B. & Chapman, R.A. (Eds) 1993. *The New Atlas of Breeding Birds in Britain and Ireland: 1988–1991*. London: T. & A.D. Poyser.

Gibson, L. 1992. Lundy flora, 1989–1992. *LFS Annual Report* 43: 104–112.

Gill, F.B. & Wright, M.T. 2006. *Birds of the World: Recommended English Names, on behalf of the International Ornithological Congress*. Princeton, New Jersey: Princeton University Press.

Gosse, P.H. 1865. *Sea and Land*. London: James Nisbet & Co. (Title page has title as *Land and Sea*.)

Griffith, S.C. & Stewart, R. 1998. Genetic confirmation of non-identical embryonic twins in the House Sparrow *Passer domesticus*. *Journal of Avian Biology* 29: 207–208.

Griffith, S.C., Stewart, I.R.K., Dawson, D.A., Owens, I.P.F. & Burke, T. 1999. Contrasting levels of extra-pair paternity in mainland and island populations of the house sparrow (*Passer domesticus*): is there an 'island' effect? *Biological Journal of the Linnaean Society* 68: 303–316.

Griffiths, S.C., Owens, I.P.F. & Burke, T. 1999. Female choice and annual reproductive success favour less-ornamented male house sparrows. *Proceedings of the Royal Society of London* B series, 266: 765–770.

Gurney, M. 1913. *The Gannet*, xli–xliii: 42–53.

Halliday, T.R. 1979. The Great Auk. *Oceans* 12: 27–31.

Harman, M.C. & Fisher, J. 1944. First breeding of fulmar in the south-west. *British Birds* 38: 97–98.

Harris, M.P. 1984. *The Puffin.* Calton: T. & A.D. Poyser.

Harris, M.P. & Birkhead, T.R. 1985. Breeding ecology of the Atlantic Alcidae, pp. 155, 177–179. In: D.N. Nettleship & T.R. Birkhead (Eds), *The Atlantic Alcidae: The Evolution, Distribution and Biology of the Auks Inhabiting the Atlantic Ocean and Adjacent Water Areas.* London: Academic Press.

Harrisson, T.H. 1932. The birds of Lundy Island from 1922 to 1931 with special reference to numerical fluctuations. *British Birds* 25: 212–219.

Harrisson, T.H. & Wynne-Edwards, V.C. 1930. Wood-sandpiper on Lundy Island. *British Birds* 24: 83.

Harrop, A.H.J. 2002. The Ruddy Shelduck in Britain: A review. *British Birds* 95: 123–128.

Harting, J.E. 1871. Quails in Lundy Island. *The Zoologist* 2521.

Harting, J.E. 1901. *A Handbook of British Birds.* London: John C. Nimmo. (pp. 5–6, White-tailed Eagle.)

Heaven, A.A., M.E. & C.H. 1870–1905. Private Diaries. (See also Boyd 1950.)

Hendy, E.W. 1922. Some further observations on the birds of Lundy, June 1914. *British Birds* 16: 214–215.

Hendy, E.W. 1933. *Here And There With Birds*, pp. 131–151. London: Jonathan Cape.

Hobbs, A.J.H. 1934. Some notes on the birds of Lundy. *Transactions of the Torquay Natural History Society* 7: 1.

Hoek Ostende, L.W. van den, Dekker, R.W.R.J. & Keijl, G.O. 1997. Type-specimens of birds in the National Museum of Natural History, Leiden. Part 1 Non-Passerines. *Nationaal Natuurhistorisch Museum, Technical Bulletin* 1: 1–248.

Hornby, C. 1943. *Rural Amateur.* London: Collins.

Hubbard, E.M. 1971. A contribution to the study of the Lundy flora. *LFS Annual Report* 22: 13–24.

Irving, R.A. Schofield, A.J. & Webster, C.J. (Eds) 1997. *Island Studies: fifty years of the Lundy Field Society.* Lundy Field Society, Bideford.

Jenks, D.G. 2004. *A History of Devonshire Ornithology: A Review of the Literature, Events and Personalities from Prehistoric Times to the end of the Twentieth Century.* Falmouth: Isabelline Books.

JNCC. 2001. *The UK SPA network: its scope and content. Vol.2: Species accounts.* JNCC, Peterborough.

Jones, M. 1965. Bimaculated Lark on Lundy: a bird new to Great Britain and Ireland. *British Birds* 58: 309–312.

Jourdain, F.C.R. 1922. Editorial comment on Loyd, L.R.W. 1922. Observations on the birds of Lundy, May and June. *British Birds* 16: 154.

Joy, N.H. 1922. The birds of Lundy. *British Birds* 16: 188.

Kehoe, C. 2006. Racial identification and assessment in Britain: a report from the RIACT subcommittee. *British Birds* 99: 619–645.

King, J.M.B. 1985. Weights and probable origin of an exceptional movement of Blackcaps etc. on Lundy in October 1984. *LFS Annual Report* 36: 21–22.

Lack, D. 1934. Birds on Lundy. *British Birds* 28: 77.

Langham, A.F. 1994a. The Great Auk on Lundy: its possible nesting site. *LFS Annual Report* 45: 33–34.

Langham, A.F. 1994b. *The Island of Lundy.* Stroud: Alan Sutton Publishing Ltd.

Langham, A. & M. 1970. *Lundy.* Newton Abbot: David & Charles. (Second edition 1984.)

Langman, M., Jewels, A. & Reay, P. 2007. A Review of Devon Subspecies. *Devon Birds* 60(2): 16–29.

Langton, I. 1864. Cream-coloured woodcock. *The Field*, 30 January 1864.

Lea, D. 1951. Lundy Bird Observatory, 1950. *British Birds* 44: 233–235.

Lea, S.E.G., Daley, C., Boddington, P.J.C. & Morrison, V. 1996. Diving patterns in shags and cormorants (*Phalacrocorax*): tests of an optimal breathing model. *Ibis* 138: 391–398.

Lewis, S. 1924. Sand Martins and Blackcaps on Lundy. *British Birds* 18: 78.

LFS. 1962. The Winter of 1962-63 on Lundy: Taken from Notes and Observations made by the Islanders. *LFS Annual Report* 15: 34–35.

Lock. L. 2001. The breeding land birds of Lundy. *LFS Annual Report* 51: 104–112.

Lock. L. 2004. The breeding land birds survey of Lundy 2004. *LFS Annual Report* 54: 51–62.

Loyd, L.R.W. 1922. Observations on the birds of Lundy, May and June. *British Birds* 16: 148–159.

Loyd, L.R.W. 1923. Further observations on the birds of Lundy, June and July, 1923. *British Birds* 17: 158.

Loyd, L.R.W. 1925. *Lundy, its history and natural history*. London: Longmans, Green & Co.

Mapleton-Bree, H.W. 1932. Woodcocks in Lundy. *British Birds* 25: 276.

Mathew, G.F. 1866a. Additions to Rowe's Catalogue of the mammals, birds, &c.. of Devon. *The Naturalist* 2: 357–360.

Mathew, M.A. 1861. Occurrence of the Spotted Eagle (*Falco nævius*) at Lundy Island. *The Zoologist* 19: 7380.

Mathew, M.A. 1866b. The Great Auk on Lundy Island. *The Zoologist* 1866: 100–101.

McShane, C. 1996. Eastern Phoebe in Devon: new to the Western Palearctic. *British Birds* 89: 103–107.

Mitchell, P.I., Newton, S., Ratcliffe, N. & Dunn, T.E. (Eds) 2004. *Seabird Populations of Britain and Ireland*. London: T. & A.D. Poyser.

Moore, E. 1837. On the Web-footed Birds of Devonshire. *The Magazine of Natural History* Vol. 1 (New Series): 360–366.

Moore, R. 1969. *The Birds of Devon*. Newton Abbot: David & Charles.

Morrey Salmon, H. & Lockley R.M. 1934. The Grassholm gannets – a survey and a census. *British Birds* 27: 142–152.

Nakagawa, S. 2004. Changes in House Sparrow population size, breeding success and breeding pattern on Lundy. *LFS Annual Report* 54: 63–70.

Nettleship, D.N. & Evans, P.G.H. 1985. Distribution and Status of the Atlantic Alcidae, pp. 53, 61–69. In: D.N. Nettleship & T.R. Birkhead (Eds), *The Atlantic Alcidae: The Evolution, Distribution and Biology of the Auks Inhabiting the Atlantic Ocean and Adjacent Water Areas*. London: Academic Press.

Newton, I., Hobson, K.A., Fox, A.D. & Marquiss, M. 2006. An investigation into the provenance of northern bullfinches *Pyrrhula p. pyrrhula* found in winter in Scotland and Denmark. *Journal of Avian Biology* 37: 431–435.

Odin, N. 2006. Racial determination of Great Spotted Woodpeckers *Dendrocopos major* in Britain. *Ringers' Bulletin* 11: 106.

Oldham, C. 1932. Lundy birds. *British Birds* 25: 275–276.

Palmer, M.G. (Ed.) 1946. *The fauna and flora of the Ilfracombe District of North Devon*. (Bird section by N.V. Allen, pp. 8–43). Exeter: James Townsend & Sons.

Parfitt, E. 1876. The Fauna of Devon, Part XIV – Birds: Lundy Island, pp. 303–310. *Trans. Devon Assoc.* Vol. 8. July 1876. Plymouth.

Parsons, A.J. 1983. Notes on some mammals on Lundy. *LFS Annual Report* 34: 40.

Parsons, A.J. 2002. Densities and distributions of fifteen bird species on Lundy in June 2000. *LFS Annual Report* 52: 94–98.

Patient, R. 2001. Black-faced Bunting on Lundy – first for Devon. *Devon Bird Report* 74: 227–229.

Pennington, M., Osborn, K., Harvey, P., Riddington, R., Okill, D., Ellis P. & Heubeck, M. 2004. *The Birds of Shetland*. London: Christopher Helm.

Perry, R. 1940. *Lundy, Isle of Puffins*. London: Drummond.

Perry, R. 1942. Birds. *National Review* 64–71.

Perry, R. 1942. Razorbills on Lundy. *Nineteenth Century and After* 132 (July–December): 80.

Perry, R. 1943. Fulmar petrel comes south. *Country Life*, 10 December 1943, pp. 1043–1044.

Perry, R. 1944. Five months with guillemots. *Geographical Magazine*, June 1944, pp. 84–95.

Perry, R. 1945. The Manx Shearwater on Lundy. *British Birds* 38: 240.

Perry, R. 1945. Sea-birds on Lundy. *British Birds* 38: 259–260.

Perry, R. 1947. Operation Fledge. *The Field*, 6 January 1947, pp. 631–632.

Perry, R. 1949. Lundy, isle of puffins. *Trident* 11: 5–7.

Perry, R. 1950. Operation Fledge. *Everybody's Weekly*, 22 July 1950.

Pidsley, W.E.H. 1891. *The Birds of Devonshire*. London: W.W. Gibbings & Exeter: J.G. Commin.

Price, D.J. 1996a. *Lundy – Breeding Seabirds: Population Trends and Distribution 1939–1996 (Auks, Kittiwakes, Fulmars and Shags)*. Published privately, November 1996.

Price D.J. 1996b. Surveys of breeding seabirds on Lundy: 1981–96. *LFS Annual Report* 47: 28–35.

Price, D.J. 2004. Lundy Seabirds, Gulls and Oystercatchers. Unpublished report.

Price, D.J. Undated. Site Register: Lundy census of breeding birds 1981–1996. Unpublished report.

Price, D. & Booker, H. 2001. Manx Shearwaters on Lundy. *LFS Annual Report* 51: 95–103.

Pring, C.J. 1922. Large clutch of oystercatcher's eggs. *British Birds* 16: 136–37.

Ratcliffe, D.A. 1993. *The Peregrine Falcon*. London: T. & A.D. Poyser. 2nd edition.

Roberts, A.J.R. Not dated but pre-1897. Lundy Island and its sea birds. *The Country Magazine* pp. 143–144.

Roberts, A.J.R. 1903. *The Bird Book*, pp. 110–123. London: John Lane.

Robinson, P. 2003. *The Birds of the Isles of Scilly*. London: Christopher Helm.

Rogers, H.M. 1943. Hoopoes on the Isle of Man and Lundy. *British Birds* 37: 38.

Rogers, M.J. 1998. Records of Western Bonelli's Warbler in Britain, 1948–96. *British Birds* 91: 122–123.

Ross, N.J. & Rousham, A.H. 1909. *The Birds of Lundy*. (Paper read at Exeter before the R.A.M. Field Club and Nat. His. Soc., March 13 1909)

Rousham, A.H. 1908. Nature notes. *Devon and Exeter Gazette*, 25th June 1908.

Sangster, G., Knox, A.G., Helbig, A.J. & Parkin, D.T. 2002. Taxonomic recommendations for European birds. *Ibis* 144: 153–159.

Sangster, G., Collinson, J.M., Helbig, A.J., Knox, A.G. & Parkin, D.T. 2004. Taxonomic recommendations for *British Birds*: second report. *Ibis* 146: 153–157.

Schofield, J. 2004. The Archaeology of Ornithology; the Rituals of Ringing – Lundy's Heligoland Traps in Context. *LFS Annual Report* 54: 93–107.

Sharpe, R. 1984. Geoffrey-Le-Baker Aves-Ganymedis, Lundy Island, and Neckam, Alexander. *Notes and Queries* 31: 31–36.

Sharrock, J.T.R. (Ed.) 1973. *The Natural History of Cape Clear Island*. Berkhamsted: T. & A.D. Poyser.

Sharrock, J.T.R. 1976. *The Atlas of Breeding Birds in Britain and Ireland*. Berkhamsted: T. & A.D. Poyser, Berkhamsted.

Sharrock J.T.R. & Grant P.J. (Eds) 1982. *Birds New to Britain and Ireland*. Calton: T. & A.D. Poyser.

Smith, F.R. & the Rarities Committee. 1973. Rare birds in Great Britain 1972. *British Birds* 66: 339.

Snow, B.K. 1960. The breeding biology of the Shag (*Phalacrocorax aristotelis*) on the island of Lundy, Bristol Channel. *Ibis* 102: 554–575.

Snow, B.K. 1963. The behaviour of the Shag. *British Birds* 56: 77–103 & 164–186.

Society for the Protection of Birds. 1904. Three Islands. *Bird Notes and News* 1(7): 41–42.

Southern, H.N. & Reeve, E.C.R. 1941. Quantitative Studies in the Geographical Variation of Birds – The Common Guillemot (*Uria aalge* Pont.). *Proc. Zool. Soc.* 1941, Ser. A., pp. 255–276.

Southern, H.N. & Tucker, B.W. 1944. The Manx Shearwater on Lundy. *British Birds* 38: 122-129.

Studdy, R. 1949. Birdwatching on Lundy. *Wild Life*, Spring 1949.

Taylor, A.M. 1985. Manx Shearwaters on Lundy: ringing information and other observations. *LFS Annual Report* 36: 23–24.

Taylor, A.M. 1989. Manx Shearwaters on Lundy: further ringing studies and observations on breeding status. *LFS Annual Report* 40: 31–33.

Ternstrom, M. 1995. A brief history of the Gannet colony on Lundy. *LFS Annual Report* 46: 39–42.

Thomas, D.H. 1981. The size of the colony of Manx Shearwaters on Lundy. *LFS Annual Report* 32: 16–20.

UK Biodiversity Partnership. 2006. *The UK Biodiversity Action Plan: Highlights from the 2005 reporting round*. London: Defra.

Upton, R.C. 1968. Lundy Peregrines. *The Falconer* 5(2): 104–109.

Waldon, J. 1994. Ancient Murrelet in Devon: new to the Western Palearctic. *British Birds* 87: 307–310.

Waller, C.S. 1967a. First-winter male Black-billed Cuckoo (*Coccyzus erthrophthalmus*) on Lundy, Devon. *LFS Annual Report* 18: 14–15.

Waller, C.S. 1967b. Baltimore Orioles on Lundy, Devon. *LFS Annual Report* 18: 15–16.

Waller, C.S. 1970. Rufous-sided Towhee on Lundy. *British Birds* 63: 147–149.

Waller, C.S. 1981. Spanish Sparrow: new to Britain and Ireland. *British Birds* 74: 109–110.

Wernham, C.V., Toms, M.P., Marchant, J.H., Clark, J.A., Siriwardena, G.M. & Baillie, S.R. (Eds) 2002. *The Migration Atlas: movements of the birds of Britain and Ireland*. London: T. & A.D. Poyser.

Wetlands International. 2006. *Waterbird Population Estimates – Fourth Edition*. Wetlands International, Wageningen, The Netherlands.

Whitaker, B. 1955a. Bonelli's Warbler on Lundy. *British Birds* 48: 285.

Whitaker, B. 1955b. Melodious Warbler on Lundy. *British Birds* 48: 284.

Whitaker, B. 1955c. Sardinian Warbler on Lundy. *British Birds* 48: 515.

Whitaker, B. 1955d. Yellowthroat on Lundy: a new British bird. *British Birds* 48: 145–147.

Whitaker, B. 1956a. Results of Shag ringing, 1948–55. *LFS Annual Report* 10: 38–39.

Whitaker, B. 1956b. A summary of work on some breeding birds, 1947–56. *LFS Annual Report* 10: 50–51.

Whitaker, B. 1957. The autumn movement of tits. *LFS Annual Report* 11: 23–24.

White, S.J. 2005. *Spring passage of Whimbrel through Britain*. Downloadable PDF from www.lancswt.org.uk

Willcox, N.A. 1986. *Larus* Gulls on Lundy. *LFS Annual Report* 37: 21–25.

Willcox, N.A. 1987. Seabird Studies on Lundy. *LFS Annual Report* 38: 24–32.

Willcox, N.A. 1988. The status of Kittiwakes *Rissa tridactyla* on Lundy in 1988. *LFS Annual Report* 39: 24–30.

Workman, W.B. 1961. Myrtle Warbler in Devon. *British Birds* 54: 250–251.

Workman, W.B. 1963. Baltimore Oriole on Lundy, Devon (1958). *British Birds* 56: 52–55.

Wynne-Edwards, V.C. & Harrisson, T.H. 1932. A bird census on Lundy Island (1930). *Journal of Ecology* 20: 371–379.

Sources of useful information

The following is a brief guide to some of the bodies most closely involved with Lundy and its birds. Whether you are interested in catching up with news of the latest bird sightings, or perhaps want to visit the island for the first time, these websites should provide you with everything you need. Given that organisations restructure and society officers change, we have omitted phone numbers and postal addresses in favour of website addresses.

Devon Bird Watching & Preservation Society

www.devonbirds.org.uk

DBWPS, more often known as 'Devon Birds', is the body responsible for maintaining records of birds seen in Devon, including the assessment of county rarities. It publishes the journal *Devon Birds* three times per year, which includes the annual *Devon Bird Report*. Members also receive a newsletter, *The Harrier*, every two months. The Society works closely with many other organisations to secure more effective conservation of both species and habitats and also manages a small number of nature reserves.

Lundy Field Society

www.lundy.org.uk

The LFS was founded in 1946 and for many years had its headquarters in the Old Light. Originally concentrating on the study of birds, the Society is now a charity that has as its aims the study of Lundy, in particular its history, natural history and archaeology, and the conservation of its wildlife and antiquities. For over 50 years the LFS has been carrying out conservation work, supporting research on the island (by means of modest grants) and publishing the results in its *Annual Report*.

Lundy Birds

www.lundybirds.org.uk

Richard Campey, former island resident, maintains this site as a free service for all those with an interest in birdwatching on Lundy. News and photographs of the latest sightings are posted regularly – but remember that the site depends for its freshness on visiting birdwatchers contributing records; please consider taking a few moments to do this (via the 'submit sightings' button).

Lundy Island

www.lundyisland.co.uk

The Lundy Company's website provides details of transport to and from the island (including *MS Oldenburg's* sailing timetable and the schedule for the winter helicopter service). It also describes the various accommodation options and the range of activities available on the island, including warden-led seabird and wildlife walks and rocky shore rambles.

Landmark Trust

www.landmarktrust.org.uk

The Landmark Trust finances, administers and maintains Lundy under a 60-year lease from the National Trust and has carried out an extensive building and renovation programme – which continues to this day – since taking on responsibility for the island in 1969. The Landmark Trust's website provides information on the availability and cost of accommodation on Lundy and details of how to book.

National Trust

www.nationaltrust.org.uk

The National Trust secured Lundy for the nation by purchasing the island from the Harman family in 1969. Members of the National Trust enjoy free entry to the island and therefore benefit from a modest discount on sailing tickets, which otherwise incorporate a landing fee.

Natural England

www.naturalengland.org.uk

Natural England works for people, places and nature to conserve and enhance biodiversity, landscapes and wildlife in rural, urban, coastal and marine areas. Natural England supports and advises on the management of the Lundy Site of Special Scientific Interest, Special Area of Conservation, Marine Nature Reserve and No Take Zone.

RSPB

www.rspb.org.uk

The RSPB has undertaken regular surveys of Lundy's breeding sea and landbirds and has been a key partner in the Seabird Recovery Programme, working closely with the Landmark Trust, Natural England and the National Trust.

The Birds of Lundy

www.birdsoflundy.org.uk

We have also established a website dedicated to this book on which updates will be posted periodically. These will include sightings of species new to Lundy (subject to acceptance and publication by the BBRC, DBRC and/or LFS), other noteworthy records and corrections to any important errors in these pages that may come to light. We will also announce any plans we may hatch for a full update at some point in the future. In the meantime, do please contact us with your feedback, questions or comments using the email facility within the website.

Indexes to the Systematic List

Scientific names

English names

The index is arranged alphabetically by full name (e.g. Lesser Whitethroat is listed under 'L' for 'Lesser', not 'W' for 'Whitethroat'). Priority is given to the common name most widely used by British birdwatchers; in cases where the international common name differs, there is an appropriate cross-reference to the relevant entry (e.g. 'Black-legged Kittiwake see Kittiwake').